THE BOOK

BRAKE
Manual

Martynn Randall

The Haynes Manual for maintaining, fault finding and repairing brake systems

Haynes Publishing
Sparkford Nr Yeovil
Somerset BA22 7JJ England

Haynes North America, Inc
861 Lawrence Drive
Newbury Park
California 91320 USA

Editions Haynes
4, Rue de l'Abreuvoir
92415 COURBEVOIE CEDEX, France

Acknowledgements

We are grateful for the help and co-operation of various motor manufacturers and Sykes-Pickavant Limited for assistance with technical information and illustrations. Kent Reppert II also supplied various illustrations.

This manual is not a direct reproduction of any vehicle manufacturer's data, and its publication should not be taken as implying any technical approval by vehicle manufacturers or importers.

© Haynes Publishing 2004

A book in the Haynes Service and Repair Manual Series

Printed in the USA

ISBN 1 84425 178 0

British Library Cataloguing in Publication Data
A catalogue record for this book is available from the British Library

While every attempt is made to ensure that the information in this manual is correct, no liability can be accepted by the authors or publishers for loss, damage or injury caused by any errors in, or omissions from, the information given.

(4178-192)

Contents

Chapter 1   **Introduction**

Chapter 2   **Disc brakes**

Chapter 3   **Drum brakes**

Chapter 4   **Handbrakes**

Chapter 5   **ABS systems**

Chapter 6   **Hydraulic systems, brake servos and vacuum pumps**

Chapter 7   **Maintenance**

Chapter 8   **Reference**

Glossary

Fault finding

Index

Conversion factors

Length (distance)
Inches (in)	x 25.4	= Millimetres (mm)	x 0.0394	= Inches (in)	
Feet (ft)	x 0.305	= Metres (m)	x 3.281	= Feet (ft)	
Miles	x 1.609	= Kilometres (km)	x 0.621	= Miles	

Volume (capacity)
Cubic inches (cu in; in³)	x 16.387	= Cubic centimetres (cc; cm³)	x 0.061	= Cubic inches (cu in; in³)
Imperial pints (Imp pt)	x 0.568	= Litres (l)	x 1.76	= Imperial pints (Imp pt)
Imperial quarts (Imp qt)	x 1.137	= Litres (l)	x 0.88	= Imperial quarts (Imp qt)
Imperial quarts (Imp qt)	x 1.201	= US quarts (US qt)	x 0.833	= Imperial quarts (Imp qt)
US quarts (US qt)	x 0.946	= Litres (l)	x 1.057	= US quarts (US qt)
Imperial gallons (Imp gal)	x 4.546	= Litres (l)	x 0.22	= Imperial gallons (Imp gal)
Imperial gallons (Imp gal)	x 1.201	= US gallons (US gal)	x 0.833	= Imperial gallons (Imp gal)
US gallons (US gal)	x 3.785	= Litres (l)	x 0.264	= US gallons (US gal)

Mass (weight)
Ounces (oz)	x 28.35	= Grams (g)	x 0.035	= Ounces (oz)
Pounds (lb)	x 0.454	= Kilograms (kg)	x 2.205	= Pounds (lb)

Force
Ounces-force (ozf; oz)	x 0.278	= Newtons (N)	x 3.6	= Ounces-force (ozf; oz)
Pounds-force (lbf; lb)	x 4.448	= Newtons (N)	x 0.225	= Pounds-force (lbf; lb)
Newtons (N)	x 0.1	= Kilograms-force (kgf; kg)	x 9.81	= Newtons (N)

Pressure
Pounds-force per square inch (psi; lbf/in²; lb/in²)	x 0.070	= Kilograms-force per square centimetre (kgf/cm²; kg/cm²)	x 14.223	= Pounds-force per square inch (psi; lbf/in²; lb/in²)
Pounds-force per square inch (psi; lbf/in²; lb/in²)	x 0.068	= Atmospheres (atm)	x 14.696	= Pounds-force per square inch (psi; lbf/in²; lb/in²)
Pounds-force per square inch (psi; lbf/in²; lb/in²)	x 0.069	= Bars	x 14.5	= Pounds-force per square inch (psi; lbf/in²; lb/in²)
Pounds-force per square inch (psi; lbf/in²; lb/in²)	x 6.895	= Kilopascals (kPa)	x 0.145	= Pounds-force per square inch (psi; lbf/in²; lb/in²)
Kilopascals (kPa)	x 0.01	= Kilograms-force per square centimetre (kgf/cm²; kg/cm²)	x 98.1	= Kilopascals (kPa)
Millibar (mbar)	x 100	= Pascals (Pa)	x 0.01	= Millibar (mbar)
Millibar (mbar)	x 0.0145	= Pounds-force per square inch (psi; lbf/in²; lb/in²)	x 68.947	= Millibar (mbar)
Millibar (mbar)	x 0.75	= Millimetres of mercury (mmHg)	x 1.333	= Millibar (mbar)
Millibar (mbar)	x 0.401	= Inches of water (inH₂O)	x 2.491	= Millibar (mbar)
Millimetres of mercury (mmHg)	x 0.535	= Inches of water (inH₂O)	x 1.868	= Millimetres of mercury (mmHg)
Inches of water (inH₂O)	x 0.036	= Pounds-force per square inch (psi; lbf/in²; lb/in²)	x 27.68	= Inches of water (inH₂O)

Torque (moment of force)
Pounds-force inches (lbf in; lb in)	x 1.152	= Kilograms-force centimetre (kgf cm; kg cm)	x 0.868	= Pounds-force inches (lbf in; lb in)
Pounds-force inches (lbf in; lb in)	x 0.113	= Newton metres (Nm)	x 8.85	= Pounds-force inches (lbf in; lb in)
Pounds-force inches (lbf in; lb in)	x 0.083	= Pounds-force feet (lbf ft; lb ft)	x 12	= Pounds-force inches (lbf in; lb in)
Pounds-force feet (lbf ft; lb ft)	x 0.138	= Kilograms-force metres (kgf m; kg m)	x 7.233	= Pounds-force feet (lbf ft; lb ft)
Pounds-force feet (lbf ft; lb ft)	x 1.356	= Newton metres (Nm)	x 0.738	= Pounds-force feet (lbf ft; lb ft)
Newton metres (Nm)	x 0.102	= Kilograms-force metres (kgf m; kg m)	x 9.804	= Newton metres (Nm)

Power
Horsepower (hp)	x 745.7	= Watts (W)	x 0.0013	= Horsepower (hp)

Velocity (speed)
Miles per hour (miles/hr; mph)	x 1.609	= Kilometres per hour (km/hr; kph)	x 0.621	= Miles per hour (miles/hr; mph)

Fuel consumption*
Miles per gallon, Imperial (mpg)	x 0.354	= Kilometres per litre (km/l)	x 2.825	= Miles per gallon, Imperial (mpg)
Miles per gallon, US (mpg)	x 0.425	= Kilometres per litre (km/l)	x 2.352	= Miles per gallon, US (mpg)

Temperature
Degrees Fahrenheit = (°C x 1.8) + 32   Degrees Celsius (Degrees Centigrade; °C) = (°F - 32) x 0.56

It is common practice to convert from miles per gallon (mpg) to litres/100 kilometres (l/100km), where mpg x l/100 km = 282

Introduction

It's a beautiful summer day. You're hurtling down your favourite stretch of road, enjoying the countryside and your favourite CD. You notice, however, an annoying rattle coming from somewhere under the instrument panel. "I'll have to sort that out" you say to yourself, as you make a mental note to fix it as soon as you get home. You turn up the stereo.

Suddenly, a large estate car towing a caravan pulls out onto the road, not more than 100 yards ahead. Instinctively, you check the lane to your right for oncoming traffic and to your dismay, there's lots of it. With nowhere to go, you hit the brakes. Hard. Hard enough for the "ABS" light on the instrument panel to glow, but that isn't what you're looking at.

You breath a sigh of relief when you realise the caravan isn't rushing towards you anymore. After a few choice phrases and an exchange of hand gestures, you pass this rolling roadblock and you're back on your way - nothing lost but a little sweat.

A little sweat and a minuscule amount of friction material from the brake pads, but you're not thinking about your brakes. They performed flawlessly, and besides, you pushed the pedal so you get the credit!

When was the last time you did think about your vehicle's brakes? The sad fact is that most drivers pay more attention to annoying rattles or scratches in the paint, ignoring their brakes until they start making bad noises, the vehicle pulls to one side, the brake pedal feels mushy or, worse yet, they fail completely. Brakes are probably the most abused and neglected components on a vehicle.

While complete brake failure is not a common occurrence, some forms of brake system trouble are all too common. Most can be avoided with a little attention every few thousand miles. The braking system is the most important system on your vehicle. Your life, the lives of your passengers, pedestrians and other motorists on the road all depend upon your brakes.

All vehicles will need some form of brake system repair sooner or later. Wear is an inherent feature of all brake systems - your brakes slowly give their lives so you can retain yours. Due to this continual sacrifice, all brake pads and shoes must eventually be retired, to be replaced with the next generation of new lining. Other problems can crop up, too.

But for many, the braking system represents a portion of the vehicle that just shouldn't be tampered with, and because of this, repairs are usually left to someone else. That's where this manual comes in. It has been designed to help just about anyone repair just about any kind of problem in any type of brake system.

Most modern automotive braking systems are actually quite simple to maintain and repair, provided that each step is performed in a careful, deliberate manner. A considerable amount of money can be saved and much knowledge can be gained by taking on these tasks yourself. This will give you a great sense of satisfaction - not only because you saved a lot of money and your car wasn't tied up for a couple of days in some workshop, but because you'll know that the job was done correctly.

This manual unlocks the "mysteries" of the modern automotive braking system. The procedures illustrated throughout the book are general in nature, but with specific differences in component design pointed out where necessary to help you complete each procedure safely and properly. Included are chapters on component and system operating fundamentals, tools and equipment, fault finding, maintenance, disc brake pad renewal, drum brake shoe renewal, handbrake systems, hydraulic systems and Anti-lock Brake Systems (ABS). At the end of the manual there's a glossary of terms used throughout the book. In short, everything you need to know to successfully maintain and repair your brakes and ensure your safety and that of others around you, as well!

Chapter 1

How to use this repair manual

The manual is divided into Chapters. Each chapter is subdivided into sections, some of which consist of consecutively numbered paragraphs (usually referred to as "Steps," since they're normally part of a procedure). If the material is basically informative in nature, rather than a step-by-step procedure, the paragraphs aren't numbered.

The term *(see illustration)* is used in the text to indicate that a photo or drawing has been included to make the information easier to understand (the old cliché "a picture is worth a thousand words" is especially true when it comes to how-to procedures). Also every attempt is made to position illustrations on the same page as the corresponding text to minimise confusion. Some procedures are largely made up of illustrations and captions, with little or no accompanying text.

The terms **"Note," "Caution,"** and **"Warning"** are used throughout the book with a specific purpose in mind - to attract the reader's attention. A **"Note"** simply provides information required to properly complete a procedure or information which will make the procedure easier to understand. A **"Caution"** outlines a special procedure or special steps which must be taken when completing the procedure where the Caution is found. Failure to pay attention to a Caution can result in damage to the component being repaired or the tools being used. A **"Warning"** is included where personal injury can result if the instructions aren't followed exactly as described.

Hydraulic systems

In the early days of motorised transportation, the entire brake system on a horseless carriage consisted of nothing more than a lever that the driver pulled, causing it to rub against a tyre. Although some mechanical advantage could be built into the lever, braking power was largely determined by the strength of the driver. Of course, this was a very inadequate system and could quickly be rendered useless by driving through a little water or mud!

As cars evolved, the brakes at the wheels (drum brakes, which we'll cover in the next Section) were actuated by a linkage or a cable, or a combination of the two. This was usually sufficient for the vehicle weights and the relatively low speeds they were able to achieve. This worked, but cables and linkages were a source of high wear and a definite "weak link" in the brake system chain.

By the late 1920's/early 1930's, most cars were equipped with hydraulically actuated brakes. This greatly increased braking reliability and safety. Since mechanical advantage can easily be designed into a hydraulic system, driving a motor vehicle became a much less tiresome proposition.

Why use fluid in a brake system? Well, for three reasons:

Liquids can't be compressed
Liquids can transmit motion
Liquids can transmit force and can also increase or decrease force

This was discovered long before the automobile was even dreamed of (in 1647), by a French philosopher and mathematician named Blaise Pascal (1623 - 1662). He determined that in a confined fluid, pressure applied externally is transmitted equally in all directions. In a static fluid, force is transmitted at the speed of sound throughout the fluid and acts at right angles on all surfaces in or confining the fluid *(see illustration)*. Of course, this happens because liquids can't be compressed.

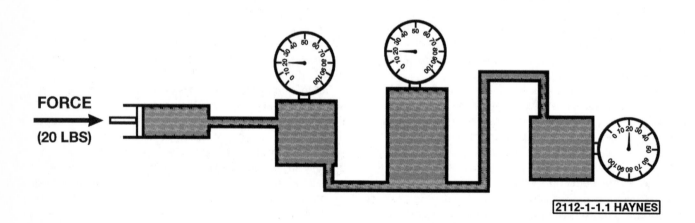

2112-1-1.1 HAYNES

Pascal's law states that "pressure, when applied to a confined liquid, is transmitted undiminished". In this example, a force of 20 pounds has been exerted on the piston, which has a surface area of one square inch. Notice that each pressure gauge registers 20 pounds per square inch (psi), regardless or the size, shape or location of its chamber.

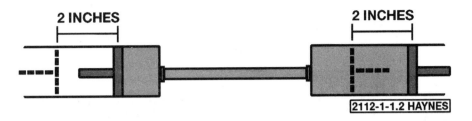

The piston in the hydraulic chamber at the left has been depressed two inches - the piston in the cylinder on the right has moved out an equal amount. The pistons are of the same surface area and the force transmitted is equal too.

Liquids can also transmit motion because of this law of physics. If a piston in a hydraulic cylinder is pushed in a certain amount, a piston in another hydraulic cylinder of equal size, connected by a tube, will move out an equal amount *(see illustration)*.

The hydraulic brake system in all motor vehicles is based on these principles. When the driver of a car pushes on the brake pedal, the force exerted on the master cylinder is converted into system pressure and is distributed through the brake lines to the wheel cylinders and/or brake calipers. This action is what applies the brake shoes to the drums or the brake pads to the discs, creating friction, which converts the kinetic energy of the moving vehicle to heat and slows the car down.

The components that make up a modern hydraulic system are only a little more complex than the examples shown in the previous illustrations. Lets take a look at the individual components and the jobs they do.

Master cylinder

The master cylinder converts mechanical input force into system hydraulic pressure. Force exerted by the driver is transmitted through the brake pedal and applied to the master cylinder piston through a pushrod. As the piston moves forward in the cylinder, brake fluid is forced from the master cylinder. Remember, though, that the entire system is filled with fluid, so this motion is transmitted, undiminished, through the brake lines and hoses to the wheel cylinders or calipers. Once all movement is taken up in the wheel cylinders or calipers, pressure in the system begins to rise. Further movement of the components is impossible, but pressure will increase within the system if the driver pushes harder on the brake pedal *(see illustration)*.

Wheel cylinders

Wheel cylinders are used in drum brake assemblies. They convert the hydraulic pressure created by the master cylinder into mechanical force, which pushes outward on the brake shoes, expanding the shoes against the brake drum.

Wheel cylinders are usually made from cast iron. The most common type is the double-piston wheel cylinder, which

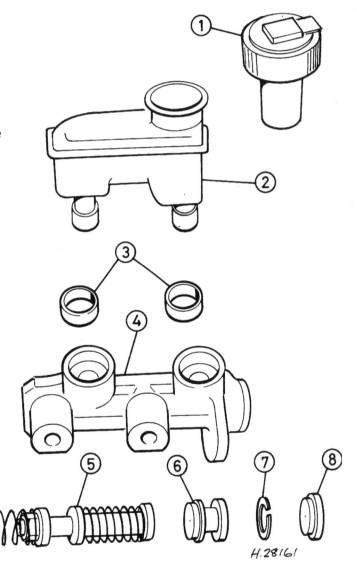

Exploded view of a typical master cylinder

1 Cap	5 Primary piston and springs
2 Reservoir	6 Secondary piston
3 Seals	7 Circlip
4 Master cylinder body	8 Seal

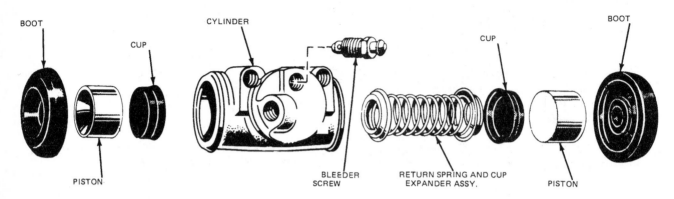

BOOT · **CUP** · **CYLINDER** · **BLEEDER SCREW** · **RETURN SPRING AND CUP EXPANDER ASSY.** · **CUP** · **BOOT** · **PISTON** · **PISTON**

Exploded view of a typical double-piston wheel cylinder

uses two pistons (usually aluminium), two rubber cups, cup expanders and a coil spring between the two piston assemblies *(see illustration)*. Some designs use pushrods connected to the brake shoes. Other styles use slotted or notched pistons, in which the ends of the brake shoes ride. At each end of the wheel cylinder is a rubber boot, which seals the unit from brake dust and other elements.

Wheel cylinders are drilled and tapped for the brake line connection and bleeder screw. They are retained to the brake backing plate with one or two bolts, or a spring steel clip.

Other types of wheel cylinders include the single-piston cylinder *(see illustration)* and the stepped cylinder. The single-piston cylinder is usually used in pairs; each cylinder actuates one brake shoe. Stepped cylinders are essentially the same as double-piston cylinders, except that one half of the cylinder bore is larger than the other. The larger piston is capable of exerting more force than the smaller one. So, stepped cylinders are only used in drum brake designs where it is necessary to apply more pressure to one of the brake shoes than the other.

Calipers

The brake calipers, used on disc brakes, are basically frames that house the brake pads and the hydraulic cylinders, which convert the system pressure from the master cylinder into mechanical force *(see illustration)*. This force squeezes the brake pads against the disc, which causes friction and heat dissipation, which in turn slows the vehicle. Calipers will be explained in greater detail in the Disc brakes Chapter.

Proportioning valve

This valve was once found only on vehicles with drum brakes on the rear wheels, but a lot of cars with four-wheel disc brakes use them, too. It's located in the hydraulic circuit to

1 Trailing shoe seat/adjuster screw
2 Adjuster star wheel
3 Adjuster detent
4 Washer
5 Screw
6 Bleed screw
7 Cover
8 Cup
9 Piston
10 Dust boot

Exploded view of a typical single piston wheel cylinder

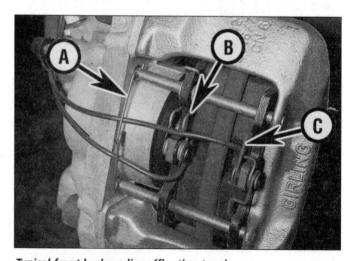

Typical front brake caliper (floating type)

A Retaining pin spring clip
B Inner pad anti-rattle spring
C Outer pad anti-rattle spring

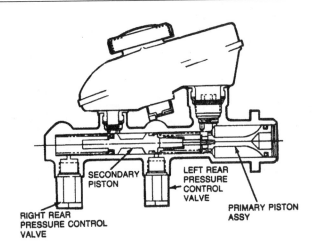

These pressure control valves, similar to proportioning valves, are screwed right into the rear brake outlets of the master cylinder (the outlets for the front brakes aren't shown in this illustration - they're on the other side of the master cylinder body)

the rear wheels and limits the amount of hydraulic pressure to the wheel cylinders or calipers to prevent rear wheel lockup during emergency stops. The proportioning valve is sometimes remotely mounted, but on some brake systems is built into the master cylinder *(see illustration)*.

On some vehicles, the proportioning valve has a fixed setting. It will regulate system pressure at the same rate, regardless of any other conditions. On other vehicles, especially (but not limited to) pick-ups and vans, a variable proportioning valve is used *(see illustrations)*. Sometimes it's called a pressure control valve or load-sensing proportioning

valve, but it does the same thing - it limits pressure to the rear brakes just as a normal proportioning valve does, but it's connected to a portion of the rear suspension by a linkage, which allows the valve to monitor ride height and the amount the rear end of the vehicle rises during hard stops. By doing so, the valve can more accurately regulate pressure to the rear brakes. If the vehicle is carrying a heavy load, the valve will allow more pressure to the rear brakes, since the rear of the vehicle won't tend to rise as much during a hard stop as the same vehicle with no load at all (which means there's more weight on the rear wheels, so they won't lock up too easily). It also helps the valve distinguish between a fairly hard stop and an all-out panic stop.

Brake hoses and pipes

Brake pipes and hoses are the conduit in which the hydraulic pressure from the master cylinder is transferred to the hydraulic cylinders at the wheel brakes. Non-flexible, steel tubing is used wherever possible. Where the brake lines must span a gap that moves - between the chassis and suspension or steering, for example - flexible brake hoses must be used.

Brake fluid

Brake fluid can be considered the "life blood" of the brake hydraulic system. Most vehicles on the road today use brake fluid conforming to DOT 3 or DOT 4 safety standards. DOT stands for (USA) Department Of Transportation, the governing body that sets the standards for brake fluid, among other things.

Never introduce any other liquid into the brake hydraulic system. Only a very small percentage of car manufacturers use anything other than brake fluid in their vehicles. Notably, some Citroëns use a type of mineral oil known as LHM in their brake systems. Brake fluid and mineral oil don't mix.

This variable rate proportioning valve is mounted to the underside of the vehicle and is connected by a rod to a rear suspension arm. When the rear of the vehicle is loaded, the valve will allow normal pressure to the rear brakes. During hard stops, the rear of the car will tend to rise, shifting the weight to the front. The valve will then reduce the pressure to the rear brakes, preventing the rear wheel from locking up

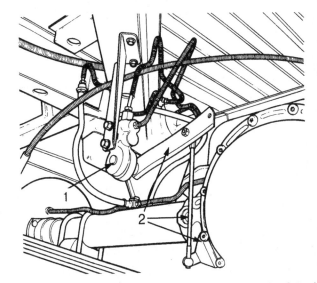

A typical example of a Load Sensing Proportioning Valve (LSPV)
1 *LSPV*   2 *Linkage*

If any other kind of fluid contaminates your brake system, the entire system must be drained, flushed and refilled with clean brake fluid. But, since it isn't possible to completely remove all fluid from the brake system, this means that every hydraulic component in the system must be removed, disassembled and fitted with new seals. Mineral oil or petroleum products are not compatible with the material that the brake system seals are made of. These liquids can cause the seals to swell and/or soften - either way, a very dangerous situation would be present.

As you can see, it is important that clean, uncontaminated brake fluid be used in the hydraulic system. It's a unique fluid, with more to its job than you might think. In addition to transmitting pressure, brake fluid must be able to:

a) *Maintain a constant viscosity.*
b) *Be compatible with the hoses and seals (i.e. all rubber/synthetic rubber components) in the hydraulic system.*
c) *Withstand heat - DOT 3 brake fluid has a 240°C boiling point.*
d) *Resist freezing.*
e) *Lubricate the sliding parts in the system.*
f) *Flow through small orifices with minimum resistance.*
g) *Resist the formation of sludge or gum deposits, regardless of temperature or pressure.*
h) *Prevent corrosion of metal parts.*
i) *Mix with other approved brake fluids.*
j) *Last, but certainly not least, last! Brake fluid must be able to do all of the above even after being in the system for an extended period of time (years).*

When adding brake fluid to the brake fluid reservoir, always use brake fluid from a small, sealed brake fluid container. Since brake fluid is hygroscopic (meaning it is able to absorb moisture), fluid stored in an open container, or even in a sealed large container (if it's been sitting on the

shelf for a long time) may contain too much moisture. If the fluid is laden with too much moisture, its boiling point is lowered. When the moisture-tainted brake fluid is subjected to the high heat of a modern brake system, the water molecules turn to gas, forming bubbles. This will cause a spongy feeling brake pedal. If the problem is serious enough it can cause complete brake failure. If this happens, the hydraulic system must be purged of all old brake fluid and filled with new fluid.

Take care when handling brake fluid. Some important points to remember are listed in the 'Hints & Tips' box.

Wheel brakes

Regardless of the type of brakes a vehicle may be equipped with, all brakes do the same thing; convert the energy of the moving vehicle into another form of energy - heat. They do this by rubbing parts together, and the resulting friction between the moving parts creates heat. The faster the brakes can create, absorb and dissipate heat, the faster the vehicle will slow down.

There are several factors that determine the efficiency of a brake. These are:

a) *The amount of pressure applied to the brake pads or shoes (more pressure = more friction).*
b) *The total area of the brake lining (greater area = more friction).*
c) *The diameter of the brake disc or drum (larger diameter = more powerful brake - like using a long lever to move a big rock).*
d) *The diameter of the vehicle's tyres (a tall tyre acts like a long lever turning the brake - the larger the diameter of the tyre, the more powerful the brake must be).*
e) *The coefficient of friction between the brake pads and disc or brake shoes and drum.*
f) *The ability of the brake to dissipate heat.*
g) *The coefficient of friction between the tyre contact patch and the ground.*

Creating friction is no problem, but dealing with the resulting heat has kept engineers busy for years, constantly searching for ways to improve braking efficiency. Even the brakes of years ago were pretty good at stopping a vehicle from a high rate of speed one or two times before allowing them to cool off, but as the brakes heated up, their ability to dissipate heat decreased, which reduced braking power. This frequently lead to brake fade, a condition that, when mild, requires more pedal effort from the driver to slow the vehicle. When severe, brake fade can lead to a complete loss of braking ability.

While the brakes fitted on modern vehicles are certainly not immune to brake fade, they are able to safely handle many more hard stops, one after the other, than the brakes on older vehicles. This is due to improved materials used in the construction of braking components and, to an even greater degree, advances in the design of wheel brakes, enabling them to disperse heat faster.

hints & tips

- Brake fluid is poisonous. If it is accidentally ingested, call a poison control centre or seek medical attention immediately.
- For the above reason, never store or dispose of brake fluid in a beverage container (when bleeding brakes, for example).
- If you get brake fluid on your skin, wash it off immediately with soap and water. It's a good idea to wear latex gloves when there's a possibility of coming into contact with brake fluid.
- Wear eye protection whenever bleeding the brakes or working around brake fluid. If you get brake fluid in your eyes, rinse them out with plenty of water, then seek medical attention.
- Brake fluid will damage paint. Be careful when working on the hydraulic system near painted components. Cover all exposed bodywork in the surrounding area. Immediately rinse off brake fluid spills with lots of water

Brake fade

Brake fade is a condition that can occur when the brakes have become overheated and lose their ability to create friction and dissipate heat. The driver of a vehicle experiencing complete brake fade finds himself/herself pushing on a hard brake pedal with no stopping ability. Eventually, glazed brake linings occur, which adds to the loss of braking power.

This problem is compounded on a drum brake set-up. The drums expand when they get hot, which adds to the distance the shoes must travel before they contact the friction surface. They also lose some of their rigidity and tend to flex outward when the brake shoes start pushing against them.

There's another danger associated with overheated brakes. If the brake fluid is not in top condition (if it's old and has absorbed a lot of moisture), the heat created by the brakes can be conducted to the hydraulic components, resulting in boiling brake fluid. If this happens, the driver is in even more trouble, because even if the brakes cool off enough to allow some degree of operation, the bubbles in the brake fluid will remain - the brake pedal will be soft and mushy and probably travel to the floor, unable to produce any pressure in the hydraulic system. This is because the gas bubbles in the brake fluid are compressible. The only way to get rid of them is to bleed the hydraulic system (at which time all of the old fluid should be purged and replaced with fresh brake fluid).

Brake fade is not only a heat problem - it can be brought on by water, too. While this condition isn't quite as dangerous as heat-induced fade (provided there isn't a parked car directly in front of you as you're trying to stop), it can take a driver by surprise.

The stopping capability of disc brakes isn't affected much by water; the spinning disc throws off the water, and any remaining moisture on the disc or pads is quickly vaporised shortly after the brakes are applied. Drum brakes, however, are very susceptible to water-induced fade.

When water enters a drum brake assembly (usually through the gap between the brake drum and the backing plate) it becomes trapped. It gets thrown outward by the centrifugal force of the spinning drum and acts like a lubricant between the shoes and the drum's friction surface. The problem is made worse when the water mixes with accumulations of brake dust. The resulting mud-like mixture takes longer to burn off than plain water.

If you find yourself experiencing water-induced brake fade, hold your foot down hard on the brake pedal - if there's no immediate change in braking action, release the brakes and apply them again (all the while trying to avoid any obstacles in your path). A couple of repeated applications of the pedal like this should clear up the problem.

Tools and equipment

Establish a place to work. It doesn't have to be particularly large, but it should be clean, safe, well-lit, organised and adequately equipped for the job. True, without a good workshop or garage, you can still service and repair brakes, even if you have to work outside. However, major repairs should be carried out in a sheltered area with a roof. Some of the procedures in this book require an environment totally free of dirt, which could cause contamination and subsequent failure if it finds its way into the brake system.

For some home mechanics, the idea of using the correct tool is completely foreign. They'll cheerfully tackle the most complex procedures with only a set of cheap open-end spanners of the wrong type, a single screwdriver with a worn tip, a large hammer and an adjustable spanner. Though they often get away with it, this cavalier approach is stupid and dangerous. It can result in relatively minor annoyances like stripped fasteners, or cause catastrophic consequences like brake failure. It can also result in serious injury.

A complete assortment of good tools is a given for anyone who plans to work on cars. If you don't already have most of the tools listed below, the initial investment may seem high, but compared to the spiralling costs of routine maintenance and repairs, it's worth while. Besides, you can use a lot of the tools around the house for other types of mechanical repairs. While some of the tools we'll describe aren't necessary to complete most brake repair operations, they are representative of the kinds of tools you would expect to find in a well-equipped workshop.

Buying tools

There are two ways to buy tools. The easiest and quickest way is to simply buy an entire set. Tool sets are often priced substantially below the cost of the same individually priced tools - and sometimes they even come with a tool box. When purchasing such sets, you often wind up with some tools you don't need or want. But if low price and convenience are your concerns, this might be the way to go. Keep in mind that you're going to keep a quality set of tools a long time (maybe the rest of your life), so check the tools carefully; don't skimp too much on price, either. Buying tools individually is usually a more expensive and time-consuming way to go, but you're more likely to wind up with the tools you need and want. You can also select each tool on its relative merits for the way you use it.

You can get most of the hand tools on our list from the tool department of any car accessory shop or similar chain that sells hand tools. Special tools are available from companies supplying the needs of professional mechanics. These companies can also supply the other tools you need, but they'll probably be more expensive.

Also consider buying second-hand tools from auctions or similar outlets. You may have limited choice in sizes, but you can usually determine from the condition of the tools if they're worth buying. You can end up with a number of unwanted or duplicate tools, but it's a cheap way of putting a basic tool kit together, and you can always sell off any surplus tools later.

Until you're a good judge of the quality levels of tools, avoid mail order firms, flea markets and car boot sales. Some of them offer good value for the money, but many sell cheap, imported tools of dubious quality. Like other consumer products counterfeited in the Far East, these tools run the gamut from acceptable to unusable.

If you're unsure about how much use a tool will get, the following approach may help. For example, if you need a set of combination spanners but aren't sure which sizes you'll end up using most, buy a cheap or medium-priced set (make sure the jaws fit the fastener sizes marked on them). After some use over a period of time, carefully examine each tool in the set to assess its condition. If all the tools fit well and are undamaged, don't bother buying a better set. If one or two are worn, renew them with high-quality items - this way you'll end up with top-quality tools where they're needed most and the cheaper ones are sufficient for occasional use. On rare occasions you may conclude the whole set is poor quality. If so, buy a better set, if necessary, and remember never to buy that brand again.

In summary, try to avoid cheap tools, especially when you're purchasing high-use items like screwdrivers, spanners and sockets. Cheap tools don't last long. Their initial cost plus the additional expense of replacing them will exceed the initial cost of better-quality tools.

Hand tools

A list of general-purpose hand tools you should have in your workshop

Adjustable spanner - 250 mm
Allen key set (4 mm to 10 mm)
Ball peen hammer
Brake bleeding kit
Brass hammer
Brushes (various sizes, for cleaning small parts)
Combination (slip-joint) pliers
Centre punch
Cold chisels
Combination spanner set (6mm to 19mm)
Dial indicator and base
Extensions - 25, 150, 250 and 300 mm
Feeler gauge set
Files (assorted)
Flare-nut (split ring) spanners
Floor jack
Gasket scraper
Hacksaw and assortment of blades
Impact screwdriver and bits
Locking pliers
Micrometer
Phillips screwdrivers
Pin punches
Pliers

Ratchet
Scraper (made from flattened copper tubing)
Scribe
Socket set (6-point sockets are preferred, but some fasteners require the use of 12-point sockets)
Soft-face hammer (plastic/rubber)
Spark plug socket (with rubber insert)
Spark plug gap adjusting tool
Standard screwdrivers
Steel ruler
Stud extractor set
Tap and die set
Thread gauge
Torque spanner (same size drive as sockets)
Torx socket(s)
Universal joint
Vacuum gauge/pump (hand-held)
Wire brush (large)
Wire cutter pliers

Special brake-related tools

Split ring spanners

These spanners, sometimes called flare nut spanners, are used for loosening and tightening hydraulic pipe fittings (tube nuts). Construction is similar to a six-point ring spanner, but a portion of one of the flats is cut out to allow the spanner to pass over a pipe or hose (*see illustration*). This design offers much more surface area of the spanner to be in contact with the flats on the fitting, which will prevent the fittings from being rounded off because the load is distributed over as much area as possible. They are also thicker than most open or ring spanners, which adds to the surface area in contact with the tube nut. **Caution:** *When*

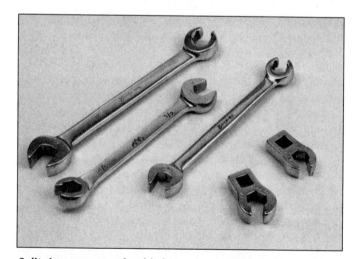

Split ring spanners should always be used when slackening or tightening pipe unions - the two odd shaped items on the right are split ring crows' feet, which are useful for unions that require being tightened to a specific torque

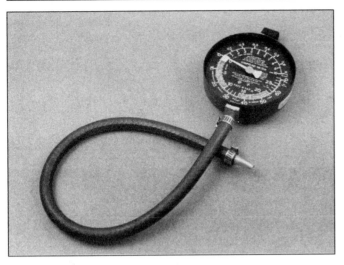

Vacuum gauge

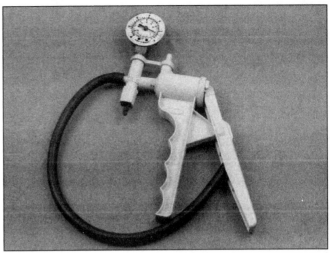

Hand operated vacuum pump

loosening a tube nut on a fitting connected to a flexible hose, always use a second spanner to hold the larger, female fitting stationary. This will prevent the hydraulic pipe from twisting.

Vacuum gauge

The vacuum gauge *(see illustration)* indicates intake manifold vacuum, in inches- or mm of mercury (in-Hg, mm-Hg). Brake servos depend on a healthy vacuum to operate properly. A hard pedal on a vehicle equipped with a vacuum-actuated brake servo would normally indicate a faulty servo, but before replacing anything it would be a good idea to check the intake manifold vacuum with a gauge like this.

Vacuum/pressure pump

The hand-operated vacuum/pressure pump *(see illustration)* can create a vacuum, or build up pressure, in a circuit to check components that are vacuum or pressure operated, such as brake servos.

Torx Bits

Many owners become surprised, sometimes even frustrated, when they tackle a service or repair procedure and run into a fastener with a little six-pointed, star-shaped recess in its head. These are called Torx head bolts and are becoming increasingly popular with automobile manufacturers, especially for mounting brake calipers *(see illustration)*. It's very important to use the proper Torx bit on these fasteners. Never try to use an Allen key on a Torx fastener - you'll strip the head out and really create a problem!

Caliper piston retraction tool

When replacing brake pads, the caliper piston(s) must be pushed back into the caliper to make room for the new pads. On some caliper designs (sliding calipers) this can be done before the caliper is removed, using an ordinary C-clamp. On other kinds of calipers (especially multiple-piston calipers) a caliper retraction tool is very helpful in accomplishing this task *(see illustration)*. You just unbolt the

Many late model vehicles use Torx head fasteners to secure the brake calipers - always use the proper size bit when slackening or tightening these bolts

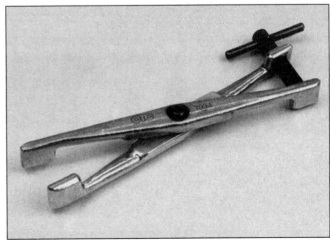

A tool like this is used for pushing the caliper piston(s) back into the caliper bore(s) to make room for the new brake pads

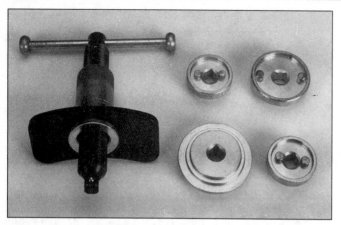

This universal brake caliper wind-back tool works on many different kinds of calipers and greatly facilitates brake pad renewal, especially on calipers with integral handbrake mechanisms

caliper, slide it off the brake disc, insert this tool between the pads and turn the screw - the piston(s) will be forced to the bottom of the bore(s).

Caliper piston wind-back tools

This kit *(see illustration)* combines two kinds of caliper piston retractors. One serves the same purpose as the tool described above. The other is for use on disc brake calipers with threaded handbrake actuators in the caliper pistons. On these calipers the pistons can't be pushed into their bores - they have to be rotated back in.

Here's another tool for turning the brake caliper pistons back into their bores *(see illustration)*. This one offers six different lug arrangements - one to fit almost any vehicle using this design caliper.

Brake spring pliers

Another kind of spring removal tool combines three spring tools in one *(see illustration)*. This is probably the most

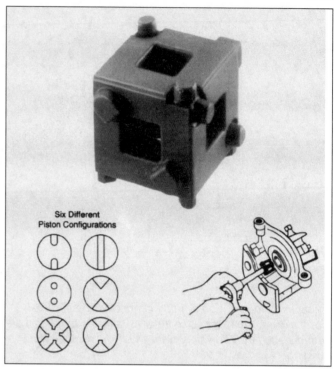

This six-in-one rear caliper piston retractor is an economical alternative to the universal disc brake caliper tool - it also simplifies the task of turning the piston and actuator screw rear calipers

versatile type of brake spring tool available and will work on just about any vehicle with drum brakes.

Hold-down spring tool

This tool, available in different sizes and designs, eases the removal of the brake shoe hold-down springs and cups *(see illustration)*. Just set the tool on the cup, push down and turn 90-degrees and ease up, and the cup and spring are removed.

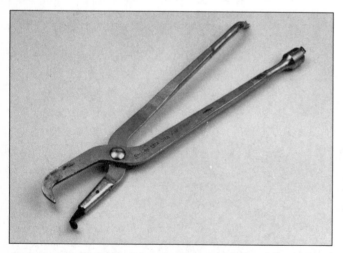

Brake spring pliers like this are able to handle just about any spring set-up you're likely to encounter and offer lots of leverage for removing and refitting those really strong springs

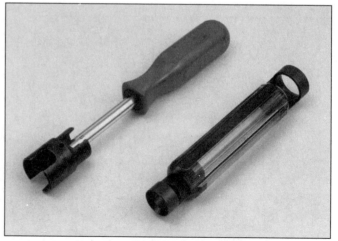

Pliers can be used to remove brake shoe hold-down springs, but if you don't want to fumble around and waste time, do it the right way and use a hold-down spring tool

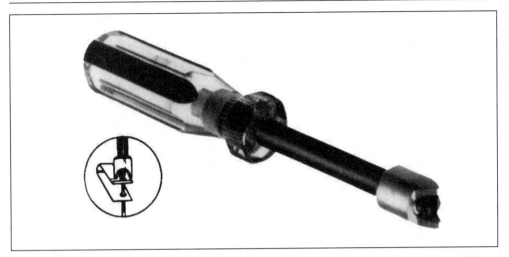

If the drum brakes you're working on use hold-down clips instead of springs, use a tool like this

Use hose clamps to prevent fluid loss and air ingress when removing brake calipers or drums etc.

Hold-down clip tool

Similar to the hold-down spring tool, this device simplifies the removal of brake shoe hold-down clips *(see illustration)*.

Brake shoe adjuster tool

These tools are available in a few different shapes to work on many different types of drum brakes, but they're all used for the same thing - to reach through the hole in the backing plate (or drum on some models) and turn the adjuster (or 'star') wheel to expand or retract the brake shoes *(see illustration)*.

Hose clamps

Hose clamps *(see illustration)*, are very useful tools, provided they are used correctly. Placed over a flexible hose and tightened, they will prevent fluid from flowing through the hose. It reduces the mess resulting from brake fluid running all over the place, and eliminates the need for completely draining the reservoir. **Warning:** *These tools should never be overtightened, or the internal structure of the hose may be permenantly damaged.*

Vacuum pump brake bleeding kit

When it's time to bleed the brakes and there aren't any friends around to pump the brake pedal for you, this device *(see illustration)* will allow you to finish the job. Just connect it to the bleed screw (follow the tool manufacturer's instructions), open the screw and operate the pump. All air will be drawn from the portion of the system you're bleeding.

One-man brake bleeding kit

This tool *(see illustration)* will also let you complete the brake bleeding procedure by yourself. It's basically a container and hose with a one-way valve in it. This allows you to open the bleed screw, pump the pedal to purge the system of air without any air or old fluid being drawn back into the system.

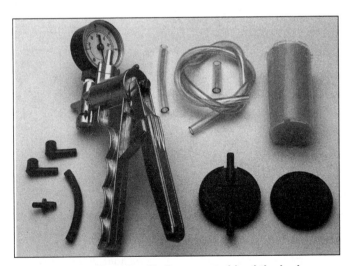

This brake bleeding kit will allow you to bleed the brake system by yourself

The one-man brake bleeder helps you achieve the same objective as the vacuum plump bleeder kit, but it's less expensive. The only drawback is that you'll have to get out from underneath the car, hop into the driver's seat, pump the pedal a few times, then get out and tighten the bleed screw

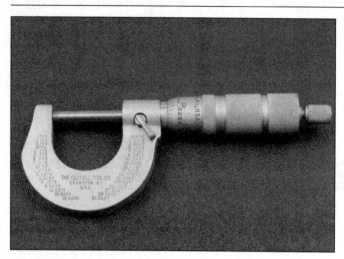

The micrometer is and essential precision measuring device for determining the thickness or brake discs

The dial test indicator (DTI) is the only way to measure brake disc runout accurately

Micrometers

The most accurate way to measure the thickness of a brake disc is with a micrometer. When doing a brake job or just checking your brakes, you'll have to confirm that the discs haven't worn down to their minimum thickness, or that there's enough material left to allow machining *(see illustration)*.

Dial test indicators

The dial indicator *(see illustration)* is another measuring mainstay. You'll use this tool for measuring brake disc runout (warpage).

Buy a dial indicator set that includes a flexible fixture and a magnetic stand *(see illustration)*. If the model you buy doesn't have a magnetic base, buy one separately. Make sure the magnet is strong. Also make sure the arm that attaches the dial indicator to the flexible fixture is sturdy and the locking clamps are easy to operate.

Safety items that should be in every workshop

Fire extinguishers

Buy at least one fire extinguisher *(see illustration)* before doing any maintenance or repair procedures. Make sure it's rated for flammable liquid fires. Familiarise yourself with its

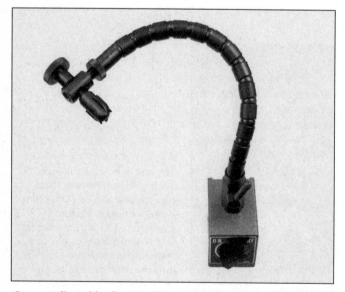

Get an adjustable, flexible fixture like this one, and magnetic base, to ensure maximum versatility from you DTI

Buy at least one fire extinguisher before you start - make sure it's rated for flammable liquid fires

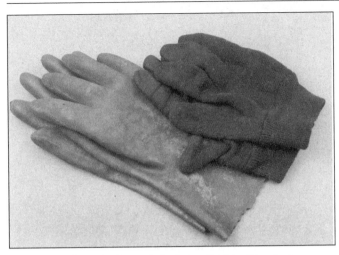

Get a pair of heavy duty work gloves for handling hot or sharp-edged objects and a pair of rubber gloves for washing parts with solvent or brake cleaner

One of the most important items you'll need in the workshop is a face shield or safety goggles, especially when using a grinder

use when you buy it - don't wait until you need it to figure out how to use it. And be sure to have it checked and recharged at regular intervals. Refer to the safety tips at the end of this chapter for more information about the hazards of fuel and other flammable liquids.

Gloves

If you're handling hot parts or metal parts with sharp edges, wear a pair of industrial work gloves to protect yourself from burns, cuts and splinters *(see illustration)*. Wear a pair of heavy duty rubber gloves (to protect your hands when you wash parts in solvent or brake cleaner.

Safety glasses or goggles

Never work on a bench or high-speed grinder without safety glasses *(see illustration)*. Don't take a chance on getting a metal sliver in your eye. It's also a good idea to wear safety glasses when you're washing parts and while bleeding brakes.

As many brake pads/shoes may contain asbestos, make sure you're wearing a filtering mask

Filtering mask

The linings of most brake pads and shoes contain asbestos, which is extremely hazardous to your health. The dust deposited all over your brakes (and wheels) is made up of a high percentage of asbestos fibres. Be sure to always wear a filtering mask *(see illustration)* when working on or around your brakes - it'll greatly reduce the risk of inhaling asbestos fibres.

Fasteners

Fasteners - nuts, bolts, studs and screws - hold parts together. Keep the following things in mind when working with fasteners: All threaded fasteners should be clean and straight, with good threads and unrounded corners on the hex head (where the spanner fits). Make it a habit to renew all damaged nuts and bolts. Almost all fasteners have a locking device of some type, either a lockwasher, locknut, locking tab or thread adhesive. Don't reuse special locknuts with nylon or fibre inserts. Once they're removed, they lose their locking ability. Fit new locknuts.

Flat washers and lockwashers, when removed from an assembly, should always be refitted exactly as removed. Renew any damaged washers. Never use a lockwasher on any soft metal surface (such as aluminium), thin sheet metal or plastic.

Apply penetrant to rusted nuts and bolts to loosen them up and prevent breakage. Some mechanics use parafin in a spout-type oil can, which works quite well. After applying the rust penetrant, let it work for a few minutes before trying to loosen the nut or bolt. Badly rusted fasteners may have to be chiselled or sawed off or removed with a special nut breaker, available at tool shops.

If a bolt or stud breaks off in an assembly, it can be drilled and removed with a special tool commonly available for this purpose. Most automotive engineers can perform this task, as well as other repair procedures, such as the repair of threaded holes that have been stripped out.

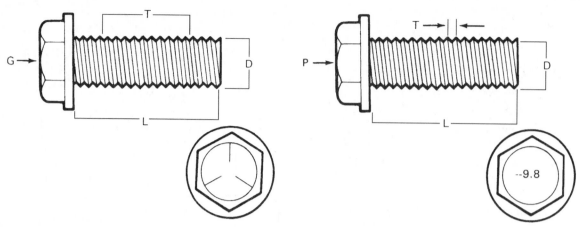

Imperial bolt dimensions/grade marks on the left, and metric bolt dimensions/grade marks on the right

G Grade marks (bolt strength)
L Length (in inches)
T Thread pitch (number of threads per inch)
D Nominal diameter (in inches)

P Property class (bit strength)
L Length (in millimeters)
T Thread pitch (distance between threads in millimeters)
D Diameter

Fastener sizes

All bolts, whether imperial or metric, are sized in accordance with their diameter, thread pitch and length (see illustration). For example, an imperial 1/2-13 x 1 bolt is 1/2 inch in diameter, has 13 threads per inch and is 1 inch long. An M12-1.75x25 metric bolt is 12mm in diameter, has a thread pitch of 1.75 mm (the distance between threads) and is 25 mm long. The two bolts are nearly identical, and easily confused, but they are not interchangeable.

In addition to the differences in diameter, thread pitch and length, metric and imperial bolts can also be distinguished by examining the bolt heads. The distance across the flats on an imperial bolt head is measured in inches; the same dimension on a metric bolt or nut is sized in millimetres. So don't use an Imperial spanner on a metric bolt, or vice versa.

Most imperial bolts also have marks radiating out from the centre of the head (see illustration) to denote the grade or strength of the bolt, which is an indication of the amount of torque that can be applied to it. The greater the number of marks, the greater the strength of the bolt. Grades 0 through 5 are commonly used on cars. Metric bolts have a property class (grade) number, rather than a mark, moulded into their heads to indicate bolt strength. In this case, the higher the number, the stronger the bolt. Property class numbers 8.8, 9.8 and 10.9 are commonly used on cars.

Strength markings can also be used to distinguish imperial hex nuts from metric hex nuts. Many imperial nuts have dots stamped into one side, while metric nuts are marked with a number (see illustrations). The greater the number of dots, or the higher the number, the greater the strength of the nut.

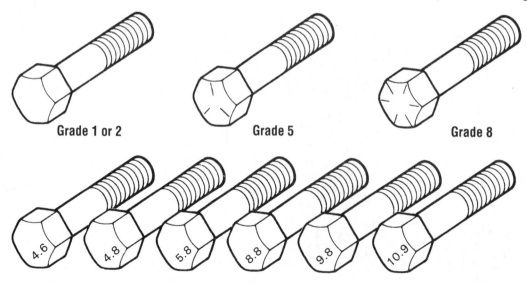

Grade 1 or 2   Grade 5   Grade 8

4.6   4.8   5.8   8.8   9.8   10.9

Bolt strength markings(top - Imperial; bottom - metric)

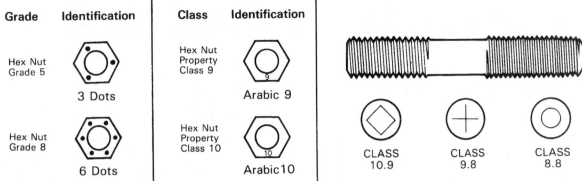

Imperial nut strength markings on the left, metric nuts in the centre, and metric studs to the right

Metric studs are also marked on their ends *(see illustration)* according to property class (grade). Larger studs are numbered (the same as metric bolts), while smaller studs carry a geometric code to denote grade.

It should be noted that many fasteners, especially Grades 0 through 2, have no distinguishing marks on them. When such is the case, the only way to determine whether it's imperail or metric is to measure the thread pitch or compare it to a known fastener of the same size.

Imperial fasteners are often referred to as SAE, as opposed to metric. However, it should be noted that SAE technically refers to a non-metric fine thread fastener only.

Since fasteners of the same size (both imperial and metric) may have different strength ratings, be sure to refit any bolts, studs or nuts removed from your vehicle in their original locations. Also, when replacing a fastener with a new one, make sure that the new one has a strength rating equal to or greater than the original.

Metric thread sizes	Ft-lbs	Nm
M-6	6 to 9	9 to 12
M-8	14 to 21	19 to 28
M-10	28 to 40	38 to 54
M-12	50 to 71	68 to 96
M-14	80 to 140	108 to 190

Pipe thread sizes		
1/8	5 to 8	7 to 10
1/4	12 to 18	17 to 24
3/8	22 to 33	30 to 44
1/2	25 to 35	34 to 47

U.S. thread sizes		
1/4 – 20	6 to 9	9 to 12
5/16 – 18	12 to 18	17 to 24
5/16 – 24	14 to 20	19 to 27
3/8 – 16	22 to 32	30 to 43
3/8 – 24	27 to 38	37 to 51
7/16 – 14	40 to 55	54 to 74
7/16 – 20	40 to 60	54 to 81
1/2 – 13	55 to 80	75 to 108

Specific torque value charts

Tightening sequences and procedures

Most threaded fasteners should be tightened to a specific torque value **(see charts)**. **Warning:** These are general torque specifications for conventional fasteners. Some fasteners used in the brake system (most notably the disc brake caliper bolts or guide pins) are specifically designed for their purposes and would not fall into the categories listed below. Torque is the twisting force applied to a threaded component such as a nut or bolt. Overtightening the fastener can weaken it and cause it to break, while undertightening can cause it to eventually come loose. Bolts, screws and studs, depending on the material they are made of and their thread diameters, have specific torque values. Be sure to follow torque recommendations closely. For fasteners not assigned a specific torque, a general torque value chart is presented here as a guide. These torque values are for dry (unlubricated) fasteners threaded into steel or cast iron (not aluminium). As was previously mentioned, the size and grade of a fastener determine the amount of torque that can safely be applied to it. The figures listed here are approximate for Grade 2 and Grade 3 fasteners. Higher grades can tolerate higher torque values.

How to remove broken fasteners

Sooner or later, you're going to break off a bolt inside its threaded hole. There are several ways to remove it. Before you buy an expensive extractor set, try some of the following cheaper methods first.

First, regardless of which of the following methods you use, be sure to use penetrating oil. Penetrating oil is a special light oil with excellent penetrating power for freeing dirty and rusty fasteners. But it also works well on tightly torqued broken fasteners.

If enough of the fastener protrudes from its hole and if it isn't torqued down too tightly, you can often remove it with self-locking pliers. If that doesn't work, or if the fastener doesn't provide sufficient purchase for pliers, try filing it down to take a spanner, or cut a slot in it to accept a screwdriver *(see illustration)*. If you still can't get it off - and you know how to weld - try welding a flat piece of steel, or a nut, to the top of the broken fastener. If the fastener is broken off

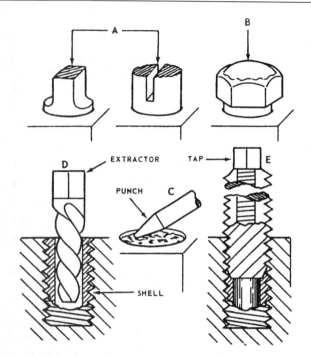

There are several ways to remove a broken fastener

A File it flat or slot it
B Weld a nut on it
C Use a punch to unscrew it
D Use a stud extractor
E Use a tap to remove the shell

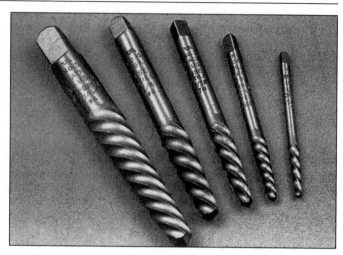

Typical assortment of stud extractors

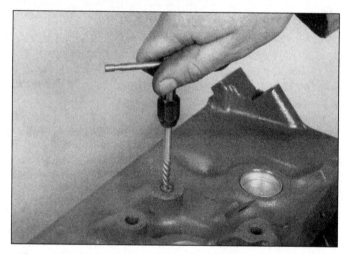

When screwing in the stud extractor, make sure it's centred properly

flush with - or below - the top of its hole, try tapping it out with a small, sharp punch. If that doesn't work, try drilling out the broken fastener with a bit only slightly smaller than the inside diameter of the hole. This leaves a shell which you can pick out with a sharp chisel.

If none of the above techniques work, you'll have to resort to some form of screw or stud extractor *(see illustration)*. These are sold in sets which can remove anything from 6 mm to 24 mm bolts or studs. Most extractors are fluted and tapered high-grade steel. To use a screw extractor, drill a hole slightly smaller than the OD of the extractor you're going to use. (Extractor sets include the manufacturer's recommendations for what size drill bit to use with each extractor size.) Then screw in the extractor *(see illustration)*. Extractors are reverse-threaded, so the action of screwing it in anti-clockwise will turn the broken fastener out of the hole.

A word to the wise: Even though a stud extractor will usually save your bacon, it can cause even more grief if you're careless or sloppy. Drilling the hole for the extractor off-centre, or using too small, or too big, a bit for the size of the fastener you're removing will only make things worse. So be careful!

Component disassembly

Disassemble components carefully to help ensure that the parts go back together properly. Note the sequence in which parts are removed. Make note of special characteristics or marks on parts that can be refitted more than one way, such

as a grooved thrust washer on a shaft. it's a good idea to lay the disassembled parts out on a clean surface in the order in which you removed them. It may also be helpful to make sketches or take a photo of the components before removal.

When you remove fasteners from a component, keep track of their locations. Thread a bolt back into a part, or put the washers and nut back on a stud, to prevent mix-ups later. If that isn't practical, put fasteners in a fishing tackle box or a series of small boxes. An egg box is ideal for this purpose - each cavity can hold the bolts and nuts from a particular area (i.e. sump bolts, valve cover bolts, engine mount bolts, etc.). A box of this type is helpful when working on assemblies with very small parts, such as the carburettor or valve train. Mark each cavity with paint or tape to identify the contents.

When you unplug the connector(s) between two wire harnesses, or even two wires, it's a good idea to identify the two halves with numbered pieces of masking tape - or a pair of matching pieces of coloured electrical tape - so they can be easily reconnected.

Disc brakes

Brake pad inspection and renewal	2
Brake disc inspection and renewal	3
Caliper overhaul	See Chapter 6
General information	1

1 General information

The disc brake differs from the drum brake in that the friction surface is external, allowing it to cool much more rapidly. There is little deflection or bending in a disc brake assembly, unlike in a drum brake. Friction is created by forcing two brake pads against a rotating disc *(see illustration)*. The disc is pinched between the pads, so the only part that could possibly flex is the caliper, but calipers don't flex very much. The result is a very efficient brake.

Most modern vehicles are equipped with disc brakes on the front wheels, at least. Many are equipped with discs at the rear, too. Since weight transfers to the front of the vehicle under braking, it is important to have more powerful brakes up front - they do most of the work.

Disc brakes have many advantages over drum brakes:

a) *Resistance to heat fade - disc brakes dissipate heat more rapidly because more of the braking surface is exposed to air. Heat also makes the discs a little thicker, which has no ill effects on braking (with a drum brake, heat tends to allow the drum to expand and flex).*

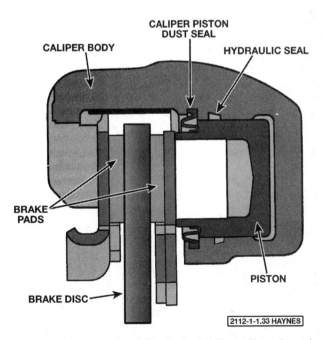

Cutaway of a typical front disc brake (sliding caliper shown)

b) *Resistance to water fade - rotation of the disc tends to throw off the water.*

c) *Better straight-line stops - because of their clamping action, disc brakes are less likely to pull.*

d) *Ease of serviceability - disc brake pads, in almost all cases, are easier to renew that drum brake shoes.*

e) *Lighter weight.*

f) *Cheaper to manufacture.*

The major components of a disc brake assembly are:

The brake disc, or rotor - This part is attached to the hub and turns with the wheel. The thickness and diameter of the disc determine how much heat the brake can absorb and dissipate. Some discs are vented to improve cooling.

The brake pads - These are composed of a steel backing plate to which the brake lining (friction material) is attached. Brake pad linings are attached by rivets or are bonded to the backing plate, just like the brake shoes in a drum brake. The composition of the lining is similar to a drum brake shoe, also.

The brake caliper - This is the component that squeezes the pads against the disc. It is a U-shaped casting that fits over the disc and pads. It contains at least one hydraulic cylinder, which converts the pressure developed by the master cylinder into mechanical energy. Calipers can have up to four pistons, or even more on exotic designs. The caliper is affixed to a mounting bracket that is bolted to the steering knuckle or suspension arm, or fastened to bosses that are integral with the knuckle.

Designs

There are three general designs of disc brakes, determined by caliper arrangement: Fixed caliper, floating calipers and sliding calipers.

Fixed caliper - In this design, the caliper is attached to the hub carrier (or a bracket attached to the carrier) and is stationary *(see illustrations).* A minimum of two opposing pistons must be used on this design - one to apply each pad. Some fixed calipers use four pistons (two per pad) and some even use three pistons (a large piston in one half of the caliper and two smaller ones in the other half).

As the brake pedal is applied, pressure from the master cylinder is distributed equally to the pistons, which are

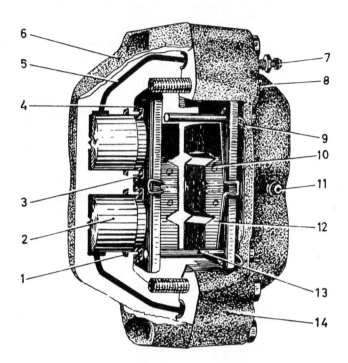

Cutaway of a typical fixed caliper

1 Piston seal	8 Bolt
2 Piston	9 Retaining clip
3 Dust boot	10 Brake pad
4 Dust boot retaining clip	11 Bleed screw
5 Fluid transfer channel	12 Anti-rattle spring
6 Caliper (outer half)	13 Pad retaining pin
7 Bleed screw	14 Caliper (inner half)

1 Caliper body
2 Outer pistons
3 Inner piston
4 Piston seals
5 Dust boot
6 Piston seal
7 Dust boot
8 Brake pad
9 Pad retaining pin
10 Clip
11 Bleed screw
12 Dust cap
13 Mounting shim
14 Anti-rattle spring

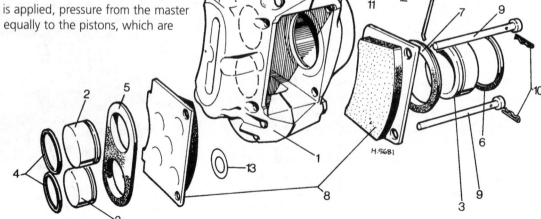

Exploded view of a three-piston fixed caliper

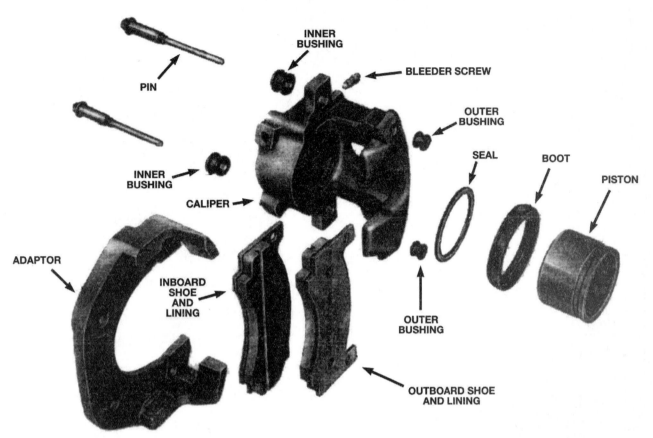

Exploded view of a typical single-piston floating caliper

forced against the brake pads, which squeeze the disc. The caliper doesn't move. Brake pads are usually retained by a pin (or pins) in this set-up.

Most fixed calipers are constructed of two castings containing the hydraulic pistons. The halves are bolted together, some having fluid passages leading from one half to the other. On other designs a fluid transfer tube leads from one side of the caliper to the other to supply the outer piston(s) with hydraulic pressure.

Some fixed calipers are equipped with springs behind the pistons, to keep the pistons from retracting more than just enough to relieve pressure on the disc. This ensures the pads stay right next to the disc (they actually rub against the disc, but with no pressure applied). The result is a firm brake pedal without an excessive amount of travel.

Floating caliper - The floating caliper uses a piston (two in some designs) only on one side of the caliper *(see illustration)*. The caliper is mounted on guide pins that ride in bushings or sleeves, so it is free to move back and forth. As hydraulic pressure builds up behind the caliper piston, the piston pushes on the inner brake pad, forcing it against the disc. As this happens, the inside of the caliper is pushed away from the disc, which simultaneously pulls the outside of the caliper into the outer brake pad, forcing it against the disc *(see illustration)*. The result is the same powerful

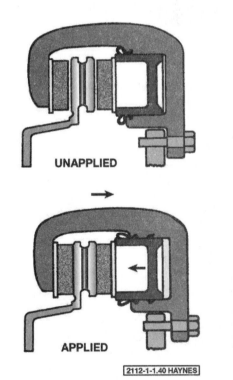

In a floating caliper, the action of the piston not only pushes the inner brake pad against the disc, it also pulls the outer brake pad against the disc (sliding calipers work like this too)

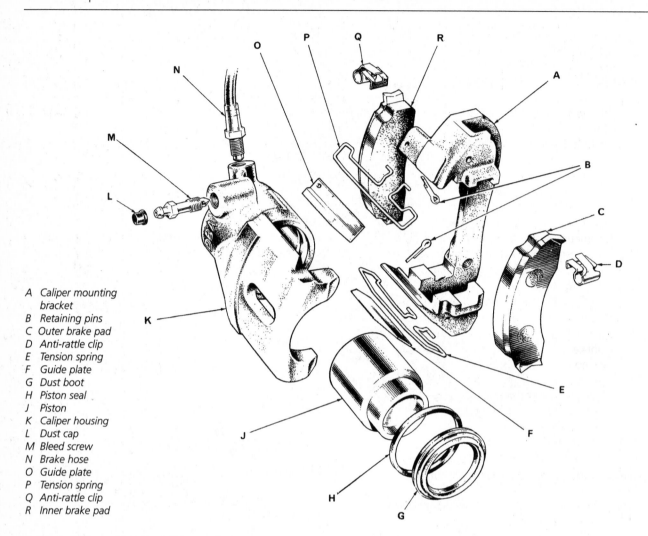

A Caliper mounting
   bracket
B Retaining pins
C Outer brake pad
D Anti-rattle clip
E Tension spring
F Guide plate
G Dust boot
H Piston seal
J Piston
K Caliper housing
L Dust cap
M Bleed screw
N Brake hose
O Guide plate
P Tension spring
Q Anti-rattle clip
R Inner brake pad

Exploded view of a typical sliding caliper

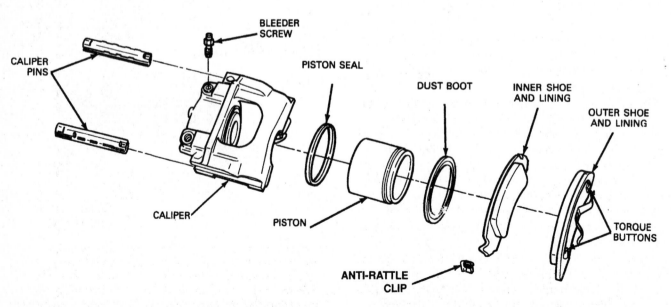

Here's another kind of sliding caliper - the caliper pins are spring steel to ensure a tight fit after they're driven into place

clamping action without the complexity of multiple pistons.

Another advantage of the floating caliper is the tendency to absorb pulsations caused by disc runout (wobble). With a fixed caliper, a warped disc will push the pistons back slightly with every rotation of the disc (this is called knockback). Under braking, this will be transmitted back through the hydraulic system to the brake pedal, causing it to pulsate under the driver's foot. In a floating caliper set-up, the caliper will move back and forth with the pads as the warped disc moves them back and forth, eliminating almost all of the pulsating at the brake pedal.

The outer brake pad in a floating caliper set-up is usually affixed to the caliper housing by a retaining spring or tangs. The inner pad is sometimes fastened to the caliper piston or is retained by the caliper mounting bolts. There are exceptions, though. On some designs, both pads ride in the caliper bracket.

In addition, floating calipers are much easier to service than fixed calipers, and are cheaper to manufacture.

Sliding caliper - The sliding caliper is a variation of the floating caliper. Unlike the floating caliper, however, the sliding caliper uses no guide pins; instead, a pair of machined abutments on the caliper adapter position and align the caliper. Retaining clips, springs, keys or "wedge"- type pins keep the caliper on machined guides (sometimes called "ways") on the adapter, allowing lateral movement of the caliper *(see illustrations)*.

In a sliding caliper set-up, the brake pads sometimes ride on the machined abutments of the caliper adapter. In other designs, one of the pads rides on the adapter and the other pad is affixed to the caliper - either the frame or the piston.

Apart from the way the caliper is mounted and the method of retaining the brake pads, operation of the sliding caliper is the same as the floating caliper.

Operation

We've actually discussed how the caliper works, but there's an important feature of brake calipers that we haven't covered yet, and that is the self-adjusting capability of the brake caliper.

The piston in a brake caliper fits in its bore with very little clearance (no more than 0.12 mm). To hold the hydraulic fluid in the caliper under pressure, the piston is surrounded by an O-ring near the opening in the piston bore. There's also a dust boot at the top of the piston, and on some calipers the boot seats in a groove just like the piston seal, but serves no purpose in fluid sealing at all. The O-ring seal is much larger than it needs to be for sealing purposes alone. It plays the main role in the self-adjusting feature of disc brakes.

When pressure from the master cylinder builds up behind the caliper piston, the piston is forced out and applies the brake pads. As the piston travels outward, the piston seal is distorted - it bends out with the piston *(see illustration)*. When the brakes are released, pressure behind the piston

subsides and the seal pulls the piston back home (remember, we're only talking about a fraction of a mm). As the pads wear down, the piston travels out a little farther, and even though the seal bends out with the piston, it can only go so far. So, the piston slides through the seal enough to take up the slack caused by the thinner brake pads. In doing so, the brake pedal remains firm and doesn't travel to the floor as the brake pads wear down.

Some older multi-piston calipers achieve the same self adjusting action by placing coil springs behind each piston.

As you can see, the disc brake has many advantages over the drum brake, but it has one disadvantage - there's no self-energising action. It could be compared to a drum brake with two trailing shoes. There are two ways to compensate for this: large caliper pistons and some form of power assist to help the driver supply the necessary pressure to the master cylinder.

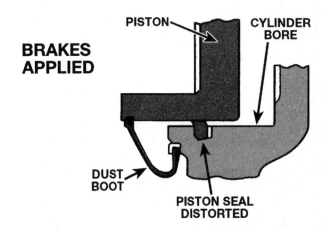

BRAKES APPLIED

PISTON — CYLINDER BORE

DUST BOOT

PISTON SEAL DISTORTED

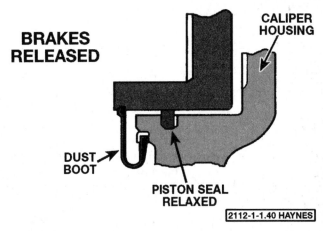

BRAKES RELEASED

CALIPER HOUSING

DUST BOOT

PISTON SEAL RELAXED

2112-1-1.40 HAYNES

These drawings illustrate the seal retraction action that takes place after the brakes are released. In the top drawing, pressure has pushed the piston from the bore a little. The piston seal has distorted and 'followed' the piston. In the bottom drawing, the brakes have been released, and the seal has pulled the piston back into the caliper.

Chapter 2

2 Brake pad inspection and renewal

> ⚠ *Warning: Disc brake pads must be renewed on both front or rear wheels at the same time - never renew the pads on only one wheel. Also, the dust created by the brake system may contain asbestos, which is harmful to your health. Never blow it out with compressed air and don't inhale any of it. An approved filtering mask should be worn when working on the brakes. Do not, under any circumstances, use petroleum-based solvents to clean brake parts. Use brake system cleaner only!*

The brake pad renewal procedures are covered through a sequence of illustrations, laid out in order from removing the old pads to fitting the new ones. The captions presented with the illustrations will walk you through the entire procedure, one step at a time. Work only on one brake assembly at a time, using the assembled brake for reference, if necessary.

Regardless of the type of brake you're working on, there are a few preliminary steps to be taken before yanking the old pads out. First, park the vehicle on a level surface, open the bonnet and locate the master cylinder - it's usually mounted on the bulkhead or the brake servo on the driver's side of the bulkhead (but on some vehicles it's on the other side of the engine compartment). Cover all painted areas around the master cylinder (wing included).

If you haven't already done so, this is a good time to put on your filtering mask, latex gloves and eye protection. Your hands aren't too dirty yet, and brake dust tends to get all over the wheels and inside of the wheel covers, so put them on before removing the wheels.

Next, remove the wheel covers (if fitted) from the front wheels and loosen the wheel nuts about one-half turn. Raise the vehicle and support it securely on axle stands. Remove the wheels, but remember to only work on one brake at a time.

Before touching or disassembling anything, clean the caliper, pads and disc with brake system cleaner and allow it to dry *(see illustration)*.

Now, refer to the appropriate procedure under Fixed caliper brake pad renewal, Sliding caliper brake pad renewal or Floating caliper brake pad renewal. Be sure to stay in order and read the captions that accompany each illustration. Before fitting the new pads, inspect the brake discs as outlined later in this Chapter, and replace them if necessary.

After you have successfully fitted the pads on one side of the vehicle, repeat the procedure on the other brake.

There are also a couple of things you must do before you can call the job complete. As soon as you have lowered the vehicle and tightened the wheel nuts securely, check the brake fluid level in the master cylinder reservoir. If necessary,

Before removing anything, clean the caliper and pads with brake cleaner and allow it to dry. Position a drain pan under the brake to catch the residue. Do NOT use compressed air to blow the dust from the parts.

add some to bring it to the desired level. Refit the reservoir cover or cap, but don't close the bonnet yet.

Before starting the engine, depress the brake pedal a few times to bring the pads into contact with the disc. The pedal will go to the floor for the first couple of pumps, but will build up after that. If this is not done, you'll probably crash into something on the other side of the street after you back out of your driveway!

Now that you have a solid brake pedal, recheck the fluid level. It may have gone down some as the piston(s) in the caliper were forced outward, shoving the pads up against the discs.

Lastly, before committing the vehicle to normal service, road test it in an isolated area, if possible. For the first few hundred miles or so, try to avoid hard braking to allow the new pads to bed in.

Fixed caliper

Tools required (these will suffice for most applications, however, the calipers on your vehicle may differ slightly):
Jack and axle stands
Wheel brace
Filtering mask
Safety glasses or goggles
Latex gloves
Hammer
Pin punch
Needle-nose pliers
Crowbar or large screwdriver (two in the case of three- or four-piston calipers)
Brake fluid receptacle

Materials required
Brake pads
Brake system cleaner
High temperature anti-seize compound
Brake fluid
Split pins (if applicable)

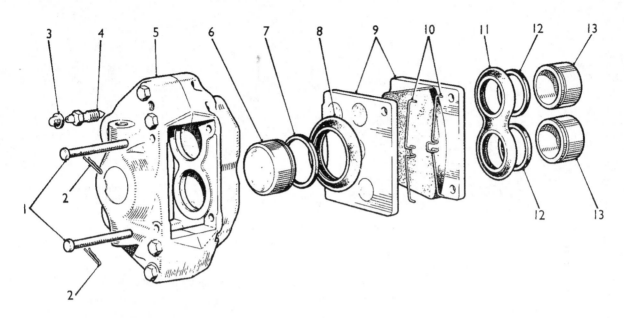

Exploded view of a typical fixed brake caliper assembly

1 Retaining pins	3 Dust cover	6 Piston (inner)	9 Pad assembly	11 Dust boot
2 Spring clip or	4 Bleeder screw	7 Piston seal	10 Anti-rattle	12 Piston seal
cotter pin	5 Caliper body	8 Dust boot	spring	13 Piston (outer)

Remove the old brake pads (fixed caliper)

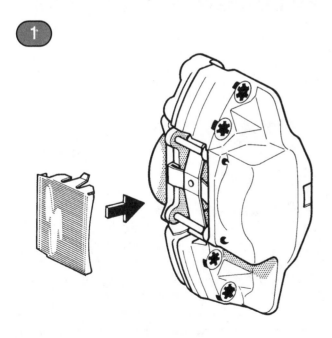

If equipped, prise off the cover from the caliper, noting how it's fitted.

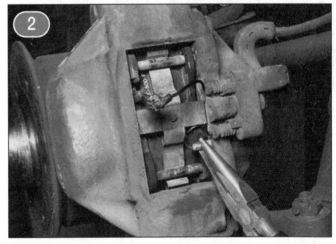

Some vehicles are equipped with electric wear sensors that plug into the pad backing plates. When the pads wear down to the sensors, the probes on the sensors earth out on the brake disc, completing the circuit and illuminating a warning light on the instrument panel. To remove these sensors, pull them out of the mounting holes with a pair of pliers. Note: If the pads have worn down to the sensors, be sure to renew the sensors.

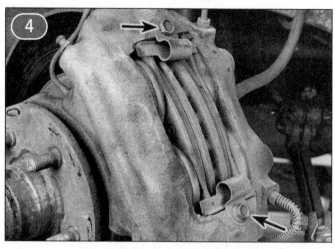

The brake pads on most fixed calipers are retained by one or two retaining pins. The retaining pins are usually secured by split pins, spring-steel clips or the ends of the anti-rattle springs. If your retaining pin has a split pin like this one, remove the split pin and discard it (a new pin must be used when refitting). If spring steel clips or the ends of the anti rattle springs secure the retaining pins, pull them out with a pair of pliers.

On some vehicles, the pads aren't secured by retaining pins, but are trapped in the caliper with two hold-down clips. To remove the clips, unscrew the bolts (arrowed).

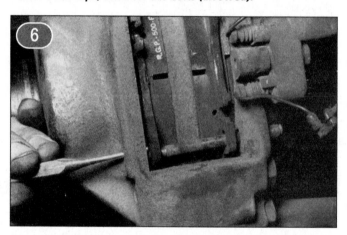

This caliper has retaining pins secured by spring steel clips. It is also equipped with anti-rattle springs - be careful not to let the springs fly out as you remove the retaining pins.

Use a hammer and a small punch to knock the retaining pins out of the caliper. Note: Some retaining pins, like the pins on this Mercedes, don't have retaining clips or split pins. Instead, the retaining ins are fitted with spring-steel collars around their heads that fit tightly into the holes in the caliper frame (if they don't fit tightly, renew them).

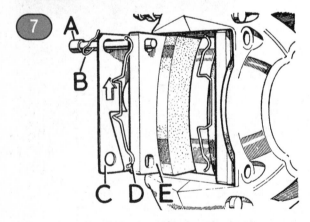

Typical brake pad arrangement on a fixed caliper

A Pin   B Retaining clip   C Shim   D Anti-rattle spring   E Pad backing plate

After removing the pad retaining pin(s), pull out one of the old brake pads (not both). You may need to use a pair of pliers to free the pad.

Preparation for fitting (fixed caliper)

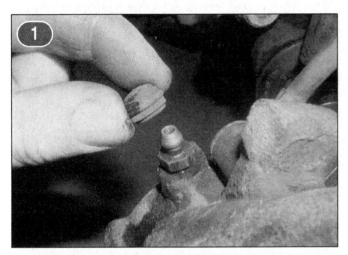

To make room for the new, thicker pad, the piston(s) must be pushed back into its bore as far as possible. However, it is essential that the old brake fluid is not forced back up the hoses/pipes, where it could cause problems with any ABS components fitted, or in some cases, may cause damage to the master cylinder seals. Fit a clamp to the flexible brake hose fitted to the caliper, and tighten moderately. Prise off the rubber cap (where fitted) ...

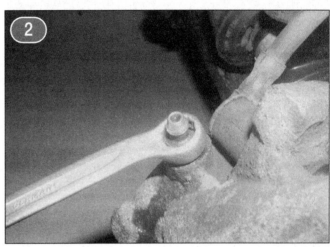

... fit a ring spanner over the bleed screw on the caliper, and connect a plastic hose to the screw. The other end of the hose should be in a suitable receptacle (jam jar etc.) ...

... slacken the bleed screw half a turn and push the piston(s) back into their bores. Old fluid should flow into the receptacle. A lever bar or large screw driver will work. If the caliper has two pistons, you'll need two levers/screwdrivers. Take care not to cock the pistons sideways at all. Damage to the piston, bore or seal could result. Before fitting the new pads, check for fluid leakage around the caliper piston. If any is found, the caliper should be overhauled.

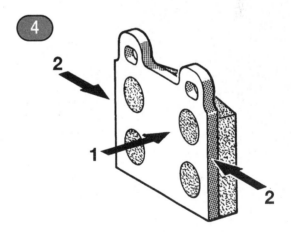

Prepare the new brake pads for fitting by applying an anti-seize compound to the backing plate (1) and to the edges (2) of the pads where they ride in the caliper. Note: Be sure to clean the caliper in the area where the brake pads make contact. Warning: Do not touch the pad friction material - if you get any grease on the pad, remove it immediately with brake system cleaner

Chapter 2

Fit the new pads (fixed caliper)

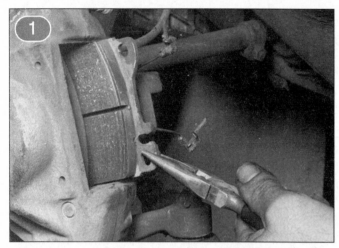

Insert the new pad into the caliper, along with the anti-rattle shim, if one was present when you tool the oil pad out. Note: Many anti-rattle shims are directional - they have an arrow stamped in them that must point in the same direction as the forward rotation of the brake disc. Remember, don't get any grease on the pad lining. After fitting the pad, repeat the procedure on the remaining pad.

Refit the retaining pins and anti-rattle springs (if equipped), of the hold-down springs. On this design, the rather stiff anti-rattle spring must be held down as the retaining pin is inserted.

Continue to drive the pins fully in. On models that use clips to secure the retaining pins, they can simply be pushed in, but on pins with spring-steel collars, like this Mercedes, you'll have to knock them in until they're seated. Install the retaining pin clip(s) or split pin(s). If equipped with pad wear sensors, insert the probes of the sensors into the holes in the pad backing plate.

All models

Repeat the entire procedure to renew the pads on the other wheel. Don't forget to pump the pedal a few times to bring the pads into contact with the disc. Be sure to then check the brake fluid level.

Sliding caliper

Tools required (these will suffice for most applications, however, the calipers on your vehicle may differ slightly):
Jack and axle stands
Wheel brace
Filtering mask
Safety glasses or goggles
Latex gloves
Large C-clamp or pad retraction tool
Needle-nose pliers
Length of wire (a straightened-out coat-hanger will work)
Spanner, socket, Allen key or hammer and punch, depending on caliper design (to remove caliper bolts or pins)
Brake fluid receptacle

Materials required
Brake system cleaner
Brake pads
Retaining clips, anti-rattle springs, caliper pins or keys (depending on caliper design), if damaged
High temperature anti-seize compound
Thread locking compound (non-hardening) (for calipers that are secured by bolts)
Brake fluid

Remove the caliper (sliding caliper)

To make room for the new, thicker pad, the piston(s) must be pushed back into its bore as far as possible. However, it is essential that the old brake fluid is not forced back up the hoses/pipes, where it could cause problems with any ABS components fitted, or in some cases, may cause damage to the master cylinder seals. Fit a clamp to the flexible brake hose fitted to the caliper, and tighten moderately. Prise off the rubber cap (where fitted), and connect a plastic pipe to the screw. The other end of the pipe should be in a suitable receptacle (jam jar etc.).

On most calipers, a C-clamp can be used to push the piston into its bore after the bleed screw has been opened half a turn. The old fluid should flow along the plastic pipe into the receptacle. Once the pistons have been retracted, tighten the bleed screw and remove the clamp. Due to the design of some calipers, the piston can only be retracted after the pads have been removed. DO NOT attempt to push back the pistons using this method on calipers with integral handbrake mechanisms.

On calipers held in place with a retainer clip and anti-rattle spring, unscrew the bolt and remove the clip and spring from each end of the caliper. Inspect the clip and anti-rattle spring from cracks and distortion.

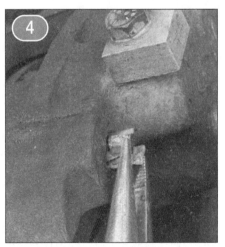

If your caliper is retained by pins that are driven into the slot between the caliper and the caliper mounting bracket, squeeze the end of the lower caliper pin with a pair of pliers and knock the pin into the groove as far as possible ...

... then use a hammer and punch to drive the pin out completely. Proceed to remove the upper pin in the same manner. Check the pins for rust or other damage. If they were very easy to remove or damaged, renew them.

If the caliper is secured by a key, remove the key retaining bolt ...

... then drive the caliper key out with a hammer and punch (take care not to lose the caliper support spring)

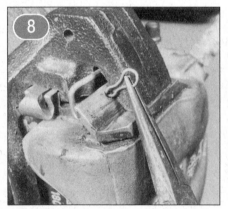

Another retention method (commonly used on Fiats), uses guide plates that wedge the caliper into the mounting bracket. To remove the caliper, pull out the retaining pin from the guide plate ...

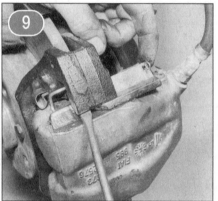

... the remove the guide plates ...

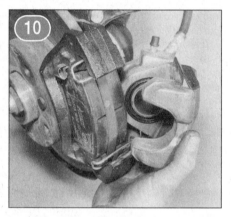

... and remove the caliper

If the caliper isn't to be removed for service, suspend it with a length of wire - don't let it hang by the brake hose.

Remove the brake pads (sliding caliper)

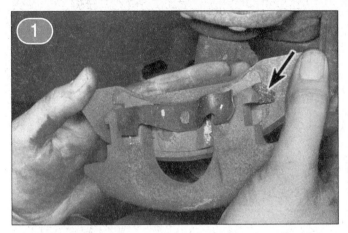

On some calipers, the outer pad is secured to the caliper by a spring clip. To remove the pad, push it towards the piston to dislodge the torque buttons (arrowed), then slide the pad out of the caliper

Some outer pads are held in the caliper frame by 'ears' on the pad backing plate. Most of the time these can simply be snapped out of the caliper, but if the pad sticks, knock it out with a hammer.

Remove the inner brake pad from the caliper bracket.

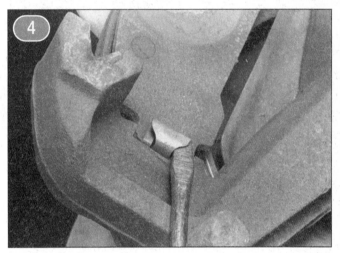

On models with an anti-rattle clip on the pad, use a screwdriver to prise the pad from the bracket

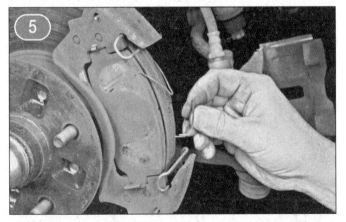

On some calipers, both pads ride in the caliper mounting bracket. Take note of any springs and shims that may be present, remove them, then prise the pads from the mounting bracket

Chapter 2

Preparation for fitting (sliding caliper)

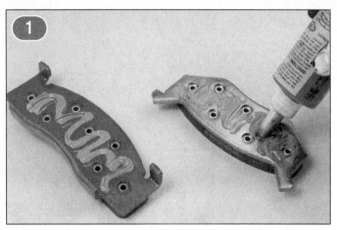

Apply a coat of anti-seize compound to the backing plates of the new pads.

If applicable, fit a new anti-rattle clip(s) onto the pad. Most sliding caliper designs use these clips on only one end of the inner pad (usually at the bottom)

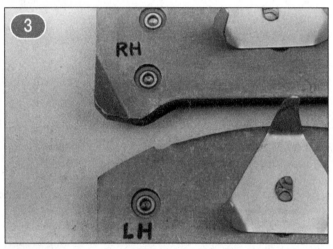

Some brake pads are marked for left and right sides of the vehicle - ensure they are fitted in the correct positions

If not already done so, a C-clamp can be used to push the piston into its bore after the bleed screw has been opened half a turn. DO NOT attempt to push back the pistons using this method on calipers with integral handbrake mechanisms.

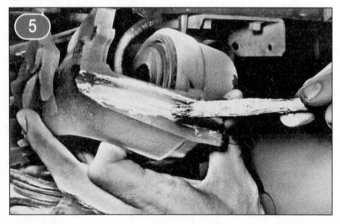

Clean the grooves on the ends of the caliper where it slides into the bracket. Also clean the grooves of the bracket, then apply a light film of high-temperature anti-seize compound to the sliding surface of the caliper ...

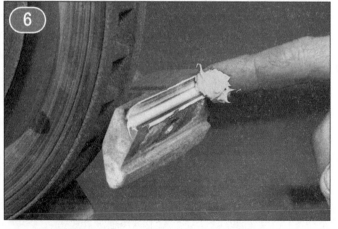

... or the sliding surfaces of the mounting bracket

Fit the new pads (sliding caliper)

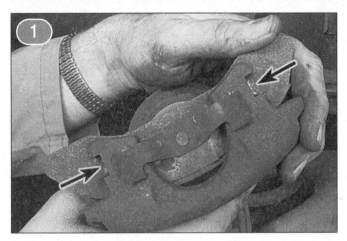

If the outer pads on your vehicle are secured to the caliper with a spring clip like this, push the pad into position on the caliper body, ensuring the torque buttons seat fully into the cut-outs (arrowed).

When you fit the new inner brake pad on a design like this, ensure the 'ears' (arrowed) at either end of the pad backing plate are properly seated into the machined surfaces of the caliper mounting bracket

On models that have an anti-rattle clips(s), set the lower end of the pad into the caliper mounting bracket, compress the clip and slide the upper end of the pad into position.

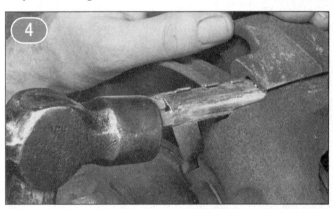

Refit the caliper over the brake pads and disc. On calipers retained by pins, set the pins in their grooves and drive them into place ...

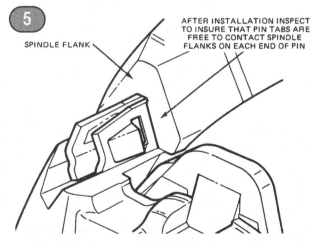

SPINDLE FLANK

AFTER INSTALLATION INSPECT TO INSURE THAT PIN TABS ARE FREE TO CONTACT SPINDLE FLANKS ON EACH END OF PIN

... making sure they are driven in completely. Make sure the pin tabs on each side of the mounting bracket are exposed

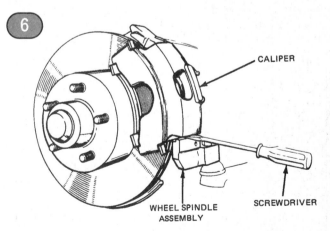

CALIPER

WHEEL SPINDLE ASSEMBLY

SCREWDRIVER

If the caliper is secured by a caliper key, insert a screwdriver between the mounting bracket and the caliper to create a gap for the key ...

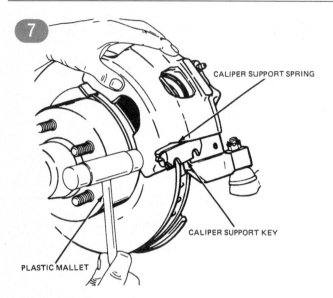

... then insert the caliper support key and spring clip into the slot. Drive the key and spring into place, then refit the bolt, tightening it securely.

If your caliper is retained by an anti-rattle spring and retainer clip, refit them. Apply a drop of locking compound to its threads, then tighten the bolts securely.

If your caliper is secured by guide plates, slide the plates into the gaps between the caliper and the mounting bracket, then refit the retaining pins.

All models

Repeat the entire procedure to renew the pads on the other wheel. Don't forget to pump the pedal a few times to bring the pads into contact with the disc. Be sure to then check the brake fluid level.

Floating caliper

Tools required (these will suffice for most applications, however, the calipers on your vehicle may differ slightly):
Jack and axle stands
Wheel brace
Filtering mask
Safety glasses or goggles
Latex gloves
Large C-clamp or brake pad retractor
Needle-nose pliers
Length of wire (a straightened-out coat-hanger will work)
Spanner, socket, Allen key or Torx key, depending on caliper design (to remove caliper bolts or pins)
Brake fluid receptacle

Materials required
Brake system cleaner
Brake pads
Caliper bushes and mounting bolts or guide pins (if worn or damaged)
High-temperature anti-seize compound
Brake fluid
Thread locking compound

Remove the caliper (floating caliper)

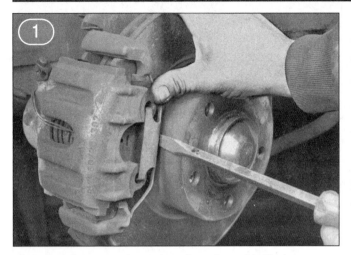

If equipped, remove the anti-rattle spring - this kind can simply be prised off

To remove the wire-type spring, prise out the ends of the spring from the caliper body …

… and pull them from place

To make room for the new, thicker pad, the piston(s) must be pushed back into its bore as far as possible. However, it is essential that the old brake fluid is not forced back up the hoses/pipes, where it could cause problems with any ABS components fitted, or in some cases, may cause damage to the master cylinder seals. Fit a clamp to the flexible brake hose fitted to the caliper, and tighten moderately. Prise off the rubber cap (where fitted), and connect a plastic pipe to the bleed screw. The other end of the pipe should be in a suitable receptacle (jam jar etc.).

A C-clamp can be used to push the piston into its bore after the bleed screw has been opened half a turn. The old fluid should flow along the plastic pipe into the receptacle. When the piston is fully retracted, tighten the bleed screw and remove the clamp. Due to the design of some calipers, the piston can only be retracted after the pads have been removed. With the piston retracted, remove the hose clamp. DO NOT attempt to push back the pistons using this method on calipers with integral handbrake mechanisms.

Some calipers are secured only by the upper and lower guide pin bolts (arrowed)

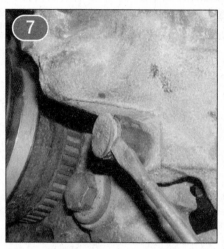

Prise out the rubber cap ...

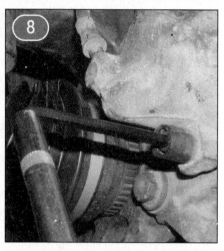

... and use an Allen key or Torx bit to slacken ...

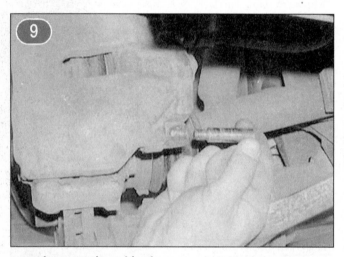

... and remove the guide pins

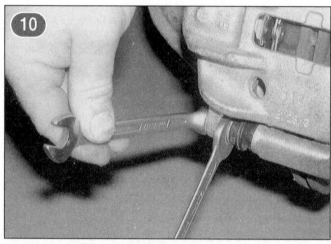

On some calipers, slacken the guide pin bolts whilst counterholding the guide pins with a second spanner

On many designs of floating caliper, it's only necessary to remove the lower guide pin/bolt, then pivot the caliper upwards to gain access to the pads

Don't allow the caliper to hang by the brake hose - suspend it from the coil spring or other suspension part with a piece of wire

Remove the brake pads (floating caliper)

On some calipers, the outer pads are fitted to the mounting bracket ...

... whilst the inner pad clips into the caliper piston

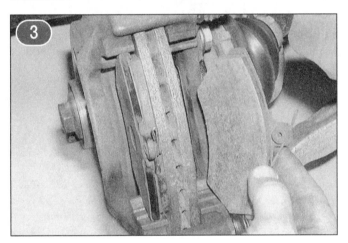

On others, both pads are fitted into the caliper mounting bracket

Some outer pads are clipped to the caliper. Push the pad away from the caliper and slide it off

Preparation for fitting (floating caliper)

If not already done so, to make room for the new, thicker pad, the piston must be pushed back into its bore as far as possible. However, it is essential that the old brake fluid is not forced back up the hoses/pipes, where it could cause problems with any ABS components fitted, or in some cases, may cause damage to the master cylinder seals. Fit a clamp to the flexible brake hose fitted to the caliper, and tighten moderately. Prise off the rubber cap (where fitted), and connect a plastic pipe to the bleed screw. The other end of the pipe should be in a suitable receptacle (jam jar, brake bleed kit etc.).

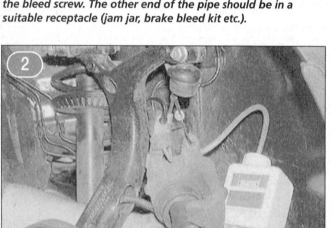

Undo the bleed screw half a turn, and push the piston back using a C-clamp, or ideally, a piston retraction tool. As the piston retracts fluid should flow into the receptacle. As soon as the piston is fully home, tighten the bleed screw, and remove the clamp. DO NOT attempt to push back the pistons using this method on calipers with integral handbrake mechanisms.

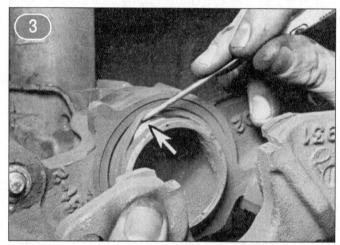

Carefully peel back the piston boot (arrowed) and check for corrosion and leaking fluid. If any is present, overhaul or renew the caliper.

Check the anti-rattle clips, if present, for cracks and distortion. Fit new ones if necessary.

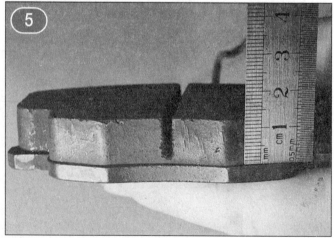

Measure the thickness of the pad, and replace them if one is below the specification given in the appropriate Service and Repair manual. Note that some manufacturers specify a minimum thickness of the friction material, whilst others specification includes the thickness of the backing plate

Fit the new brake pads (floating caliper)

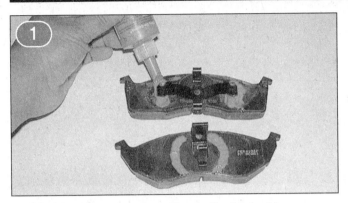

If the new pads don't come with an adhesive backing, sparingly apply a film of high-temperature anti-seize compound (Copperslip) to the backing plates.

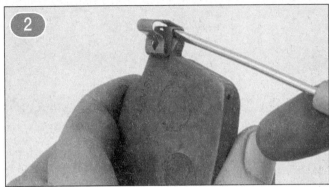

If the old pads were equipped with anti-rattle springs like this, prise them off and transfer them to the new pads. If they are worn or bent, renew them.

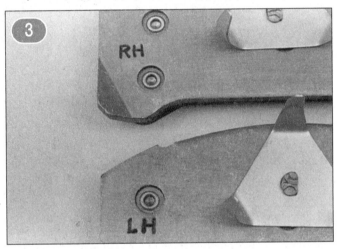

Some pads are marked for the left and right sides of the vehicle - ensure they are fitted correctly.

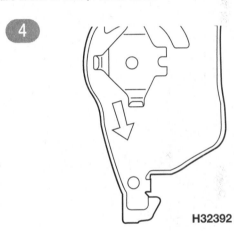

H32392

Some pads are marked for normal rotational direction. Fit the pads with the arrows pointing in the normal direction of rotation.

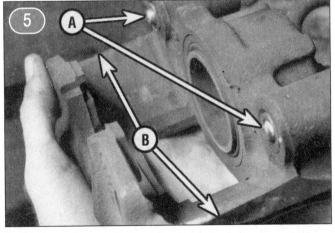

Inspect the caliper bolts, and bushes (A) for damage and the contact surfaces (B) for corrosion. Clean the contact surfaces with brake system cleaner and emery paper if they are dirty. Check the guide pin gaiters for damage. Replacement gaiters may be available - check with your retailer.

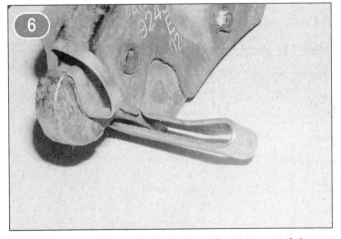

On some, an audible warning sensor is fitted to one of the pads. As the pad wears down the sensor comes into contact with the spinning disc, and emits a screech to alert the driver.

Some pads come with a chamfer at one end of the friction material. Fit the pads so that this chamfered end is the leading edge, ie. the first edge of the pad to contact the disc as it spins.

Refit the pads (and anti-rattle shims where fitted) to the caliper mounting bracket ...

... or to the caliper - where applicable.

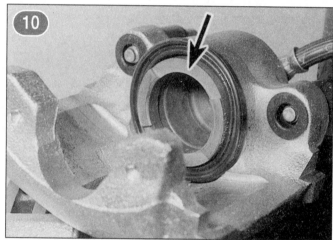

On some, the caliper piston must be rotated into a certain position. Here the piston cutaway (arrowed) must be parallel with the caliper body.

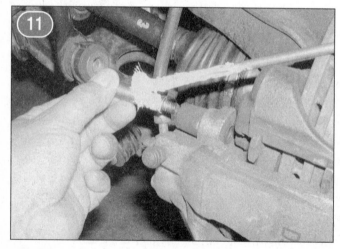

Install the caliper over the disc. then clean and lubricate the guide pins with high-temperature anti-seize compound. Fit the pins and tighten them to the correct torque. Don't forget to refit the rubber caps.

Where separate guide pin bolts are used, manufacturers often insist that the bolts are renewed. If the old bolts are to be reused, apply a little thread locking compound to the threads ...

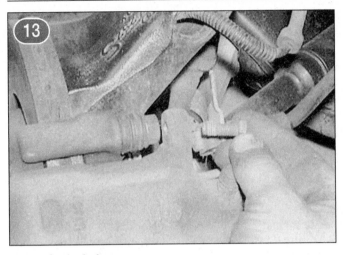

.. then fit the bolts ...

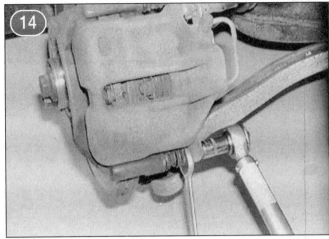

.. and tighten them to the correct torque.

All models

Repeat the entire procedure to renew the pads on the other wheel. Don't forget to pump the pedal a few times to bring the pads into contact with the disc. Be sure to then check the brake fluid level.

Brake pad renewal - calipers with integral handbrake mechanisms

To renew the brake pads on vehicles that have handbrake mechanisms built into the calipers, follow the procedure under the appropriate heading (fixed, sliding or floating caliper brake pad renewal) to remove the caliper and extract the brake pads. The only differences you'll encounter when replacing the pads on a caliper with an integral handbrake mechanism are these:

a) Sometimes it's necessary to unclip the brake hose and/or the handbrake cable from a bracket to allow caliper removal. In almost all cases, though, the brake hose can remain attached to the caliper.

b) DO NOT attempt to push the piston into the caliper bore by using a C-clamp. To make room for the new pads, the caliper piston will have to be bottomed in its bore, but on most models you can't do it by only pushing the piston in. The piston will have to be turned at the same time as being pushed in, like a big screw (see illustrations).

c) After the job has been completed, operate the handbrake until satisfactory handbrake pedal or lever travel is obtained.

On calipers with integral handbrake mechanisms, the piston must be pushed back and screwed in at the same time, using a special tool (easy) ...

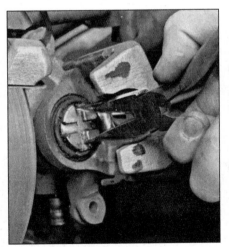

... or a pair of pliers (difficult)

Often the piston must be positioned so that a cutout in its face aligns with a peg (arrowed) on the pad backing plate.

Chapter 2

3   Brake disc inspection and renewal

> ⚠️ *Warning: The dust created by the brake system may contain asbestos, which is harmful to your health. Never blow it out with compressed air and don't inhale any of it. An approved filtering mask should be worn when working on the brakes. Do not, under any circumstances, use petroleum-based solvents to clean brake parts. Use brake system cleaner only!*

Inspection

If you haven't already done so, loosen the wheel nuts/bolts, raise the front of the vehicle and support it securely on axle stands. Remove the wheels.

Refit the wheel nuts/bolts and tighten them securely. This clamps the disc tightly against the hub and will allow for an accurate runout (warpage) check. If you tighten the wheel nuts but there's still a gap between the nut/bolt and the hub, fit washers between the nuts/bolts and the hub.

Turn the brake disc - if it is difficult to turn, depress the piston(s) in the caliper with a C-clamp (sliding and floating calipers) or, in the case of fixed calipers, prise the brake pads away from the disc a little.

Visually inspect the disc surface for score marks and other damage *(see illustration)*. Light scratches and shallow grooves are normal after use and won't affect brake operation. Deep grooves - over 0.40 mm deep - require disc replacement. Be sure to check both sides of the disc.

To check disc runout, place a dial indicator at a point about 12 mm from the outer edge of the disc *(see illustration)*. Set the indicator to zero and turn the disc. Generally, the indicator reading should not exceed 0.01 mm. If it does, the disc should be refinished by an automotive machine shop.

The brake pads on this vehicle were obviously neglected, as they wore down to the rivets and cut deep grooves into the disc - wear this severe means the disc must be renewed.

To check disc runout, mount a dial test indicator as shown and rotate the disc.

Some manufacturers allow for more runout than 0.01 mm, but runout is not desirable - the less the better. Some manufacturers regard a runout of 0.01 mm to be excessive.

The minimum wear dimension is stamped or cast into the centre of the disc ...

... on the disc 'hat' area ...

... or on the edge of the disc.

Use a micrometer to measure the disc thickness.

The disc must not wear below the specified minimum thickness. The minimum (or discard) thickness is sometimes cast into the disc *(see illustrations)*. The disc thickness can be checked with a micrometer *(see illustration)*. Measure the thickness in several places around the disc. You shouldn't wind up with readings that are more than 0.013-mm different. If you do, the disc parallelism is out of the range that most manufacturers specify as acceptable. If the disc can be reused, use a swirling motion and deglaze them with sandpaper or emery cloth *(see illustration)*.

Renewal

Remove the brake caliper. On sliding and floating calipers, follow the caliper removal steps described in the Brake pad renewal procedure. Then, on models with mounting brackets that would interfere with removal of the disc, remove the mounting bracket. To do this, remove the two mounting bracket-to-hub carrier bolts *(see illustration)*. On vehicles with fixed calipers, remove the two bolts that retain the caliper to the hub carrier *(see illustration)*.

Using a swirling motion, remove the glaze from the disc with sandpaper or emery cloth.

To remove the caliper mounting bracket, remove these two bolts (arrowed).

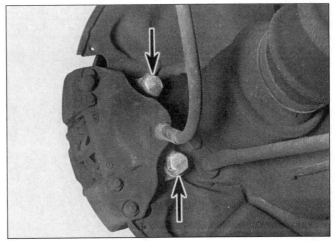

On vehicles with fixed calipers, remove the two caliper-to-hub carrier bolts (arrowed).

Some vehicles have brake discs that are bolted to the hubs.

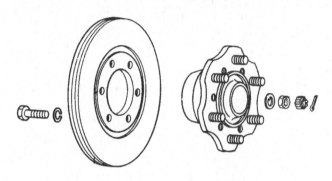

On the front brake of many four wheel drive vehicles the discs are also bolted to the hubs, but the entire assembly must be removed because the disc fits against the backside of the hub.

On some vehicles, the disc appears to be an integral part of the hub, but is actually detachable. Remove the hub as described in the appropriate Service and Repair Manual, then unbolt or press the disc from the hub *(see illustrations)*.

On most† vehicles the brake disc slips over the hub and wheel studs, and can simply be pulled off (of course, you'll have to remove the wheel nuts if you refitted them). An exception to this rule are the vehicles which use screws to retain the disc to the hub. Sometimes these screws become rusted and will have to be soaked with penetrating oil and removed with an impact screwdriver *(see illustration)*. It's also a good idea to apply penetrating oil around the area where the disc meets the hub.

If the disc retaining screws are stuck, use an impact driver to slacken them.

HINTS & TIPS

- Before separating the disc from the hub, mark the relationship of the disc to one of the wheel studs. If the wheels were dynamically balanced on the vehicle, returning the disc to the original position will retain the balance.

If the disc sticks to the hub, thread two bolts into the holes in the disc and tighten them to force the disc from the hub.

Even if you use penetrating oil, the disc might still refuse to come off. Check to see if the disc has two or three threaded holes in the area where the wheel seats. If it does, thread bolts of the correct size and thread pitch into the holes and tighten them to force the disc off the hub *(see illustration)*. If you're removing a rear brake disc with a drum-type handbrake inside the centre of the disc, and the disc won't come off, remove the plug from the handbrake adjusting access hole. On some vehicles the adjuster is accessed through one of the wheel bolt holes in the hub *(see*

On some vehicles, the adjuster is accessed through one of the wheel bolt holes in the hub (shown with the disc removed).

illustration). Engage the notches in the adjusting star wheel with a suitable tool (such as a screwdriver) and retract the handbrake shoes. Now pull the disc off the hub.

Refitting is the reverse of removal. If you're refitting a hub, repack the wheel bearings, refit the disc and adjust the bearings as described in the appropriate Service and Repair manual. If your fitting new discs, degrease them prior to fitment - they are normally coated in grease to protect them during storage.

Some manufacturers recommend that the caliper mounting bracket bolts are replaced regardless of their apparent condition. Where no recommendation is made, clean the bolts, and apply a little locking compound to the threads. Refit the caliper mounting bracket (if applicable), and tighten the bolts to the correct torque. Refit the caliper, also tightening the bolts correctly.

If your vehicle is equipped with a drum-type handbrake inside of the hub of the disc, be sure to adjust the handbrake shoes (see Chapter 7).

Typical brake pad and disc replacement procedure

The following sequence of illustrations shows the pad and disc replacement procedure for a typical floating caliper. In this case it's taken from a Vauxhall Corsa.

Loosen the wheel bolts, jack up the corner of the car you're working on, and take off the wheel. Make sure you've got an axle stand under a solid part of the car in case the jack gives out. First job is to prise off the pad retaining spring.

On the inside of the caliper, prise out the two plugs covering the caliper guide bolt heads. You now need a 7 mm Allen key, to undo the two caliper guide bolts.

Lift away the caliper, complete with the inner brake pad ...

... which is clipped into the caliper piston, and easily unclipped.

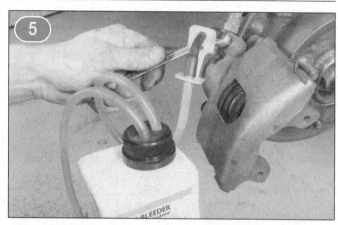

To get the new pads to fit, later on, you'll need to push the caliper piston back into the caliper. When you push the piston back, there's a slim chance that the seals in the master cylinder may be damaged. To avoid this, and eliminate any chance of old, dirty fluid going through the ABS modulator (where fitted), connect a one-man brake bleeder to the caliper bleed screw ...

... and slacken the screw whilst pushing the piston back. Tighten the bleed screw afterwards.

Don't leave the caliper swinging by its hose - tie it up with a cable-tie.

Now remove the outer brake pad.

Remove the caliper bracket bolts. These bolts must be renewed upon reassemby - new ones are pre-coated with thread-lock.

Lift off the caliper mounting bracket.

Lift the old disc from place.

When fitting new discs, check they are identical. These grooved discs must be fitted with the grooves facing a certain direction - check any instruction supplied with the discs. If the screw is undamaged, it can be reused - otherwise renew it.

All that holds the disc in place (apart from the wheel bolts, when the wheel's on) is this screw. If the screw is rusted in place, soak it with releasing agent (WD-40, Plus Gas, etc) and use an impact driver. If the screw head is damaged, drilling the screw out might be the only option.

Spend some time cleaning rust and/or debris from the disc mounting face on the hub. If the new discs don't fit completely square, then they will have excessive run-out.

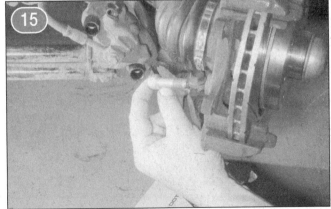

Refit the caliper mounting bracket, and secure it with new threadlock-coated bolts.

Tighten the bolts to the correct torque - refer to the appropriate Service and Repair Manual.

Set the outer pad into place on the caliper bracket.

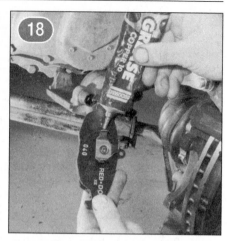

Before clipping the inner pad into the caliper, smear a little high-temperature anti-seize compound (Copperslip) on the back of the pad, around the spring legs. This helps to prevent brake squeal.

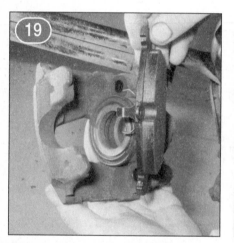

Clip the inner pad into the caliper ...

... then repeat the anti-seize compound application of the outer pad ...

... before sliding the caliper back over the disc.

Fit the caliper guide bolts, and tighten them to the correct torque.

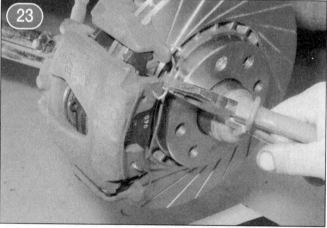

Refit the retaining spring. The spring ends fit into the holes in the caliper, and the top and bottom lugs locate around the 'ears' on the caliper bracket.

Drum brakes

Brake drum - removal, inspection and refitting   2

Brake shoes - renewal   3

General information   1

Wheel cylinder overhaul   See Chapter 6

1 General information

The first wheel brakes fitted to early cars were drum brakes. They weren't like the drum brakes on a modern vehicle, though. They worked much like a band in an automatic transmission. The friction material surrounded the outside surface of the drum and clamped tight around the spinning drum when the brakes were applied. It was a very simple arrangement, but had a couple of drawbacks; they couldn't get rid of heat very well and were almost useless if they got wet.

A major breakthrough in braking effectiveness came about when engineers placed the friction surface on the *inside* of the drum. This helped to seal the brake from the elements a little better, and allowed a much greater surface area of the drum to be in contact with the surrounding air, which allowed the brake drum to dissipate the heat it had absorbed much quicker.

The major components of a drum brake assembly are the brake drum, the brake shoes, the backing plate, the wheel cylinder(s), and all the hardware necessary to mount and connect the components *(see illustrations overleaf)*. Most rear drum brake assemblies also have self-adjusting mechanisms to keep the shoes within a predetermined distance from the drum, even as the lining material wears down.

The following is a description of each major component and its function.

Backing plate - Bolted to the axle housing (rear brake) or hub carrier (front brake), the backing plate provides a mounting place for the brake shoes and wheel cylinders. It's usually made of heavy-gauge stamped steel. It has raised areas, or lands, for the edges of the brake shoes to ride on.

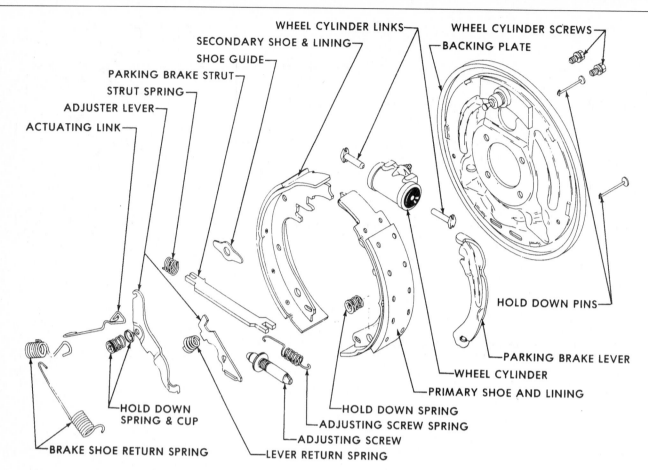

Exploded view of a typical duo-servo drum brake

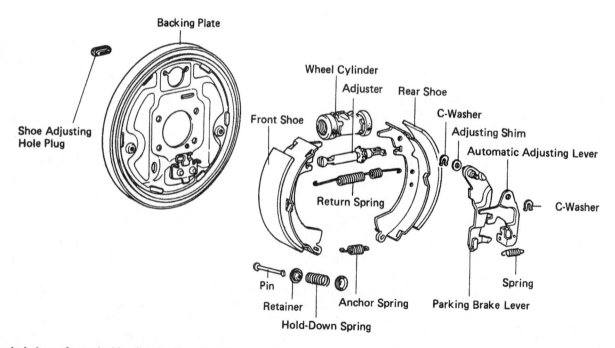

Exploded view of a typical leading/trailing drum brake

One of the most important parts of the backing plate is the anchor, or on some designs, the anchor pin. The anchor or anchor pin is the immovable rest that the end of the brake shoes rest on, and the point that all braking force for that brake (not heat dissipation, but the portion of the energy of the moving vehicle that the brake is responsible for) is transmitted through. The anchor on some vehicles is riveted to the backing plate. On others, it's bolted to the axle housing or hub carrier.

Wheel cylinder(s) - This is the component that converts hydraulic pressure into mechanical energy. Wheel cylinders are explained in detail under the *Hydraulic systems* Chapter.

Brake shoes - The brake shoe assembly usually consists of two brake shoes. A friction material is fastened to each shoe by means of rivets or by a process called bonding - a form of gluing under a heated drying process. The brake shoes are the components that the wheel cylinder pistons push out on, expanding them to rub against the friction surface of the brake drum. Brake shoes have been designed for maximum rigidity.

On a duo-servo design (we'll get to that) the shoe that faces the front of the vehicle is referred to as the primary shoe. The other one is the secondary shoe. The primary shoe is shorter (or at least the lining is) than the secondary.

On a leading/trailing brake, the front shoe is called the leading shoe; the rear shoe is called the trailing shoe.

In a drum brake set-up that has separate wheel cylinders for each brake shoe, both shoes are primary or leading shoes. This is known as a twin leading shoe arrangement.

Brake lining - The job of the brake lining is to create friction (heat) when it's pressed against the brake drum. As previously stated, the linings are riveted or bonded to the brake shoe. Most brake linings are made of asbestos-free compounds these days, although older vehicles may have asbestos linings. Some have brass or copper wires impregnated in the lining. Some linings are grooved, slotted or woven to improve cooling. Brake lining wears down in use, and must be changed when it becomes too thin (approximately 1.0 mm from the shoe [bonded linings] or the rivet heads [riveted linings]).

Brake drum - The brake drum spins with the wheel and absorbs and dissipates heat when the brakes are applied and the shoes rub against it. Brake drums are usually made from cast iron, but some are made of aluminium, fitted with cast iron liners for a friction surface. Some drums have cooling vanes cast into their outer surfaces to increase area and aid in cooling.

After a considerable amount of use, brake drums normally will become a little out-of-round. This is due to the intense temperature changes the drum is subjected to. Drums can be machined to get rid of an out-of-round condition or score marks, but all brake drums have a maximum allowable diameter, sometimes cast or stamped somewhere on the drum's surface. This dimension must not be exceeded,

because the drum wouldn't be able to dissipate heat well enough, and could even fatigue and crack.

Attaching hardware and other components - A variety of bits and pieces are required to secure the brake shoes to the backing plate and, on rear drum brakes, actuate the handbrake and ensure that the brake shoes self-adjust during operation. Not all of the following components are found on every drum brake set-up.

Hold-down pin, spring and cup - This simple device retains the brake shoe to the backing plate, but allows the brake shoe to move side-to-side a little, if necessary, to better conform to the friction surface of the brake drum. The hold-down pin is inserted from the backside of the backing plate and passes through a hole in the brake shoe. A spring is then placed over the pin and is retained by a cup, or retainer.

Shoe retracting (or return) springs - These springs pull the shoes away from the brake drum after the brake has been released. They're strong enough to overcome the residual pressure in the hydraulic system, so they push the pistons back into the wheel cylinders a little bit, preventing the shoes from dragging against the brake drum.

Handbrake lever and strut - Connected by a cable to the handbrake lever inside the vehicle, the handbrake lever inside of a drum brake assembly expands the shoes, with the help of the handbrake strut, out against the drum when the handbrake lever inside the vehicle is lifted. The handbrake lever and strut operate like a "mechanical wheel cylinder."

Self-adjusting mechanism - Self-adjusting mechanisms come in many forms, but they all work to keep the lining on the brake shoes reasonably close to the friction surface of the brake drum, as the lining wears down. On most set-ups, a small lever, actuated by a cable or linkage, turns an adjuster, or "star" wheel, located between the brake shoes. As the adjuster is turned, the shoes are expanded outward a little bit. Some self-adjusters are activated during normal braking, while others operate when the handbrake is used or the vehicle is driven in reverse and the brakes are applied.

Operation

We've covered the master cylinder and how it creates pressure in the hydraulic system, and how this pressure is converted into mechanical energy by the wheel cylinder. The pistons in the wheel cylinder then push outward on the brake shoes, forcing them against the brake drum, which creates the friction. The heat caused by this friction is then stored in the brake drum and dissipated to the air.

All modern drum brakes are self-energising, which means the braking force is multiplied by the spinning action of the drum as the brake shoe is applied to it. This self-energising action is accomplished by the toe (top) of the leading or primary shoe moving out and making contact with the rotating drum. The drum attempts to take the shoe with it - the shoe tends to stick to the drum along its entire span. Of course, it can't begin to spin with the drum, because it's prevented from doing so by the anchor plate or pin.

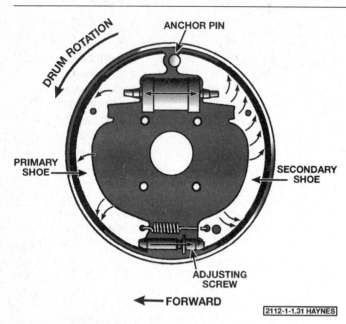

The self-energising, or servo-action drum brake uses the rotation of the brake drum to increase the pressure on the brake shoes, making the driver's job easier

A duo-servo design drum brake takes this self-energising action one step further *(see illustration)*. Since there is only one anchor pin in this type of brake, the self-energising force imposed on the primary shoe is transferred to the secondary shoe through a link, or more commonly, the adjusting screw. This forces the bottom of the secondary shoe onto the spinning drum, and the self-energising process is applied to the secondary shoe to an even greater extent, forcing the top of the secondary shoe into the anchor pin (this is why secondary shoes have more lining material on them). At the same time, the wheel cylinder is also pushing against the secondary shoe. As you can imagine, braking force is greatly multiplied. With this design, the self-energising action takes place when the brakes are applied when the vehicle is moving forwards or reversing - it doesn't matter. Brake designs that have a similar brake shoe/anchor pin layout, but use a single-sided wheel cylinder, are called uni-servo brakes (and only have servo-action brakes when going forwards).

There's one drawback to the duo-servo design - sometimes they work too well, and can lock up the rear wheels. For the most part, duo-servo brakes are used on heavier, rear-wheel drive vehicles. Many other vehicles use self-energising brakes, but without the duo-servo action. In these designs, the wheel cylinder acts on one end of the brake shoe, but the other end rests against an anchor plate or pin.

One variation of this set-up arranges the brake shoes and wheel cylinder in a similar manner to that of the duo-servo design, but instead of the anchor pin at the top and a connecting link between the shoes at the bottom, the bottom of each shoe resting against an anchor (sometimes each shoe has its own anchor pin). This type of brake is commonly referred to as a leading/trailing or double-anchor design. When the vehicle is travelling forward, only the leading shoe will be self-energised. When the vehicle is braked in reverse, the trailing shoe will be self-energised.

A less common design uses two leading, or primary, shoes. This is called a double-anchor, double-cylinder brake, also called a leading/leading or twin leading shoe brake *(see illustration)*. Each shoe has its own wheel cylinder, and each shoe is self-energising when the brakes are applied, but only when the vehicle is travelling forwards. In reverse there is no self-energising action at all, and much more muscle power is required to stop the vehicle.

Braking ratio

When the brakes are applied, the natural tendency of the vehicle is to dip forward, placing the greater stopping requirement on the front wheels and less on the rear wheels.

Through increased friction area and a larger cylinder bore on the front brakes (whether they are disc or drum brakes, it doesn't matter), a greater capacity for braking is the result.

Most modern vehicles split the ratio of braking to 60-percent on the front wheels and 40-percent on the rear wheels (this is why most vehicles have disc brakes up front). Under severe braking this ratio can become even more imbalanced, but thanks to the proportioning valve (or pressure control valve), pressure is limited to the rear brakes to keep them from locking up as the rear of the vehicle lightens up.

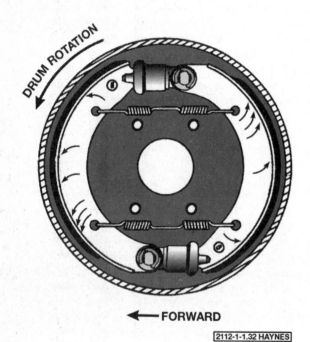

Double-anchor, double-cylinder design drum brake. This set-up makes for a powerful brake, as long as the vehicle is travelling forward

2 Brake drum removal, inspection and refitting

⚠ *Warning: The dust created by the brake system may contain asbestos, which is harmful to your health. Never blow it out with compressed air and don't inhale any of it. An approved filtering mask should be worn when working on the brakes. Do not, under any circumstances, use petroleum-based solvents to clean brake parts. Use brake system cleaner only!*

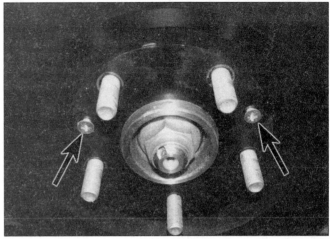

Unscrew the drum retaining screws (arrowed)

Removal

Loosen the wheel nuts/bolts, raise the vehicle and support it securely on axle stands. Chock the wheels at the opposite end of the vehicle so it can't roll. If a rear brake drum is to be removed, release the handbrake. Remove the wheel(s).

If you're removing a drum that is integral with the hub assembly (one that can't be separated from the hub), refer to the appropriate Service and Repair manual for the drum removal procedure.

If you're removing a brake drum that simply slips off an axle or hub flange, apply penetrating oil around the area where the drum meets the hub or axle flange, and also around the wheel studs. Allow the penetrant a few minutes to seep in.

Check the drum for the presence of screws that secure the drum to the hub or axle flange. If present, remove them. It may be necessary to use an impact screwdriver to break the screws loose *(see illustration)*.

Mark the relationship of the brake drum to one of the wheel studs or to the hub *(see illustration)*. This will preserve the balance if the wheels have been dynamically balanced on the vehicle. Try to pull the drum off. If it sticks, the brake shoes will have to be retracted. Refer to Chapter 7 and follow the procedure described under the "Drum brakes" portion of the "Rear brakes" section.

If the drum is stuck to the hub or axle flange, look for two or three threaded holes in the drum that look like they have no apparent purpose. If your drum is equipped with such holes, fit two (or three) bolts of the correct size and thread pitch into the threaded holes in the drum. Tighten the bolts, a little at a time, until the drum is forced off *(see illustration)*.

Mark the relationship of the drum to the hub (or one of the wheel studs) so the balance will be retained

Inspection

Check the drum for cracks, score marks, deep scratches and hard spots, which will appear as small discoloured areas. If the hard spots cannot be removed with sandpaper or emery cloth, or if any of the other conditions listed above exist, the drum must be taken to an automotive engineering workshop to have it refaced.

If the brake drum refuses to slide off the hub, screw two bolts of the proper size and thread into the threaded holes and tighten them evenly, a little at a time. The drum will be pushed off by the bolts

The maximum drum diameter is cast or stamped into the inside or outside of the brake drums.

Note: *Professionals recommend resurfacing the drums whenever a brake job is done. Resurfacing will eliminate the possibility of out-of-round or tapered drums. If the drums are worn so much that they can't be resurfaced without exceeding the maximum allowable diameter (sometimes stamped into the drum) (see illustration), then new ones will be required. At the very least, if you elect not to have the drums resurfaced, remove the glazing from the surface with emery cloth or sandpaper using a swirling motion (see illustration).*

If you have an internal micrometer or a vernier caliper that's large enough, measure the inside diameter of the drum at four different locations around the drum (45-degree intervals) *(see illustration)*. Write down each measurement. Generally, a drum that is 0.25 mm out-of-round needs to be machined. Some manufacturers would consider 0.25 mm out-of-round too much.

Also, check the diameter of the brake drum at the innermost portion of the friction surface and at the outermost portion of the friction surface. Subtract one measurement from the other to calculate drum taper. If the drum exhibits a taper of 0.12 mm or more, it should be resurfaced.

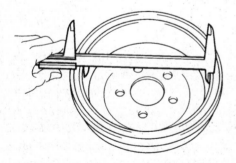

Measuring the diameter of the brake drum with a large vernier caliper

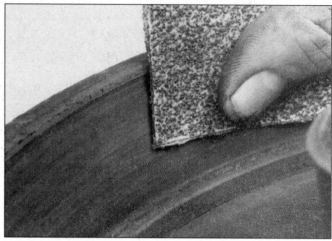

Remove the glaze from the drum surface with sandpaper or emery cloth

Note: *If the drum is to be taken to an engineering workshop for resurfacing, clean out all of the old grease from the hub (if applicable) before the machine work is done. Then, when you get it back, clean the hub out again to ensure no metal chips remain.*

Refitting

Before refitting the brake drum, make sure the friction surface is perfectly clean. If it isn't, or if in doubt, wash the drum thoroughly with brake system cleaner. Also confirm that the brake shoes are clean and all of the components of the drum brake assembly are in order.

If you're refitting a drum that slips over the wheel studs, do just that. Make sure the match marks you applied to the drum and wheel stud are aligned. If you're refitting a brake drum that's integral with the wheel hub, clean and repack the wheel bearings, refit the hub/drum and (where applicable) adjust the wheel bearings as described in the appropriate Service and Repair manual.

Regardless of the type of drum you've just refitted, adjust the drum brakes. This is covered in Chapter 7 entitled "Drum brake adjustment."

3   Brake shoe renewal

⊘ *Warning: Drum brake shoes must be renewed on both wheels at the same time - never renew the shoes on only one wheel. Also, the dust created by the brake system may contain asbestos, which is harmful to your health. Never blow it out with compressed air and don't inhale any of it. An approved filtering mask should be worn when working on the brakes. Do not, under any circumstances, use petroleum-based solvents to clean brake parts. Use brake system cleaner only!*

Regardless of the type of brake you're working on, there are a few preliminary steps to be taken before disassembling the brake. First, park the vehicle on a level surface, open the bonnet and locate the master cylinder - it's usually mounted on the bulkhead or the brake servo on the driver's side of the bulkhead (but on some vehicles it's on the other side of the engine compartment). Cover all painted areas around the master cylinder (wing included), remove the reservoir cover or cap(s) and remove about one-quarter of the fluid from the reservoir. It is necessary to do this so the reservoir doesn't overflow when the wheel cylinder pistons are pushed back into their bores to make room for the new linings. This can be accomplished with a suction pump, a siphoning kit or an old poultry baster or hydrometer.

> **Warning:** Brake fluid is poisonous - don't start the siphoning action by mouth. If you use a poultry baster, never again use that baster for cooking! Discard the fluid.

If you haven't already done so, this is a good time to put on your filtering mask, latex gloves and eye protection. Your hands aren't too dirty yet, and brake dust tends to get all over the wheels and inside the wheel covers, so put them on before removing the wheels.

Next, remove the wheel trim (if applicable) from the wheels and loosen the wheel nuts/bolts about one-half turn. Raise the vehicle and support it securely on axle stands. Remove the wheels, but remember to only work on one brake at a time. You can use the other side as a model if you aren't sure about something. Another good idea is to make

sketches or take photos of the areas you think you might have trouble with. The handbrake actuator and the adjuster mechanism are good examples of areas to concentrate on. Always note the orientation of the adjuster screw star wheel and all of the various springs.

Remove the brake drum by following the procedure under the heading "Brake drum removal, inspection and refitting".

Before touching or disassembling anything, clean the brake assembly with brake system cleaner and allow it to dry *(see illustration)*. Don't ever use compressed air or a brush to remove the brake dust.

Now, refer to the appropriate procedure under "Duo-servo brake shoe renewal" or "Leading/trailing brake shoe renewal". Be sure to stay in order and read the captions that accompany each illustration. Before refitting the brake drum, inspect it as outlined previously in this Chapter. If machining is necessary, remove the drums and have them resurfaced by an automotive engineering workshop (if they are still thick enough to undergo machining).

Note: *Professionals recommend resurfacing of brake drums whenever replacing the brake shoes, as this will produce a smooth, flat surface that will eliminate brake pedal pulsations and other undesirable symptoms related to questionable drums. At the very least, if you elect not to have the drums resurfaced, de-glaze them with sandpaper or emery cloth, using a swirling motion to ensure a non-directional finish. Be careful not to get grease on the brake drum or brake shoes.*

After you have successfully fitted the shoes on one side of the vehicle, repeat the procedure on the other brake. Then refer to Chapter 7 and adjust the shoes, referring to the section entitled "Drum brake adjustment."

As soon as you have lowered the vehicle and tightened the wheel nuts securely, check the brake fluid level in the master cylinder reservoir. If necessary, add some to bring it to the desired level. Pump the brake pedal a few times, then recheck the fluid level.

Adjust the handbrake (see Chapter 7).

Lastly, before committing the vehicle to normal service, road test it in an isolated area, if possible. For the first few hundred miles or so, try to avoid hard braking to allow the new shoes to bed in.

Duo-servo brake

> **Warning:** *The dust created by the brake system may contain asbestos, which is harmful to your health. Never blow it out with compressed air and don't inhale any of it. An approved filtering mask should be worn when working on the brakes. Do not, under any circumstances, use petroleum-based solvents to clean brake parts. Use brake system cleaner only!*

Before beginning work, wash away all traces of brake dust with brake system cleaner

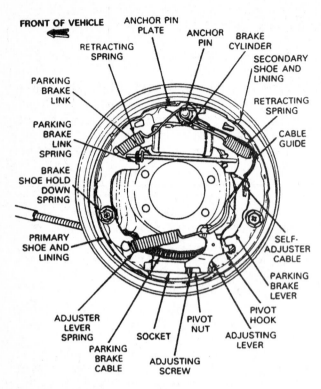

FRONT OF VEHICLE

ANCHOR PIN PLATE
ANCHOR PIN
BRAKE CYLINDER
RETRACTING SPRING
SECONDARY SHOE AND LINING
PARKING BRAKE LINK
RETRACTING SPRING
PARKING BRAKE LINK SPRING
CABLE GUIDE
BRAKE SHOE HOLD DOWN SPRING
PRIMARY SHOE AND LINING
SELF-ADJUSTER CABLE
PARKING BRAKE LEVER
ADJUSTER LEVER SPRING
PIVOT HOOK
SOCKET
PIVOT NUT
ADJUSTING LEVER
PARKING BRAKE CABLE
ADJUSTING SCREW

Rear drum brake components (with cable operated self-adjusting mechanism) - left side

Note: *The following procedure depicts the brake shoe renewal sequence for drum brakes with lever-actuated self-adjusters and cable-actuated self adjusters. Follow the photo sequence and read the accompanying caption, but simply ignore the steps which do not apply to the type of brake you are working on. The same goes for front drum brakes - just ignore all of the references to handbrake components.*

Tools required:

Jack and axle stands
Wheel nut (or bolt) spanner
Filtering mask
Safety glasses or goggles
Latex gloves
Brake spring pliers
Brake hold-down spring tool
Brake shoe adjusting tool (or a suitable screwdriver)

Materials required:

Brake shoes
Brake hardware kit
Brake system cleaner
High-temperature anti-seize compound
Brake fluid

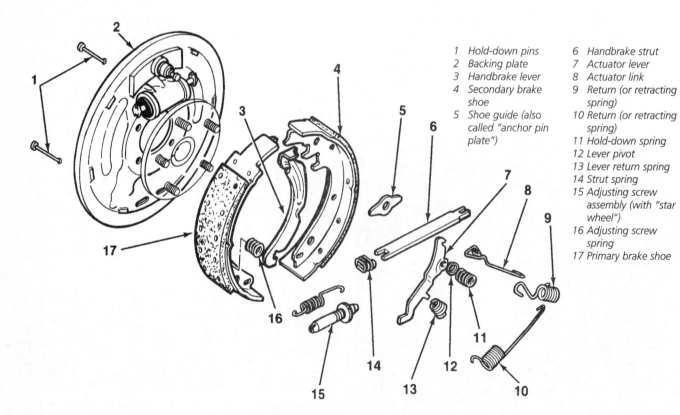

1 Hold-down pins
2 Backing plate
3 Handbrake lever
4 Secondary brake shoe
5 Shoe guide (also called "anchor pin plate")
6 Handbrake strut
7 Actuator lever
8 Actuator link
9 Return (or retracting spring)
10 Return (or retracting spring)
11 Hold-down spring
12 Lever pivot
13 Lever return spring
14 Strut spring
15 Adjusting screw assembly (with "star wheel")
16 Adjusting screw spring
17 Primary brake shoe

Exploded view of a typical rear drum brake (with lever operated self-adjuster mechanism) - left side

Remove the old brake shoes (duo-servo brake)

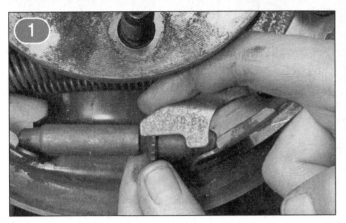

Pull back on the adjuster lever and turn the star wheel to retract the brake shoes (this will make removal of the return springs easier and, on models with cable operated adjusters, will ease removal of the adjuster cable)

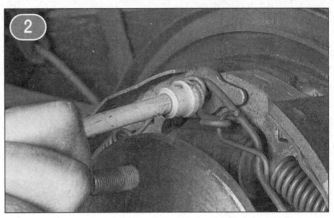

Remove the shoe return springs - the tool shown here is available at most motor factors and makes this job much easier and safer

On models with cable-actuated adjusters, remove the return spring and cable guide from the secondary shoe ...

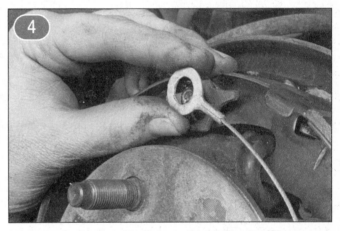

... then remove the self adjuster cable and anchor pin plate

On models with lever-actuated adjusters, pull the bottom of the actuator lever toward the secondary brake shoe, compressing the lever return spring. The actuator link can now be removed from the top of the lever ...

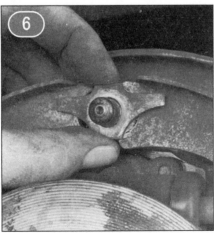

... followed by the anchor pin plate

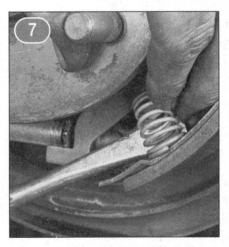

Also on models with lever-actuated adjusters, prise the actuator lever spring out with a large screwdriver

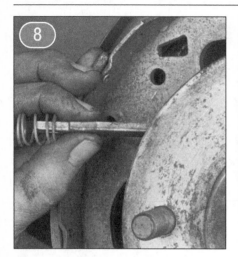

Slide the handbrake strut out from between the axle flange and the primary shoe

Remove the hold-down springs and pins. The hold-down spring tool shown here is available at most tool shops. To remove the springs, push down the retainer, turn it 1/4 turn to align the slot in the retainer with the blade on the pin, then release

On models with lever-actuated adjusters, remove the actuator lever and pivot - be careful not to let the pivot fall out of the lever

Spread the top of the shoes apart and slide the assembly around the hub

Unhook the handbrake lever from the secondary shoe, if the design of the brake permits

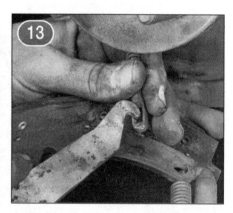

Some handbrake levers simply hook onto the cable and are easily detached. On this design, the lever is usually fastened to the secondary brake shoe with a clip and is not easily separated (it's easier to do it on the workbench)

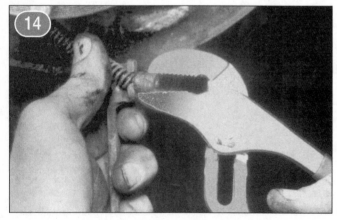

Other handbrake levers are fastened with a clip, but don't readily separate from the cable either. In this case, pull on the cable end with a pair of pliers and swing the cable out of the slot

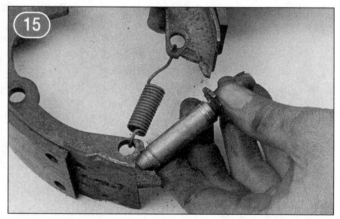

Spread the bottom of the shoes apart and remove the adjusting screw assembly

Preparation for refitting (duo-servo brake)

If the handbrake lever is still fastened to the secondary shoe, remove it by prising off the E-clip. Take note of any washers that may be present

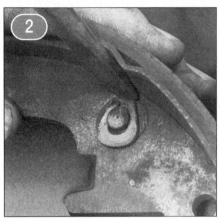

Here's another kind of clip that is commonly used to retain the handbrake lever. Spread the ends of the clip and prise it off the pin

Clean the adjusting screw with brake system cleaner, dry it off and lubricate the threads and end with high-temperature anti-seize compound (Copperslip). The screw portion of the adjuster will need to be threaded in further than before to allow the drum to fit over the new shoes

Feel the brake shoe contact points on the back plate. If they are rough or a ledge has worn into them, file them smooth. Lubricate these contact points with high-temperature anti-seize compound

If the handbrake lever was mounted to a pin on the old shoe, fit a new adjuster lever pin in the new shoe ...

... then refit the lever and a new E-clip

If your brake uses this type of clip, fit a new clip over the pin and squeeze the ends together (note the spring washer under the clip)

Fit the new shoes (duo-servo brake)

On models with cable-actuated adjusters, you may find it easier to fit the shoes on the backing plate, then refit the adjuster screw, adjuster spring and lever. Connect the adjuster spring between the new shoes (with the long portion of the spring pointing to the rear shoe on most designs), refit the adjuster screw assembly (with the long part pointing to the front shoe on most designs), then connect the handbrake cable (if disconnected from the lever)

Spread the shoes apart and slide them into position on the backing plate

Insert the handbrake lever into the opening in the secondary brake shoe. If you separated the handbrake cable from the end of the lever, connect it now if you haven't already done so

Refit the hold-down pin through the backing plate in the primary shoe, then refit the spring and retainer. If you're working on a brake with a cable-actuated self-adjuster, refit the hold-down pin, spring and retainer through the secondary shoe also

On models with lever-actuated adjuster, insert the lever pivot into the actuator lever, place the lever over the secondary shoe hold-down pin and refit the hold-down spring and retainer

Guide the handbrake strut behind the hub flange and engage the rear end of it in the slot on the handbrake lever. Spread the shoes enough to allow the other end of the strut to seat against the primary shoe

Place the anchor pin plate over the anchor pin

On models with lever-actuated adjusters, hook the lower end of the actuator link to the actuator lever, them loop the top end over the anchor pin ...

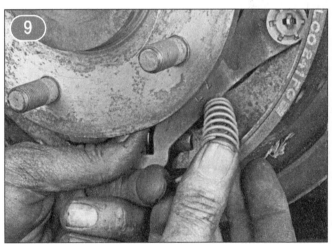

... and refit the lever return spring over the tab on the actuator lever. Push the bottom of the spring up onto the brake shoe

If you're working on a model with cable-actuated adjusters, place the end of the cable over the anchor pin ...

... then hook the end of the secondary shoe return spring through the cable guide and into the hole in the shoe. Make sure the cable sits in the guide

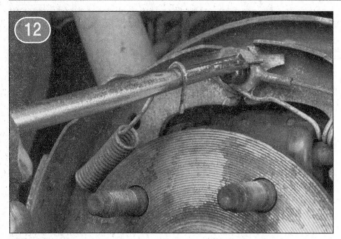

Refit the shoe retractor springs. The tool shown here is actually the handle of the brake spring pliers. This tool makes this stop much easier and safer

Bend the ends of the return springs around the anchor pin, so that the end of the spring is parallel with the long part of the spring

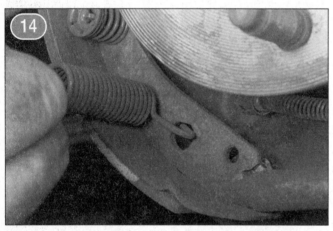

If you're working on a model with cable-actuated adjusters, hook the adjuster lever spring into the proper hole at the bottom of the primary shoe ...

.. then hook the adjuster lever spring and cable into the adjuster lever. Pull the cable down and to the rear, inserting the hook on the lever in to the hole in the secondary shoe

Wiggle the brake assembly to ensure that the shoes are centred on the backing plate. Make sure the handbrake strut and the wheel cylinder pushrods (if applicable) engage properly with the brake shoes

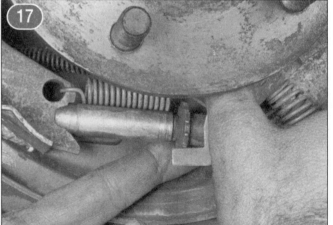

Turn the adjusting screw star wheel to adjust the shoes in or out as necessary. The brake drum should slide over the shoes and turn with a very slight amount of drag

Leading/trailing brake

> ⚠ *Warning: The dust created by the brake system may contain asbestos, which is harmful to your health. Never blow it out with compressed air and don't inhale any of it. An approved filtering mask should be worn when working on the brakes. Do not, under any circumstances, use petroleum-based solvents to clean brake parts. Use brake system cleaner only!*

Note 1: *The following procedure depicts a rear brake shoe renewal sequence for leading/trailing type drum brakes. Follow the photo sequence and read the caption below each illustration, but simply ignore the steps which do not apply to the type of brake you are working on. The same goes for front drum brakes - just ignore all of the references to handbrake components.*

Note 2: *Most leading/trailing drum brakes are similar in design, regardless of manufacturer. The differences lie primarily in the handbrake actuating mechanism. As there are many different handbrake actuator set-ups, it is not possible to cover every variation in a manual of this size. Before disassembling any components, be sure to pay close attention to the way all of the components are situated. Note how the retractor springs are fitted - is there a long,* straight portion of the spring passing over the self-adjuster star wheel? If so, make a note. Also note the mounting holes of all springs. It's a good idea to make sketches or even take instant photographs of the brake assembly, especially the handbrake components, before actually removing them. Remember to work only on one brake at a time, referring to the other brake for reference, if necessary.

The following pages contain views of typical brake drum assemblies. The removal and refitting procedure starts on page 3•33.

Tools required:
Jack and axle stands
Wheel nut (or bolt) spanner
Filtering mask
Safety glasses or goggles
Latex gloves
Brake spring pliers
Brake hold-down spring tool
Brake shoe adjusting tool (or a suitable screwdriver)

Materials required:
Brake shoes
Brake hardware kit
Brake system cleaner
High-temperature brake grease
Brake fluid

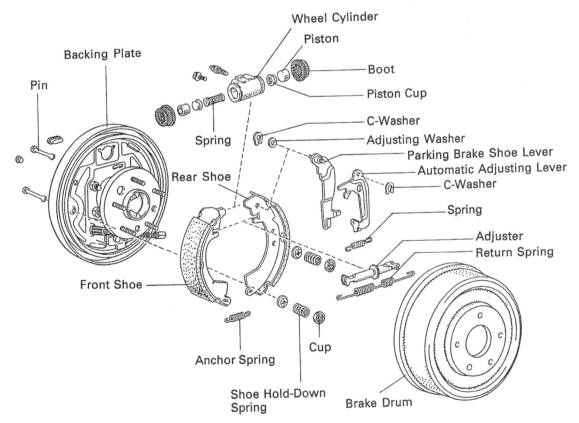

Exploded view of a typical leading/trailing drum brake assembly (Toyota)

Bedford Rascal rear brakes

1 Brake shoe retaining clip
2 Lower return spring
3 Upper return spring
4 Wheel cylinder
5 Brake shoe
6 Handbrake actuating lever

Arrow indicates the front of the vehicle

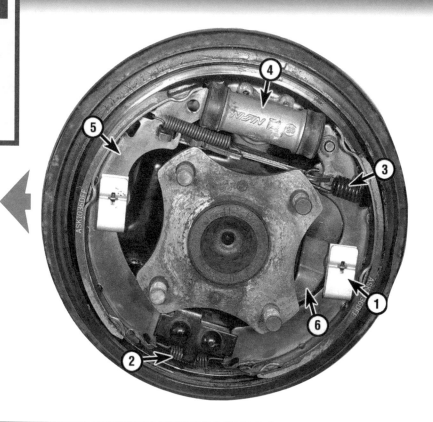

BMW 3 & 5 Series rear brakes

1 Upper anchor plate
2 Upper return spring
3 Brake shoe retaining clip and pin
4 Lower return spring
5 Wheel cylinder
6 Inner handbrake cable

Arrow indicates the front of the vehicle

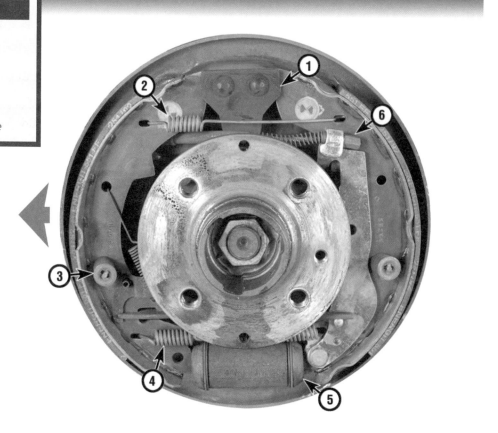

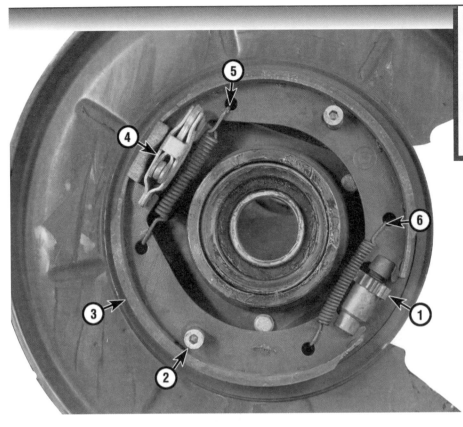

BMW 3 & 5 Series handbrake shoes

1   Adjuster 'wheel'
2   Brake shoe retaining pin and clip
3   Brake shoe friction lining
4   Actuating mechanism
5   Upper return spring
6   Lower return spring

Arrow indicates the front of the vehicle

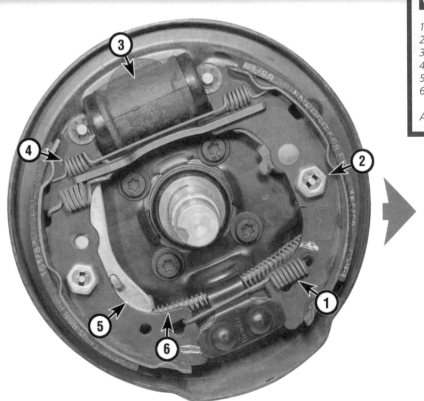

Citroën AX rear brakes

1   Lower return spring
2   Brake shoe retaining clip
3   Wheel cylinder
4   Upper return spring
5   Handbrake actuating lever
6   Inner handbrake cable

Arrow indicates the front of the vehicle

Citroën C15 rear brakes

1 Self-adjusting lever
2 Self-adjusting lever ratchet pawl
3 Lower return spring
4 Inner handbrake cable
5 Upper return spring
6 Wheel cylinder

Arrow indicates the front of the vehicle

Citroën Saxo rear brakes

1 Lower return spring
2 Inner handbrake cable
3 Self-adjusting mechanism spring
4 Upper return spring
5 Wheel cylinder
6 Brake shoe retaining clip

Arrow indicates the front of the vehicle

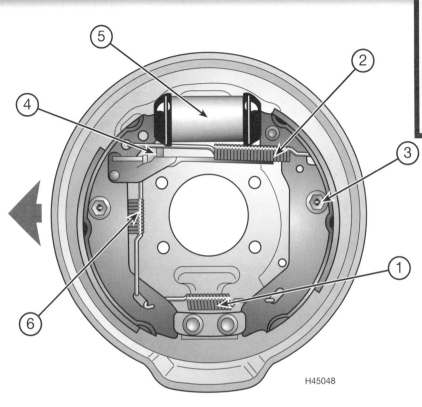

Citroën Xsara rear brakes

1   Lower return spring
2   Upper return spring
3   Brake shoe retaining clip and pin
4   Self-adjusting mechanism
5   Wheel cylinder
6   Self-adjusting mechanism spring

Arrow indicates the front of the vehicle

H45048

Fiat Cinquecento rear brakes

1   Wheel cylinder
2   Upper return spring
3   Friction disc for self-adjusting function
4   Brake shoe retaining clip
5   Lower return spring
6   Upper link strut

Arrow indicates the front of the vehicle

Ford Fiesta rear brakes

1 Brake shoe retaining clip
2 Lower return spring
3 Inner handbrake cable
4 Self-adjusting mechanism spring
5 Upper return spring
6 Wheel cylinder

Arrow indicates the front of the vehicle

Ford Focus rear brakes

1 Wheel cylinder
2 Brake shoe retaining clip and pin
3 Lower return spring
4 Inner handbrake cable
5 Self-adjusting mechanism 'ratchet'
6 Upper return spring

Arrow indicates the front of the vehicle

Ford Ka rear brakes

1 Self-adjusting mechanism 'ratchet'
2 Wheel cylinder
3 Upper return spring
4 Brake shoe retaining clip and pin
5 Lower return spring
6 Anchor plate

Arrow indicates the front of the vehicle

Honda Civic rear brakes

1 Lower return spring
2 Brake shoe retaining clip and pin
3 Self-adjusting mechanism
4 Wheel cylinder
5 Upper return spring
6 Inner handbrake cable

Arrow indicates the front of the vehicle

Chapter 3

Hyundai Pony rear brakes

1 Self-adjusting mechanism spring
2 Lower return spring
3 Brake shoe retaining clip
4 Wheel cylinder
5 Self-adjusting strut/mechanism
6 Inner handbrake cable

Arrow indicates the front of the vehicle

Land Rover Discovery handbrake assembly

1 Brake shoes
2 Expander assembly
3 Adjuster assembly
4 Return springs
5 Backplate and retaining bolt
6 Brake drum

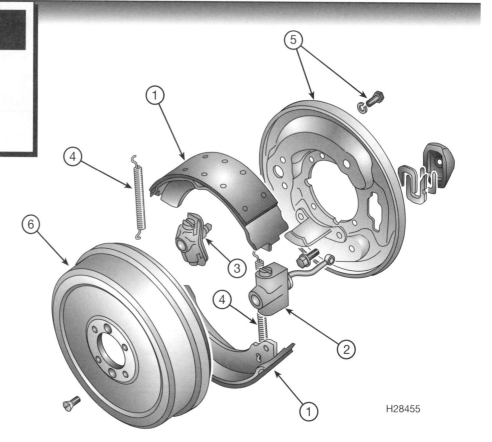

H28455

Land Rover Freelander rear brakes

1 Wheel cylinder
2 Upper return spring
3 Self-adjusting mechanism
4 Brake shoe retaining clip and pin
5 Inner handbrake cable
6 Lower return spring

Arrow indicates the front of the vehicle

Mazda 323 rear brakes

1 Self-adjusting mechanism spring
2 Lower return spring
3 Anchor plate
4 Brake shoe retaining clip and pin
5 Upper return spring
6 Wheel cylinder

Arrow indicates the front of the vehicle

Mercedes 124 Series handbrake shoes

1 Expander mechanism
2 Handbrake shoes
3 Lower return spring
4 Adjuster knurled ring
5 Adjuster body
6 Upper return spring

Arrow indicates the front of the vehicle

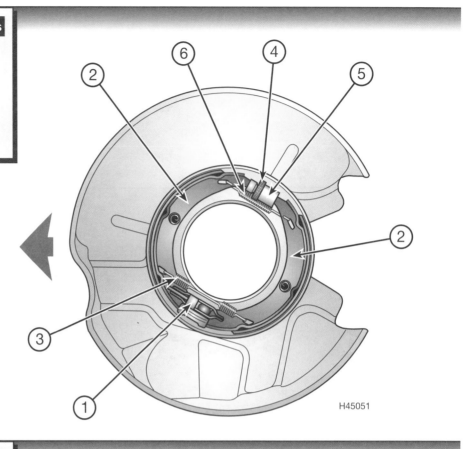

H45051

Nissan Micra rear brakes

1 Brake shoe retaining spring
2 Lower return spring
3 Wheel cylinder
4 Inner handbrake cable
5 Self-adjusting mechanism spring and lever
6 Upper return spring

Arrow indicates the front of the vehicle

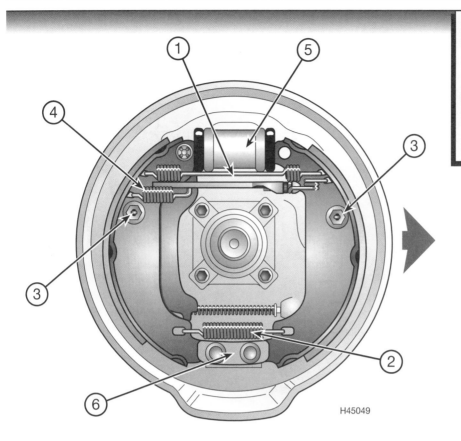

Peugeot 206 rear brakes - Bosch

1 Upper return spring
2 Lower return spring
3 Brake shoe retaining clip and pin
4 Adjuster strut-to-trailing shoe spring
5 Wheel cylinder
6 Anchor plate

Arrow indicates the front of the vehicle

H45049

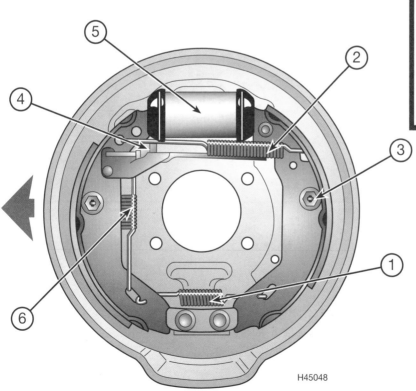

Peugeot 306 rear brakes - Girling

1 Lower return spring
2 Upper return spring
3 Brake shoe retaining clip and pin
4 Self-adjusting mechanism
5 Wheel cylinder
6 Self-adjusting mechanism spring

Arrow indicates the front of the vehicle

H45048

Proton rear brakes

1 Wheel cylinder
2 Self-adjusting strut
3 Brake shoe retaining clip
4 Lower return spring
5 Main return spring
6 Horseshoe clip

Arrow indicates the front of the vehicle

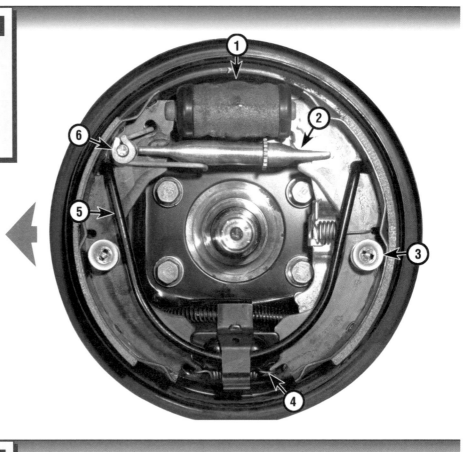

Renault Laguna rear brakes

1 Brake shoe retaining clip
2 Upper return spring
3 Wheel cylinder
4 Self-adjusting strut/mechanism
5 Inner handbrake cable
6 Lower return spring

Arrow indicates the front of the vehicle

Renault Megane rear brakes

1 Wheel cylinder
2 Retaining clip - Handbrake actuating
   lever-to-brake shoe
3 Self-adjusting mechanism spring
4 Handbrake actuating lever
5 Inner handbrake cable
6 Upper return spring

Arrow indicates the front of the vehicle

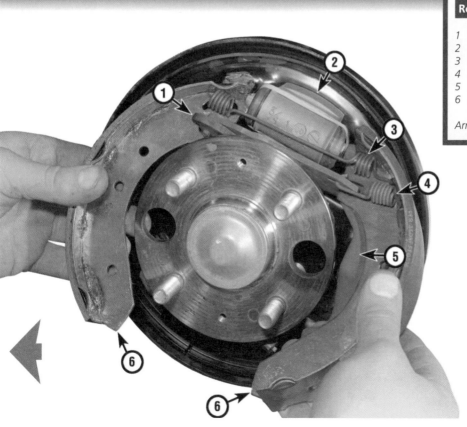

Rover 414, 416, 420 rear brakes

1 Self-adjusting mechanism
2 Wheel cylinder
3 Upper return spring
4 Self-adjusting strut/mechanism spring
5 Handbrake actuating lever
6 Brake shoes

Arrow indicates the front of the vehicle

Skoda Felicia rear brakes

1 Self-adjusting mechanism compensating
   'wedge'
2 Brake shoe retaining clip and pin
3 Lower return spring
4 Inner handbrake cable
5 Upper return spring
6 Wheel cylinder

Arrow indicates the front of the vehicle

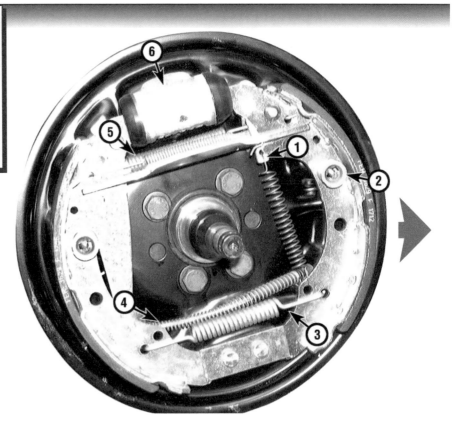

Toyota Carina-E rear brake

1 Upper return spring
2 Brake shoe retaining pin and clip
3 Lower return spring
4 Brake shoe
5 Self-adjusting ratchet lever
6 Self-adjusting strut/mechanism

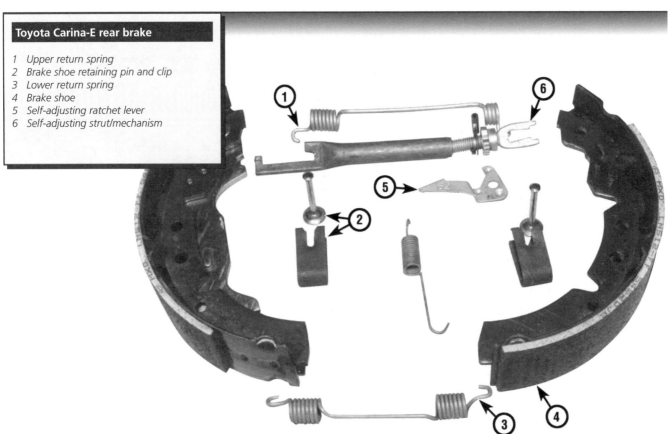

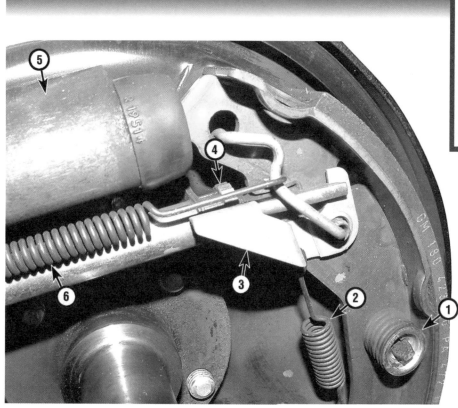

Vauxhall Corsa rear brakes

1 Brake shoe retaining pin and clip
2 Spring
3 Latch for self-adjusting mechanism
4 Self-adjusting mechanism ratchet wheel
5 Wheel cylinder
6 Upper return spring

Arrow indicates the front of the vehicle

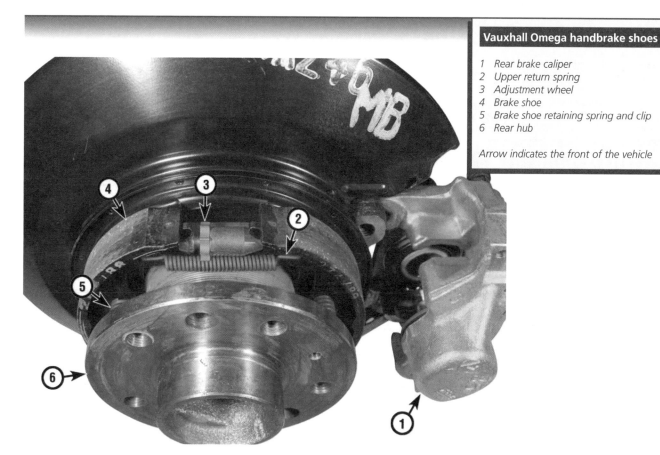

Vauxhall Omega handbrake shoes

1 Rear brake caliper
2 Upper return spring
3 Adjustment wheel
4 Brake shoe
5 Brake shoe retaining spring and clip
6 Rear hub

Arrow indicates the front of the vehicle

VW Golf rear brakes

1 Self-adjusting mechanism 'wedge' spring
2 Inner handbrake cable
3 Upper return spring
4 Wheel cylinder
5 Self-adjusting mechanism compensating 'wedge'
6 Handbrake actuating lever

Arrow indicates the front of the vehicle

VW Polo rear brakes

1 Brake shoe retaining clip
2 Wheel cylinder
3 Upper return spring
4 Self-adjusting strut spring
5 Self-adjusting mechanism compensating 'wedge'
6 Spring

Arrow indicates the front of the vehicle

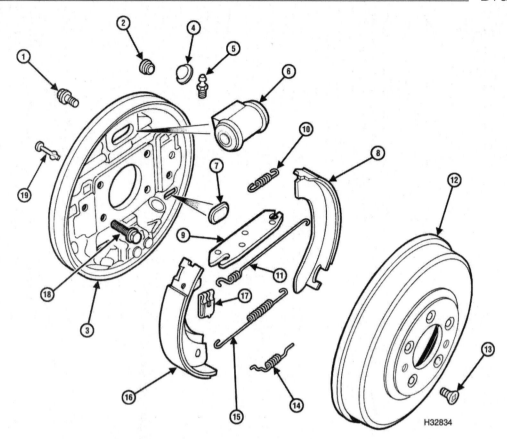

Typical rear drum brake assembly (Land Rover Freelander right-hand)

1 Wheel cylinder bolt
2 Blanking plug
3 Backplate
4 Dust cap
5 Bleed screw
6 Wheel cylinder
7 Blanking plug
8 Leading brake shoe
9 Adjuster strut
10 Adjuster spring
11 Upper shoe return spring
12 Brake drum
13 Drum retaining screw
14 Spring
15 Lower shoe return spring
16 Trailing brake shoe
17 Shoe retaining clip
18 Backplate fixing bolt
19 Shoe retaining pin

H32834

Exploded view of Hyundai, Mitsubishi drum brake assembly

1 Backing plate
2 Adjuster spring
3 Adjuster
4 Handbrake lever
5 Brake shoe
6 Piston
7 Wheel cylinder
8 Hold-down pin
9 Hold-down spring
10 Anchor spring
11 Shoe retracting spring
12 Clip spring
13 Bleed screw
14 Wheel cylinder boot

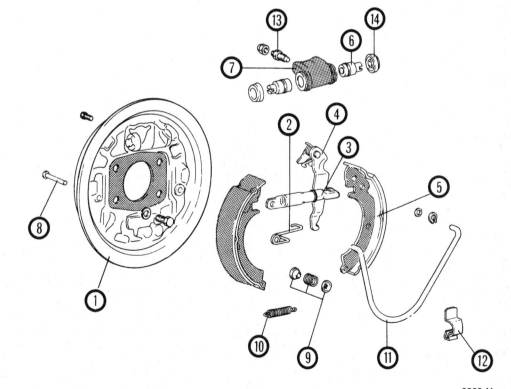

0069-H

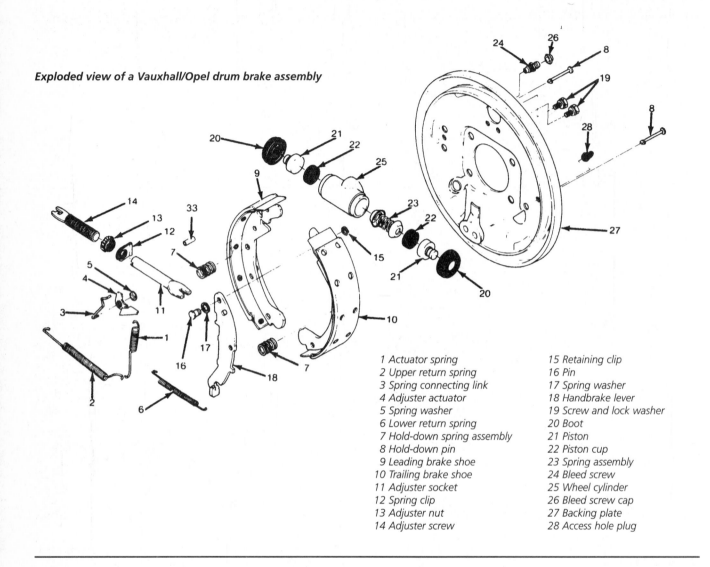

Exploded view of a Vauxhall/Opel drum brake assembly

1 Actuator spring
2 Upper return spring
3 Spring connecting link
4 Adjuster actuator
5 Spring washer
6 Lower return spring
7 Hold-down spring assembly
8 Hold-down pin
9 Leading brake shoe
10 Trailing brake shoe
11 Adjuster socket
12 Spring clip
13 Adjuster nut
14 Adjuster screw

15 Retaining clip
16 Pin
17 Spring washer
18 Handbrake lever
19 Screw and lock washer
20 Boot
21 Piston
22 Piston cup
23 Spring assembly
24 Bleed screw
25 Wheel cylinder
26 Bleed screw cap
27 Backing plate
28 Access hole plug

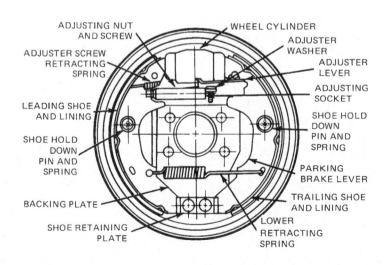

Typical Ford drum brake assembly

Remove the old brake shoes (leading/trailing brake)

Unhook the return spring (also called the retractor spring) from the leading brake shoe. A pair of locking pliers can be used to stretch the spring and pull the end out of the hole in the shoe

Remove the shoe hold-down springs. On this type, depress the hold-down spring and turn the retainer 90°, then release it. This special tool makes it much easier

If your brake is equipped with a spring steel type of hold-down clip, push down on the clip and turn the hold-down pin with a pair of pliers

Some brakes aren't equipped with hold-down springs, by have a 'horseshoe' type spring which serves as a hold-down spring and return spring. If your brake is like this, wedge a flat-bladed screwdriver under the spring and prise it out of the leading brake shoe, then remove the shoe

Remove the leading shoe from the backing plate and unhook the anchor spring from the bottom end of the shoe. If the brake you are working on has a lower shoe-to-shoe return spring instead of a spring that passes under the anchor plate, remove it using the technique shown previously, if necessary

Remove the hold-down spring from the trailing shoe

If the brake you're working on is equipped with a horseshoe spring, prise it out of the trailing shoe

Pull the trailing shoe (and adjuster assembly, if applicable) away from the backing plate ...

... then hold the end of the handbrake cable with a pair of pliers and pull it out of the handbrake lever

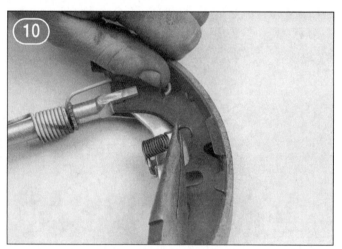

If your brake has a handbrake set-up like this, remove the adjusting lever spring

If the brake is equipped with a captive adjuster screw (retained by the return spring), unhook the spring from the shoe and slide the adjuster and spring off

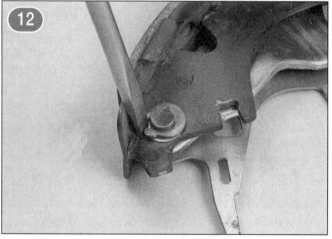

Prise the C-clip apart and remove it to separate the handbrake lever and adjuster lever from the rear shoe. Take note of any washers or shims that may be present

Preparation for refitting (leading/trailing brake)

Assemble the handbrake lever and adjuster lever to the new rear show and crimp the C-clip closed with a pair of pliers. Always use a new clip and be sure to refit any shims or washers that were present upon separation

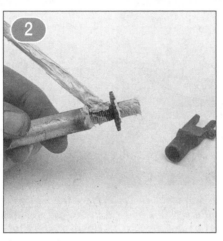

Clean the adjusting screw with brake system cleaner, dry it off and lubricate the threads and end with high-temperature anti-seize compound (Copperslip). The screw portion of the adjuster will need to be threaded in further than before to allow the drum to fit over the new shoes

Feel the brake shoe contact points on the backing plate. If they are rough or a ledge has worn into them, file them smooth. Lubricate these contact points with high-temperature anti-seize compound (Copperslip)

Fitting the new shoes (leading/trailing brake)

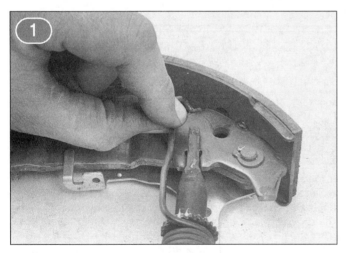

If the adjuster screw is a captive type, refit it onto the rear shoe. Ensure the end fits properly into the slot in the shoe and hook the spring into the opening in the shoe

Refit the adjuster lever spring, if applicable

Hold the trailing shoe assembly up to the backing plate, pull the handbrake cable spring back and hold it there with a pair of pliers, then place the cable into the hooked end of the handbrake lever

Place the trailing shoe against the backing plate being careful not to get any grease on the friction linings. Pass the hold-down pin through its hole in the shoes and refit the hold-down spring and retaining clip

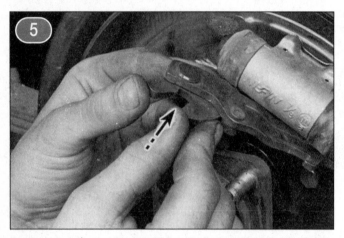

If your brake has a quadrant-type adjuster mechanism, refit it now and push the lever in about half-way (arrowed)

Connect the anchor spring (if applicable) to the bottom of each shoe and mount the leading shoe to the backing plate (again, be careful not to get any grease on the lining material). Refit the hold-down spring and retaining clip

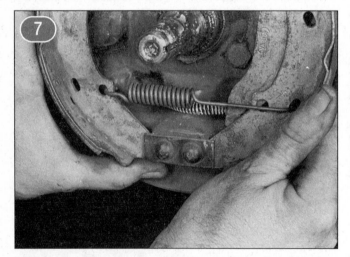

If the brake has a shoe-to-shoe return spring, refit it between the two shoes, making sure the straight portion of the spring is connected to the trailing shoe (it's designed like this so as not to interfere with the handbrake lever)

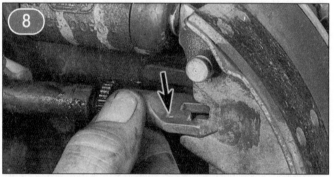

If the adjuster assembly on your brake is non-captive (not retained by the return spring), refit it now. Spread the shoes apart and insert each end of the adjuster in the proper slots in the shoes. If the slot in the handbrake lever end of the adjuster is stepped, like this one, make sure the longer part of the slot is positioned over the handbrake lever. Note: Some adjuster screws are marked (arrowed) to indicate which side of the vehicle they go on. If this is the case, be sure to refit the adjuster on the proper side. Also, this mark usually faces up

Refit the adjuster lever (if it is a detachable one like this) on the handbrake lever pivot pin ...

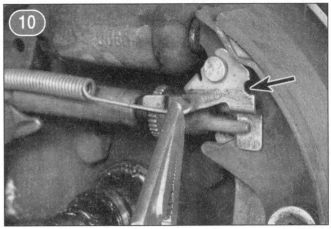

... then refit the leading shoe hold-down pin, spring and clip - stretch the return spring, with the straight part of the spring over the adjuster lever, and hook it in the notch on the adjuster lever (arrowed)

Make sure the shoes are seated properly in the slots in the wheel cylinders and are engaged with the adjuster screw assembly

Using a screwdriver, stretch the return spring into its hole in the front shoe

Prise the handbrake lever forward and check to see that the return spring (arrowed) didn't come unhooked from the trailing shoe

Wiggle the assembly to make sure it is seated properly against the backing plate. Refit the brake drum, then adjust the brakes

If your brake has a quadrant type adjuster mechanism and the brake drum won't go back on after replacing the shoes, it will be necessary to retract the shoes. Put a screwdriver between the two parts of the ratchet and push in - spring pressure will retract the shoes

Chapter 3

Handbrakes

Component renewal   2   Introduction   1

Handbrake adjustment   See Chapter 7

1   Introduction

The handbrake is sometimes called the parking brake, because its main use is for preventing the vehicle from moving when it is parked. It is also referred to as the emergency brake, but on most vehicles it would be quite useless in an emergency situation where the regular service brakes have failed, unless there were plenty of straight, unoccupied road ahead.

Almost all car manufacturers place the handbrake at the rear wheels. The most popular exceptions to this rule are Subaru, Saab and (needless to say) Citroën. They usually place the handbrakes on the front wheels. Some older vehicles had the handbrake mounted on the transmission extension housing, with a small brake drum on the driveshaft. This arrangement is still used on some Land Rovers.

There are four basic types of handbrake or parking brakes in use today, but regardless of design they share two things in common. One, they are all actuated by a lever, a pedal or a pullrod in the driver's compartment. Two, a cable or set of cables (sometimes one, sometimes two or more) connects the pedal, lever or pullrod with the handbrakes at the wheels.

On models with drum brakes at the rear wheels, the handbrake is simply incorporated into the drum brake assembly. A lever is connected to the top of the secondary, or trailing brake shoe (depending on brake design) and attached to the handbrake cable at the bottom. A strut (duo-servo type) or strut/adjuster screw (leading/trailing type) is placed between the two brake shoes, near the top. When the lever attached to the brake shoe is pulled by the handbrake cable it pushes (via the handbrake strut) the primary, or leading shoe against the brake drum. This causes

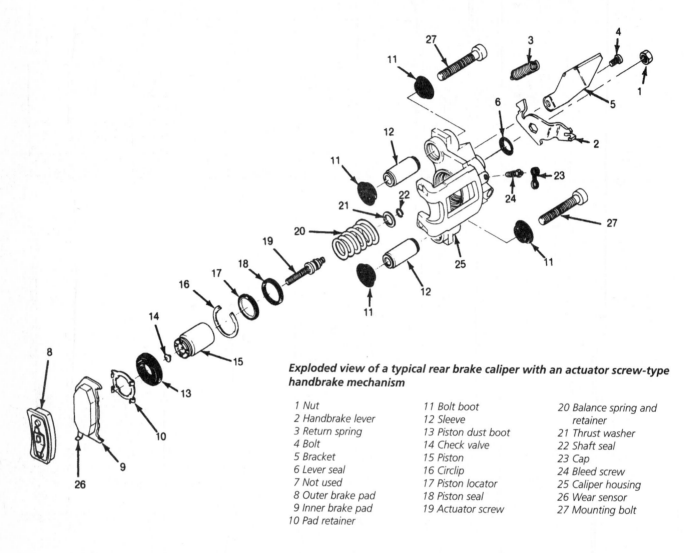

Exploded view of a typical rear brake caliper with an actuator screw-type handbrake mechanism

1 Nut	11 Bolt boot	20 Balance spring and
2 Handbrake lever	12 Sleeve	retainer
3 Return spring	13 Piston dust boot	21 Thrust washer
4 Bolt	14 Check valve	22 Shaft seal
5 Bracket	15 Piston	23 Cap
6 Lever seal	16 Circlip	24 Bleed screw
7 Not used	17 Piston locator	25 Caliper housing
8 Outer brake pad	18 Piston seal	26 Wear sensor
9 Inner brake pad	19 Actuator screw	27 Mounting bolt
10 Pad retainer		

the pivot of the lever to bear against the secondary, or trailing brake shoe, forcing it against the brake drum, thereby locking the wheel. See Chapter 3 for more information on the drum brakes.

There are three common kinds of handbrake set-ups on vehicles with disc brakes on the rear wheels (actually, if the handbrakes are situated on the front wheel brakes, only one of these designs is used). The most common type is fitted to floating or sliding calipers and operates the caliper through a large actuator screw that winds into the back of the caliper piston (see illustration). When the handbrake is set, the cable pulls on a lever attached to the actuator screw, causing the screw to turn. The helical thread on the screw tries to turn the piston, but the piston is prevented from turning because it is engaged with the brake pad by one or two lugs that fit into the backing plate of the inner brake pad. This causes the piston to move out, applying the brake pads the same way it does when hydraulic pressure pushes it

out. This system works well, but with age the actuator screws tend to seize in the caliper piston, and the seal around the actuator screw is a potential source of brake fluid leakage.

A similar type of handbrake arrangement that is integral with the caliper uses a cam-driven adjuster spindle (or pushrod) to force the piston out from the caliper (see illustration).

Another type of handbrake on vehicles with disc brakes at the rear wheels is like a little drum brake mounted inside the hub, or "hat" portion of the brake disc (see illustration). The brake shoes are anchored to a small backing plate and operate just like the handbrake mechanism on a vehicle with drum brakes. The nice thing about this design is that it is virtually trouble-free, unless you forget to release the handbrake from time to time.

A less common kind of handbrake set-up employs an extra set of small brake pads mounted in a fixture attached to

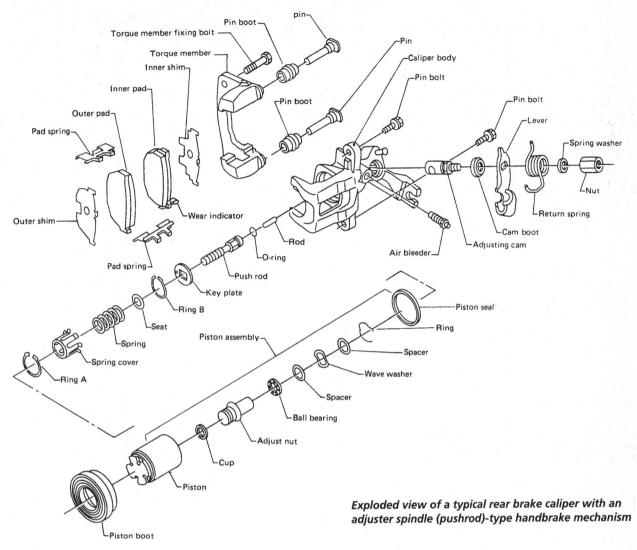

Pin boot
pin
Torque member fixing bolt
Pin
Torque member
Caliper body
Inner shim
Pin bolt
Inner pad
Pin bolt
Outer pad
Pin boot
Lever
Pad spring
Spring washer
Pin boot
Nut
Outer shim
Return spring
Wear indicator
Cam boot
Pad spring
Rod
Adjusting cam
O-ring
Air bleeder
Push rod
Key plate
Piston seal
Ring B
Ring
Seat
Spacer
Spring
Piston assembly
Wave washer
Spring cover
Spacer
Ring A
Ball bearing
Adjust nut
Cup
Piston
Piston boot

Exploded view of a typical rear brake caliper with an adjuster spindle (pushrod)-type handbrake mechanism

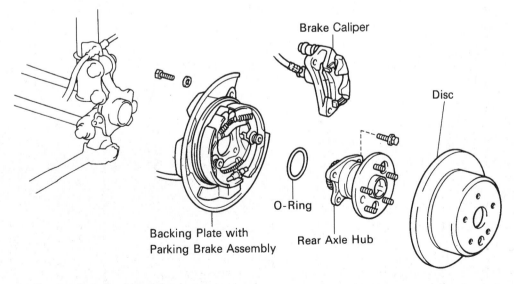

Brake Caliper

Disc

Backing Plate with
Parking Brake Assembly

O-Ring

Rear Axle Hub

Typical drum-in-disc type handbrake mechanism

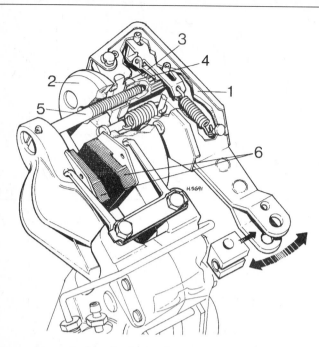

Cutaway view of a handbrake mechanism that is attached to a rear caliper and uses separate pads

1 Operating lever
2 Pad carrier assembly
3 Pawl assembly
4 Adjuster nut
5 Adjuster bolt
6 Handbrake pad

each rear caliper *(see illustration)*. They're like small, mechanically actuated calipers mated to the hydraulic calipers. Automatic adjusters in the handbrake pad carriers compensate for wear. On some vehicles that use this system, a single handbrake cable is connected to an operating lever on each mechanism *(see illustration)*, or to a linkage that operates both mechanisms.

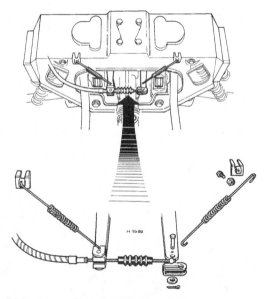

Some vehicles use a single handbrake cable to operate both handbrake mechanisms, like on this Jaguar

2 Component renewal

Handbrake lever

On most vehicles you'll have to remove the centre console for access to the handbrake lever bolts. Once this has been done, unscrew the upper handbrake cable nut (the adjusting nut) and pull the cable from the lever *(see illustration)*. Some vehicles have both cables attached to the lever. It may be necessary to remove a trim piece from the lever for access to the adjuster nut.

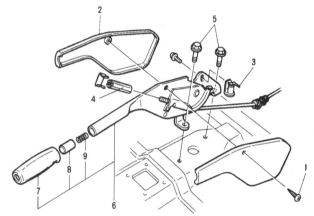

Typical handbrake lever details

1 Screw
2 Covers
3 Handbrake switch connector
4 Adjusting nut
5 Bolts
6 Lever assembly
7 Grip
8 Release button
9 Return spring

Remove the nuts or bolts holding the lever to the floorpan *(see illustration)* and detach the lever. On some models it may be necessary to unplug the electrical connector from the handbrake light switch.

Refitting is the reverse of removal, but be sure to adjust the handbrake cable(s) by following the procedure outlined in Chapter 7.

Handbrake lever mounting nuts (arrowed) - Vauxhall Zafira

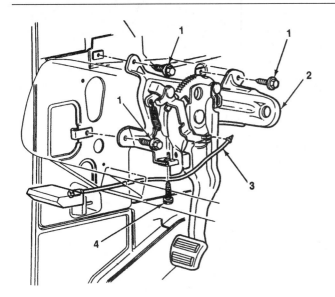

Typical parking brake pedal mounting details

1 Bolt   2 Pedal assembly   3 Release rod   4 Bolt

Parking brake pedal or pullrod

If necessary for access to the pedal, remove the under-dash panel and/or the kick panel trim. Unplug the electrical connector from the warning light switch.

If you're removing a pedal assembly, disconnect the release rod or cable from the pawl lever on the mechanism (*see*

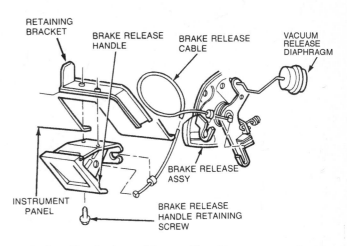

Typical parking brake pedal assembly with a vacuum release diaphragm

illustration). If equipped with a vacuum-operated release, disconnect the vacuum hose or, if the vacuum release diaphragm is not mounted on the pedal assembly, disconnect the link rod from the assembly (*see illustration*).

Remove the bolts or nuts and detach the pedal or pullrod assembly. Refitting is the reverse of removal, but be sure to adjust the handbrake as described in Chapter 7. If you're removing a handbrake pullrod, detach the cable from the end of the pullrod (*see illustration*) or remove the clevis pin and detach the rod from the lever (*see illustration*).

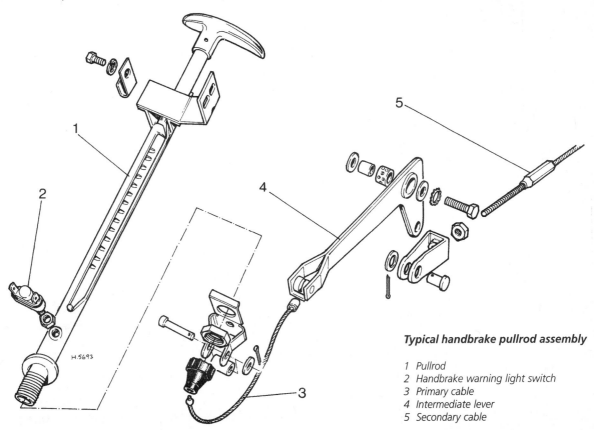

Typical handbrake pullrod assembly

1 Pullrod
2 Handbrake warning light switch
3 Primary cable
4 Intermediate lever
5 Secondary cable

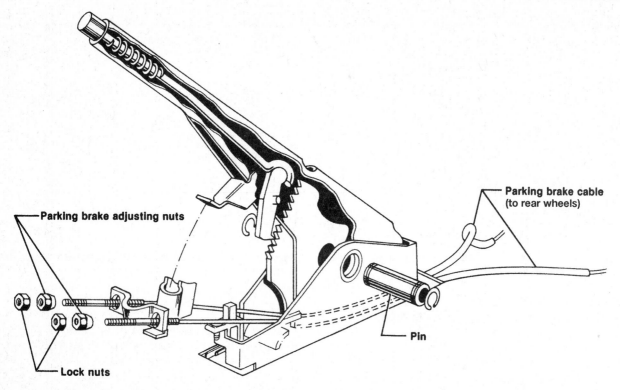

Typical two-cable handbrake cable arrangement

Handbrake cable(s)

Some vehicles are equipped with only one handbrake cable, but chances are that your vehicle has two, maybe even three or four cables to actuate the handbrake mechanisms *(see illustrations)*. These cables are retained by a series of clips or clamps and sometimes also by guide wires and springs, to keep tension on the cables to prevent them from interfering with other parts.

Before renewing a handbrake cable, loosen the adjusting nut(s) to provide some slack. See Chapter 7 for a sampling of handbrake cable adjusters.

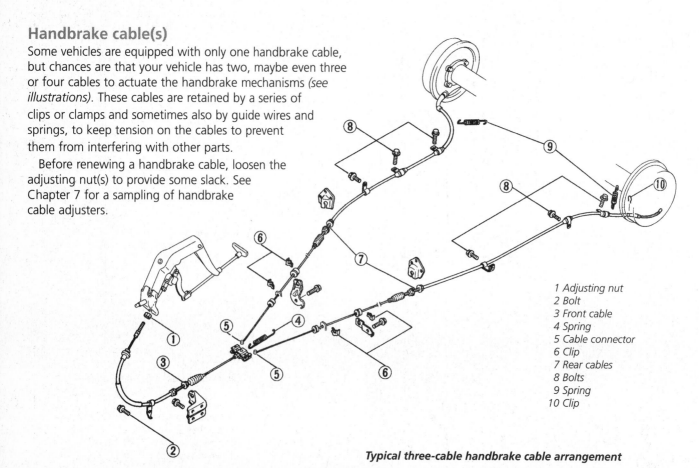

1 Adjusting nut
2 Bolt
3 Front cable
4 Spring
5 Cable connector
6 Clip
7 Rear cables
8 Bolts
9 Spring
10 Clip

Typical three-cable handbrake cable arrangement

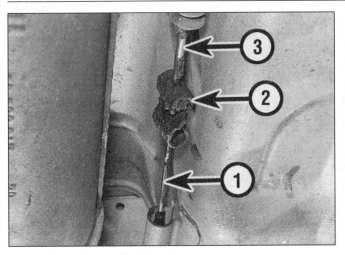

On this model (Cavalier), the front section of the cable is connected by an 'S' shaped link

1 Handbrake cable   2 Connecting link   3 Handbrake lever operating rod

Front cable

If the vehicle is equipped with a lever-actuated handbrake, remove the centre console. If the brake is pedal-actuated, remove the kick panel, if it's in the way.

Detach the cable from the lever, pedal or pullrod. In most cases this will involve removing a nut or a clip from the end of the cable *(see illustration)*.

Raise the vehicle and support it securely on axle stands.

Remove any bolts or clips retaining the cable casing, then push the cable and casing through the grommet and out from the floorpan. Some casings are retained by locking tangs which must be depressed to allow them to pass through the bracket *(see illustration)*. If the cable casing does not continue out through the floorpan, however, pull the cable and casing into the interior of the vehicle instead.

Detach the other end of the cable from the equaliser or cable connector *(see illustrations)*. Refitting is the reverse of removal. Make sure the grommet around the cable casing where it passes through the floor is properly seated. Adjust the brake by following the procedure described in Chapter 7.

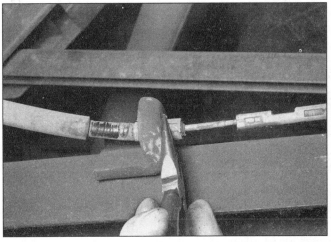

Depress the locking tangs to allow them to pass through the bracket

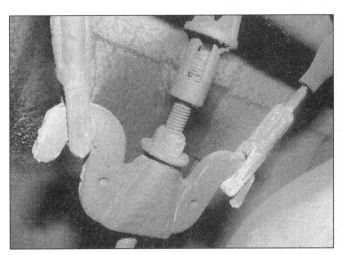

Slacken the nut and unhook the cables from the equaliser plate ...

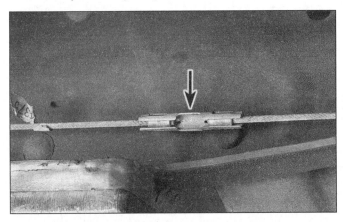

... or the cable connector (push the cable toward the centre opening (arrowed) and pull it out)

On this type of rear cable set-up, prevent the rod from turning by holding it with a pair of locking pliers, then remove the adjuster nut. The rear cables can now be separated from the adjuster

Unclip the handbrake cable end from the handbrake lever on the trailing shoe, then remove the shoe and lever assembly

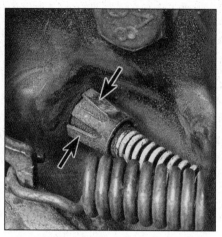

Depress the retention tangs (arrowed) to free the casing and cable from the backing plate. A pair of pliers can be used for this

On some vehicles the handbrake cable casing is attached to the backing plate by a bolts (arrowed)

Rear cable

Loosen the rear wheel nuts/bolts, raise the vehicle and support it securely on axle stands. Remove the wheel.

Detach the cable from the connector, equaliser or adjuster *(see illustrations on page 4•7)*.

Disconnect the cable casing from any mounting brackets or clips.

If the vehicle has rear drum brakes, remove the brake drum (see Chapter 3) and detach the end of the cable from the handbrake lever *(see illustration)*. In some cases this will require removal of the brake shoes. Depress the tangs on the cable casing retainer and push the cable and casing out through the backing plate *(see illustration)*, or unscrew the bolt retaining the casing to the backing plate *(see illustration)*.

If the vehicle has disc brakes, detach the cable from the handbrake lever on the caliper (or from the actuating lever on vehicles with drum-in-disc handbrake assemblies),

separate the cable casing from its bracket (it's usually retained by a clip) and remove the cable *(see illustrations)*.

Refitting is the reverse of removal. Be sure to adjust the brake as outlined in Chapter 7.

Handbrake shoes (drum-in-disc type handbrake)

> ⚠ *Warning: The dust created by the brake system may contain asbestos, which is harmful to your health. Never blow it out with compressed air and don't inhale any of it. An approved filtering mask should be worn when working on the brakes. Do not, under any circumstances, use petroleum-based solvents to clean brake parts. Use brake system cleaner only!*

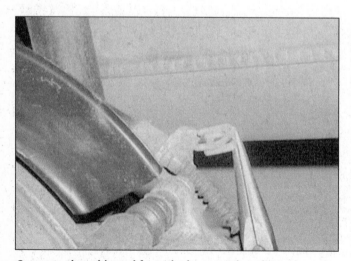

Separate the cable end from the lever on the caliper ...

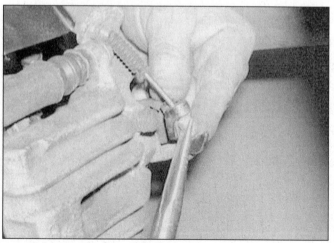

... then remove the clip and separate the cable casing from the bracket

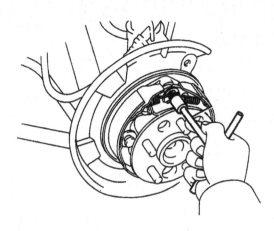

Unhook the handbrake shoe return springs from the anchor pin (where applicable)

Note: *All four handbrake shoes should be renewed at the same time, but only work on one brake assembly at a time, using the other side for reference, if necessary.*

Loosen the rear wheel nuts/bolts, raise the vehicle and support it securely on axle stands. Remove the wheels.

Remove the brake disc (see Chapter 2). Before removing anything else, clean the handbrake assembly with brake system cleaner. Position a drain pan under the brake to catch the fluid and residue.

Remove the handbrake shoe return springs from the anchor pin *(see illustration)*. Some designs don't have an anchor pin, but have two shoe-to-shoe springs instead.

Spread the tops of the shoes apart and remove the shoe strut and spring assembly, if equipped *(see illustration)*. Take note as to how the strut is positioned.

Remove the hold-down springs from the shoes *(see illustration)*. Pull the front shoe from the backing plate and remove the adjuster *(see illustration)*, then detach the shoe-to-shoe spring *(see illustration)*.

Turn and lift out the shoe strut and spring - if fitted

Remove the shoe hold-down spring. This particular type requires and Allen key. Other styles are like the more conventional hold-down spring retainers as found in a drum brake assembly

Pull the front shoe out and remove the adjuster screw

Twist the shoe and remove the shoe-to-shoe spring

Pull the cable out and up to free it from the lever on the rear shoe (some designs don't use a lever attached to the shoe - the shoes are spread apart by an actuator on the backing plate)

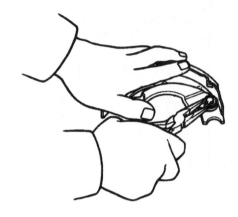

Use a pair of pliers to crimp the C-clip to the pivot pin

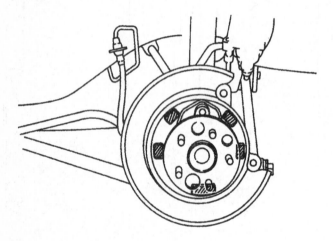

Apply a light coat of high-temperature anti-seize compound (Copperslip) to the handbrake shoe contact areas (shaded areas) on the backing plate

If the handbrake is actuated by a lever attached to the rear shoe, detach the cable from the lever (see illustration), then remove the shoe. Using a screwdriver, spread the C-clip on the handbrake lever pivot pin then remove the lever, shim (if equipped) and pin. Transfer the parts to the new rear shoe and crimp the C-clip to the pin using a pair of pliers (see illustration).

Thoroughly wash the backing plate with brake system cleaner. Feel the shoe contact areas on the backing plate - it they're rough, smooth them out with a file or sandpaper. Apply a thin coat of high-temperature grease to the contact areas (see illustration).

Clean the adjuster screw threads, then apply a film of high-temperature grease to the moving parts of the adjuster (see illustration).

If it was necessary to detach the cable from the handbrake lever on the rear shoe, reattach it now. Mount the rear shoe to the backing plate and refit the hold-down spring.

Connect the shoe-to-shoe spring between the bottom of each shoe, then refit the adjuster (see illustration). Position

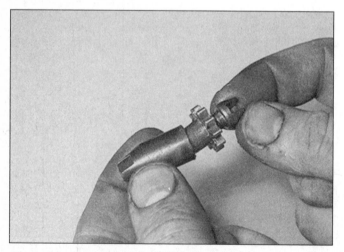

Clean the adjuster assembly and coat the moving parts with high-temperature anti-seize compound

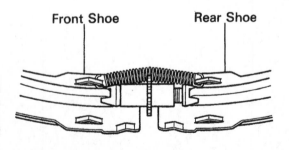

When reassembled, the tension spring and adjuster screw should be arranged something like this

the front shoe on the backing plate and refit the hold-down spring. Refit the handbrake strut. Make sure you refit it with the spring end facing the proper direction. Refit the shoe return springs.

Refit the brake disc. If the disc isn't retained by screws, temporarily refit a couple of wheel nuts to hold the disc in place. **Note:** *If the axle flange has a notch machined into it that corresponds with the adjuster hole in the disc, be sure to refit the disc with the adjuster hole over the notch (see illustrations).*

Adjust the handbrake shoes by referring to the Chapter 7 section entitled "Drum brake adjustment."

Refit the brake caliper and wheel. Lower the vehicle and tighten the wheel nuts/bolts securely.

Be sure to align the access hole with the adjuster cut-out (arrowed) when refitting the disc over the parking brake assembly

On some BMWs, position one of the wheel bolt holes as shown ...

... and insert a screwdriver to access the adjuster (disc removed for clarity)

Chapter 4

ABS systems

Components	2
Fault finding	5
General information	1

Operation	3
Precautions	4

1   General information

Note: *The following system and component descriptions offer a general overview of the ABS system, how it works, and the components that comprise a typical ABS system. It is not possible to cover the specifics of all ABS systems nor include in-depth fault finding and repair procedures in a manual of this size.*

What is ABS?

When a vehicle is rolling down the road and the driver applies the brakes, the energy of the moving vehicle is converted to heat through the brakes, which slows down the vehicle. The coefficient of friction between the road and the tyres increases too, as the tyres "grab" at the road. If the coefficient of friction exceeds that which the tyre can effectively deal with, the tyre begins to skid along the road surface. This is an example of wheel slip.

Wheel slip can be defined as the difference between the speed of the vehicle and the speed of the wheel against the ground. When a wheel is locked up and sliding, wheel slip of 100-percent is present. If the wheel is rolling along with the vehicle and the brakes are not applied, zero wheel slip is taking place. Normal braking takes place somewhere between these extreme percentages.

Unfortunately, not all instances of slowing down a vehicle fall under the "normal" category. During emergency stops or hard braking on slippery surfaces, it's easy to lock up the wheels. When the wheels are locked up, it is impossible to maintain control of the vehicle - the wheels must be rolling in order to have directional control. Besides that, engineers have discovered that a rolling wheel with a slip factor of 8 to 35-percent under braking generates a much greater coefficient of friction between the tyre and the road than a sliding tyre does. When the wheels stop rolling but the vehicle keeps moving, it will follow the path of least resistance. To the dismay of many a motorist, this path of least resistance has led right into an object of great resistance - like a telegraph pole or the proverbial brick wall!

Anti-lock Brake Systems work to avoid such situations by monitoring the rotational speed of the wheels. When the system senses a wheel turning too slowly in relation to the others, the hydraulic pressure to the brake at that wheel is reduced, preventing it from locking up.

The latest systems now also correctly proportion the braking force to the front and rear brakes - known as 'Electronic Brake Force Distribution (EBFD or EBD), and if equipped with EBA (Emergency Brake Assist), the system detects when an emergency stop is intended, and applies the maximum braking force according to the grip level available at each wheel.

All current anti-lock systems are fail-safe. They all have some form of mechanical override - in the event of a malfunction such as failure of the Electronic Control Unit (ECU), the brakes will function just like a standard (non-ABS) system.

Advantages

Anti-lock Brake Systems have three distinct advantages over a non-ABS brake system:

a) *Since brake systems with ABS don't allow the wheels to lock up, tyre wear is improved. It is impossible for the tyres to get flat-spotted with an ABS system.*

b) *The driver of a vehicle equipped with ABS has a much greater degree of control over the vehicle than the driver of a vehicle not equipped with ABS. Even under hard braking, a vehicle with ABS can be steered.*

c) *A vehicle with ABS has a reduced tendency to aquaplane when braking in wet road conditions.*

Limitations

Although a vehicle equipped with ABS will stop in the shortest possible distance achievable under the design parameters of the system (how much wheel slip the system will allow), there is certainly no guarantee that all accidents will be avoided. Tyres are still a limiting factor, and if the brakes are applied hard during cornering there is a good possibility that the tyres will lose traction. Remember, the system monitors rotational speed of the wheels, not lateral motion against the road (although some systems incorporate a lateral acceleration sensor or switch which, when activated, tells the control unit to reduce braking pressure so the tyres don't get overloaded and break traction).

If the driver applies the brakes too late, the ABS system will do its job just as it was designed to do, but the vehicle won't come to a complete stop before it hits the object that the driver is trying to avoid.

HINTS & TIPS

- When braking on snowy or icy road surfaces, or in dirt or gravel, an Anti-lock Brake System will not bring the vehicle to a stop in the shortest possible distance. A locked or nearly locked wheel is preferred under these conditions, because a wedge of snow or dirt will build up under the front of the tyres and help stop the vehicle. This can't happen with ABS, so some vehicles equipped with ABS have an override switch on the dash to defeat the ABS system during snowy conditions or when driving on dirt roads.

ABS facts

Here are some important things to know regarding ABS brakes:

a) *When the ABS is activated (when a wheel begins to lock up), it is normal for the driver to feel pedal pulsations. This is the result of the modulator valves cycling to reduce pressure in the brake lines. During normal braking no pulsations should be felt.*

b) *The amount of force on the brake pedal that is required to activate the ABS system depends on the road surface. If the surface of the road is very slippery it won't take much to slide the tyres, in which case the ABS will kick in.*

c) *If the system experiences a malfunction, it will revert to a normal hydraulic brake system. You won't lose your brakes completely on account of a problem with the ABS portion of the brake system.*

d) *Consult the appropriate Service and Repair Manual before carrying out any service operations other than brake pad or shoe renewal. In order to bleed the modulator, pump or valves, access to specialist equipment may be required.*

e) *If you renew a brake disc, brake drum, driveshaft, axleshaft or differential assembly (depending on system design) and the component being renewed is equipped with a toothed signal rotor, make sure the new part is equipped with a signal rotor also. In some cases the signal rotor is pressed onto the component, in which case it will have to be removed from the old part and pressed onto the new one.*

f) *ABS systems aren't just fitted on vehicles with four-wheel disc brakes. Some vehicles with disc brakes in the front and drum brakes in the rear are equipped with ABS.*

g) *The presence of an ABS system does not affect normal brake service. Brake pads or shoes must still be checked at the recommended intervals. They don't last any longer, either. Calipers, wheel cylinders, hoses and handbrake mechanisms are also subject to the same amount of wear as in a non-ABS system.*

h) *Finally, a vehicle equipped with ABS can't out-brake an identical non-ABS vehicle driven by an expert driver on a dry, straight road. This is because a typical ABS system allows the amount of tyre slip to drop as low as 5-percent, which is below the point at which maximum traction is achieved. A skilled driver can use his or her judgement to increase the amount of tyre slip without locking the wheels.*

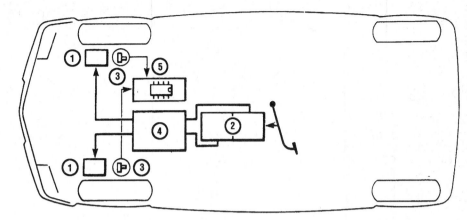

Schematic view of a typical front-wheel anti-lock braking system

1 Brake calipers
2 Master cylinder
3 Wheel speed sensors
4 Hydraulic modulator
5 ECU

Types of systems

There are two basic types of ABS systems - front-wheel anti-lock systems and four-wheel anti-lock systems. Within these two groupings are two sub-groupings - component systems and integral systems.

Front-wheel anti-lock systems

Front-wheel ABS systems operate on the front wheels only, and have no effect on the rear wheels *(see illustration)*.

Although the system cannot prevent the rear wheels from locking under extreme braking conditions, the most significant advantage of the system is that it allows the driver to brake as hard as possible and steer the vehicle at the same time.

Most vehicles have a proportioning valve fitted in the rear brake hydraulic circuit, which prevents the rear wheels from locking before the front wheels under heavy braking - this valve is not part of the ABS system, and does not sense the rotational speed of the wheels.

Front-wheel ABS systems monitor the rotational speeds of the front wheels. Most systems use electronic wheel speed sensors, which produce a signal in conjunction with toothed rotors mounted on the driveshafts or wheel hubs (these components are described in more detail later in this Chapter). An alternative system was developed by Ford for use on some of their early front-wheel-drive vehicles, using mechanical hydraulic modulators (one for each front brake), driven by toothed belts from the driveshafts.

On some systems, the hydraulic pressure to each front brake is controlled independently, according to the rotational speed of the relevant wheel. On systems where the hydraulic pressure to the front wheels is controlled through a single circuit, the pressure regulation is controlled by the signals from the wheel with the least amount of traction (this is known as the "select-low" principle).

Four-wheel anti-lock systems

Four-wheel anti-lock systems monitor the rotational speeds of all four wheels *(see illustrations)*.

The advantage of this type of system over a front-wheel system is that it reduces the possibility of the vehicle spinning (due to the rear wheels locking) under heavy braking.

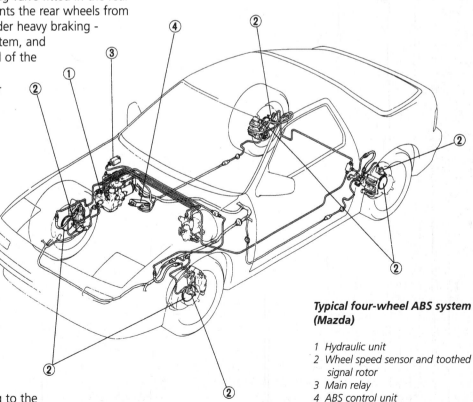

Typical four-wheel ABS system (Mazda)

1 Hydraulic unit
2 Wheel speed sensor and toothed signal rotor
3 Main relay
4 ABS control unit

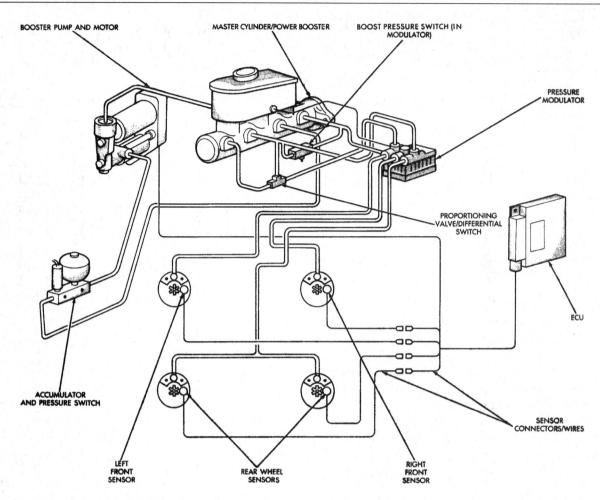

Typical four-wheel ABS system (Jeep)

On some systems, the hydraulic pressure to all four wheels is controlled independently, according to the rotational speed of the relevant wheel. An alternative type of system controls the pressure to each front brake individually, but the pressure to the rear brakes is controlled through a single circuit (the pressure to the rear brakes is controlled by the signals from the rear wheel with the least amount of grip).

Component systems

The component system is sometimes referred to as an "add-on" system. These types of systems are used on vehicles equipped with a standard master cylinder/brake servo combination. The hydraulic control unit is fitted downstream of the master cylinder.

Although referred to as an add-on system, it is not generally practical to retrofit the relevant components to convert a non-ABS brake system into an ABS system. Considerable work would be involved to achieve this (such as changing wheel hub/driveshaft components, etc).

Integral systems

Integral ABS systems are self-contained units, which combine the master cylinder, brake servo and hydraulic modulator into a single assembly *(see illustration)*.

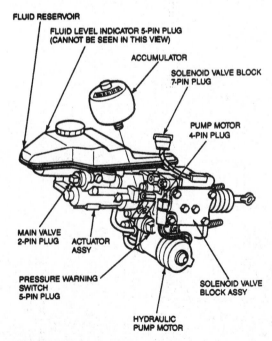

Details of an integral ABS actuation assembly

2 Components

Ford belt-driven mechanical ABS system

The system uses two belt-driven mechanical modulators, driven from the driveshafts.

Each modulator contains a shaft which drives a flywheel via a clutch. During normal driving and braking, the modulator shaft and the flywheel rotate at the same speed, and hydraulic pressure is supplied to the front brakes in the normal way. If a front wheel locks, the modulator shaft rotates more slowly than the flywheel, and the flywheel overruns the clutch to operate a hydraulic pressure dump valve, releasing the pressure on the relevant brake. At the same time as the hydraulic pressure is released, the pressure from the master cylinder operates a mechanism to slow down the flywheel. When the speed of the modulator shaft

and the flywheel are equal, the dump valve closes, and the cycle is repeated. This cycle takes place many times a second until the vehicle stops, or the brakes are released.

The system incorporates a belt breakage warning light on the instrument panel, which operates if the belt breaks, or if the belt adjustment is too slack. If the ABS system fails, normal braking is still available.

Electronic ABS systems

Most of the ABS systems likely to be encountered are electronic systems, and they comprise the following components.

 a) *Wheel speed sensors*
 b) *Toothed signal rotors*
 c) *Hydraulic modulator*
 d) *Electric fluid pump*
 e) *Hydraulic accumulator*
 f) *Electronic control unit*
 g) *Lateral acceleration sensor (not all systems)*
 h) *Brake pedal postion sensor (not all systems)*
 i) *Longitudinal acceleration sensor (not all systems)*

Wheel speed sensors

These sensors are located at all four wheels on vehicles with four-wheel ABS, or at the front wheels of vehicles with front-wheel ABS systems *(see illustrations)*.

The sensors generate small electrical impulses when the toothed signal rotors are turning. The impulses are sent to the electronic control unit, which analyses the signals to determine the rotational speed of the wheels.

All wheel sensors are of a similar design, consisting of a permanent magnet wrapped with wire.

The sensors are positioned very close to the signal rotors, and are usually mounted on the hub carriers, or sometimes in the rear brake backplates.

ABS wheel speed sensor (Vauxhall Corsa)

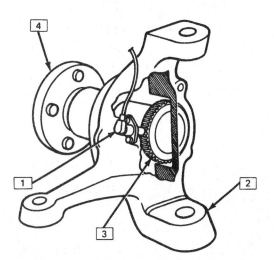

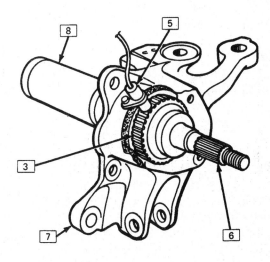

Typical wheel speed sensors

1 Front wheel speed sensor
2 Hub carrier
3 Toothed signal rotor

4 Front hub and bearing assembly
5 Rear wheel speed sensor
6 Rear driveshaft spindle

7 Rear hub carrier
8 Rear driveshaft

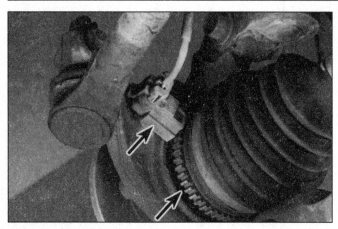

The toothed signal rotor is pressed onto the ends of the outer CV joint (lower arrow) - the wheel speed sensor is mounted on the hub carrier (upper arrow)

On some vehicles, the signal rotor is integral with the brake drum ...

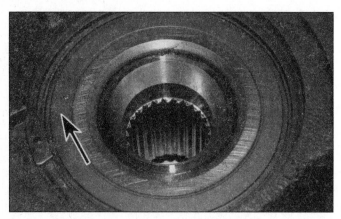

... on some, the wheel bearing oil seal (arrowed) has magnetic segments embedded which do the same job as the signal rotor teeth

On some models, the sensor is integral with the hub or carrier. If the sensor is faulty, the complete assembly must be renewed.

Toothed signal rotors

The rotors are toothed/gapped rings, which turn with the driveshafts, hubs or brake drums. On some vehicles, the signal rotor function is provided by magnetic segments embedded in the oil seal section of the wheel bearing. As the teeth/gaps/segments pass the sensor, an electrical signal (alternating current) is produced by the sensor, which is fed to the electronic control unit *(see illustrations)*.

Hydraulic modulator

The modulator regulates hydraulic pressure to the brakes, according to signals received from the electronic control unit. The modulator is able to maintain, reduce or increase hydraulic pressure.

The unit consists of a set of solenoid valves, which are opened and closed by electrical signals received from the electronic control unit. The valves are capable of cycling at a rate of many times per second, to provide fine control of the hydraulic pressure in each relevant circuit *(see illustrations)*.

ABS modulator and pipes (Vauxhall Vectra)

ABS modulator and pipes (VW Beetle)

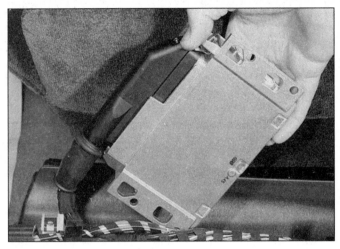

ABS ECU (Vauxhall Cavalier)

ABS ECU (BMW 3-Series)

Electric fluid pump

The pump is usually incorporated in the hydraulic modulator assembly, and operates as a transfer pump. The pump transfers fluid to and from the hydraulic circuits, according to the positions of the valves in the modulator. On some systems, the pump simply acts as a return pump to pump fluid back to the master cylinder when the brakes are released. The pump is controlled by electrical signals received from the electronic control unit.

Hydraulic accumulator

All systems use one or more accumulator to store pressurised fluid. The stored fluid is used to apply the brakes, or (on integral systems) to provide high-pressure power assistance. On some integral systems, the stored fluid is held at a very high pressure (up to 130 bar).

Electronic control unit

The electronic control unit analyses the signals from the wheel speed sensors, and any other system sensors, and uses the information to determine whether any of the wheels are about to lock-up or slip. If the control unit detects that a wheel is about to lock-up, it sends signals to the hydraulic accumulator and the electric fluid pump to control the pressure to the relevant brake(s).

On most systems, the control unit is capable of detecting problems within the system, and storing faults codes in an electronic memory. The fault codes can be read by a technician with suitable diagnostic equipment. In the event of a problem, the control unit will illuminate a warning light on the instrument panel. The ECU is usually integral with the modulator assembly, and no attempt should be made to separate it. However, on some, the ECU is remotely mounted - refer to the appropriate Service and Repair Manual *(see illustrations)*.

Lateral acceleration switch

A few systems are fitted with this component

Braking increases the coefficient of friction between the tyre and the road surface, but so does cornering. When heavy braking and hard cornering are combined, it is very easy to lock-up a wheel, which may result in a slide.

The switch operates when a certain lateral G-force is reached, and sends a signal to the electronic control unit, which reduces hydraulic pressure to the relevant brake(s).

Brake pedal position sensor

Normally only fitted to vehicles equipped with EBA (Emergency Brake Assist), this sensor provides the ABS ECU with data regarding the position of the brake pedal, and the position rate of change. From this data, the ECU can determine whether the driver is attempting an emergency stop, and apply full braking force if applicable *(see illustration)*.

The brake pedal position sensor also acts as a brake light switch (Peugeot 307)

Chapter 5

3 Operation

Although the operation of the ABS system has been described in terms of how the individual components work, the components all work together as follows.

When the driver slams on the brakes in a panic stop situation, the system must decide to do one of the following things.

a) Maintain the same pressure that the driver has applied.

b) Reduce the pressure to one or more of the hydraulic circuits.

c) Restore pressure to the original level after the pressure has been reduced.

The electronic control unit constantly monitors the inputs from the wheel speed sensors. If one (or more) of the sensors indicates a higher rate of wheel deceleration than the other sensors, the control unit knows that a wheel lock-up is likely to take place. Initially, nothing happens - the pressure to the wheel in question is maintained. This is called the "pressure holding" phase. The electronic control unit instructs the hydraulic modulator to partially close the solenoid valve, preventing any increase in brake pressure to that wheel. Fluid return is also blocked off by the solenoid, so the pressure stays the same. The electric fluid pump begins to run, but its outlet check valve stays shut unless the pump pressure exceeds the amount of pressure being created by the master cylinder.

If the wheel continues to decelerate at an abnormal rate, the control unit signals the hydraulic modulator to reduce the pressure to the brake at the wheel. The modulator closes the solenoid valve for the wheel, which prevents any more pressure from being applied. In addition, the valve is positioned in such a way as to open a passage back to the fluid reservoir. This bleeds off pressure and allows the wheel to turn.

At this point, the wheel accelerates again because it is not being braked as hard as it was. The control unit will only allow it to gain a certain amount of speed. Once it has been determined that the wheel is no longer in danger of locking up, the solenoid valve stops cycling and normal braking resumes. The hydraulic modulator allows pressure to build up to the level it was at before the pressure reduction took place.

This entire chain of events takes place many times per second, depending on how slippery the surface of the road is.

4 Precautions

There are several precautions which must be taken when working on or around the components of an anti-lock braking system. If the following points of advice are not heeded, you run the risk of incurring serious injury, either through careless working techniques, or by disabling the system due to incorrect servicing techniques.

a) Some integral ABS systems operate at very high pressures (over 130 bar). Before working on any part of the vehicle hydraulic system, consult the appropriate Service and Repair Manual to ensure that there is no risk of injury.

b) Before working on any part of the hydraulic system, ensure that, where necessary, the system has been depressurised. Most component systems operate at conventional fluid pressures, and do not need to be depressurised. On many integral systems, the system can be depressurised by pumping the brake pedal a number of times (some systems require as many as 20 pumps) with the ignition switched off - again, consult the manufacturer's servicing information before attempting to depressurise the system. Once the system has been depressurised, always open the bleed screws slowly.

c) When bleeding the complete hydraulic system, always follow the manufacturer's bleeding procedure. Note that most systems have bleed screws on the hydraulic modulator unit. Some systems cannot be bled without the use of specialist pressure-bleeding equipment.

d) Do not unplug or connect electrical connectors related to the ABS system while the ignition is switched on. This is necessary to avoid possible damage to the electronic control unit.

e) If it becomes necessary to renew a brake hose or pipe, purchase only genuine parts of original equipment quality and design. DO NOT fabricate your own components.

f) Never strike a wheel speed sensor or a signal rotor with a hammer or any other tool, and don't drop them either.

g) Don't allow grease onto the wheel speed sensors or the toothed signal rotors.

h) If the vehicle is equipped with four-wheel ABS, never fit larger diameter tyres on one end of the vehicle. All four tyres must be of the same diameter, or the electronic control unit will become confused.

i) Do not overtighten the wheel nuts or bolts, as this could damage the brake disc or drum, causing inaccurate speed signals.

j) Whenever a speed sensor is disturbed, where necessary check the gap between the sensor and the signal rotor and adjust (many sensors are not adjustable). Ensure that the sensor is clean.

k) Only use the recommended type of hydraulic fluid in the system. Never use silicone-based hydraulic fluid, unless specifically recommended by the manufacturers.

l) If any ancillary components are fitted to the vehicle, such as a mobile telephone, or a radio transmitter, ensure that the wiring is routed away from the ABS system components and wiring. Certain frequencies can interfere with the system operation.

m) Before carrying out any welding on the vehicle, disconnect the battery negative lead, and the ABS electronic control unit wiring connector.

n) Most manufacturers advise against repairing the ABS system wiring. If one wire becomes damaged, renew the relevant part of the harness. Even slight changes in resistance can lead to inaccurate speed readings from the wheel sensors.

5   Fault finding

All vehicles equipped with ABS have an "ABS" warning light on the dash. This light alerts the driver when the ECU has detected a malfunction in the system. The light will also come on whenever the ignition key is turned to the On position, as a bulb check feature. If the light doesn't come on, you should check for a blown bulb as soon as possible. Otherwise, you won't know if a problem arises in the ABS system until you need the system to work correctly and find out it doesn't.

All modern ABS systems have a self-diagnosis facility, where if the ECU detects a fault it generates and stores a fault code. Depending on the vehicle, any fault codes are 'flashed out' by the ABS warning light (the sequence and number of flashes determines the code), or retrieved using a fault code reader/scanner via the diagnostic plug - refer to the relevant Service and Repair Manual. The ABS diagnosis chapters in a manufacturer's factory service manual frequently exceed one hundred pages or so, making it impossible to provide a comprehensive ABS fault finding guide within the covers of this manual. Remember, vehicles equipped with anti-lock braking systems are also susceptible to the same problems as a vehicle that isn't equipped with ABS.

HINTS & TIPS

- Turning one wheel with the other wheels stationary and the ingition switched on will cause some ABS systems to register a fault and illuminate the warning light. If you're doing work which involves turning the wheels, make sure the ignition is switched off.

a) *Always begin diagnosis to any electrical system with a check of the fuses. If you find a blown fuse, try to figure out why the fuse blew. Never replace a fuse with one of a higher amperage rating or with a piece of foil.*

b) *Check the battery and make sure it has a full charge. ABS systems depend on an accurate supply of voltage. Batteries should put out 12 or 13 volts without the engine running, and approximately 14.2 volts with the engine running.*

c) *Make sure all electrical connectors related to the ABS system are securely connected. Remember, however, don't disconnect or connect any of the connectors with the ignition in the On position.*

d) *Check the gap between the wheel speed sensors and the toothed signal rings. While specifications vary, they should be somewhere in the neighbourhood of 0.5 to 1.0 mm. Also make sure the sensors or rings are not damaged.*

Chapter 5

Hydraulic systems, brake servos and vacuum pumps

Brake servos	3	Hoses and pipes	6
Brake system bleeding	7	Master cylinder	2
Calipers	4	Vacuum pumps	8
Introduction	1	Wheel cylinder	5

1 Introduction

This Chapter deals with the removal, refitting, bleeding and, where applicable, the overhaul procedures of the components that make up the brake hydraulic system. Because of their close relationship with the master cylinder, brake servos and vacuum pump are also included in this Chapter.

There are a few important things to remember when working on the hydraulic system:

a) *Cleanliness cannot be over-emphasised. Before opening any part of the hydraulic system, clean the fittings and surrounding area with brake system cleaner. This will prevent dirt from contaminating the fluid in the pipes.*

b) *Never re-use old brake fluid. It contains moisture which could boil as heat is conducted through the brake linings to the hydraulic components. When brake fluid boils, gas bubbles are produced. Since gas is compressible, a spongy brake pedal or a complete loss of braking pressure can result. Also, old brake fluid might be tainted with contaminants, which can cause problems. Always use new*
brake fluid from a small, sealed brake fluid container. Since brake fluid is hygroscopic (meaning it is able to absorb moisture), fluid stored in an open container, or even in a sealed large container (if it's been sitting on the shelf for a long time) may contain too much moisture.

c) ***Warning:** Brake fluid can harm your eyes and damage painted surfaces, so take great care when handling or pouring it. If you get any fluid in your eyes, immediately flush your eyes with water and seek medical attention.*

d) *Before attempting to overhaul a hydraulic component, check on the availability and cost of parts, as well as the availability and cost of a new or rebuilt unit. Sometimes rebuilt parts are cheaper than an overhaul kit! Also, not all master cylinders, calipers and wheel cylinders are rebuildable.*

e) *When overhauling a hydraulic component, work in a spotlessly clean environment. A single grain of dirt can potentially ruin the entire job.*

f) *Never use petroleum-based solvents for cleaning brake system components. Use brake system cleaner - it leaves no residue when it dries. Brake fluid will also clean hydraulic components, but if you're cleaning parts that are very dirty, it takes quite a bit of fluid to remove it all. Methylated spirit* can also be used, but it contains water - if this is used, you'll have to wait a little longer to let the parts dry. Brake system cleaner is the best way to go.

g) Don't use compressed air to dry off brake parts. Even filtered compressed air may contain too much moisture. It might even contain traces of oil.

h) Never hone an aluminium (or any non-cast iron) hydraulic cylinder.

i) Whenever any part of the hydraulic circuit is opened, that part of the system must be bled of air (refer to the Brake system bleeding procedure in this Chapter).

2   Master cylinder

⚠ Warning: This procedure does not apply to master cylinders that are directly attached to, or integral with, an Anti-lock Brake System (ABS) hydraulic control unit. Many ABS units require a special tool to cycle the valves in the ABS modulator or hydraulic control unit to ensure complete system bleeding. Vehicles equipped with such ABS systems should be taken to a dealer service department or other properly equipped garage for any master cylinder work.

The following procedure depicts the removal, overhaul and refitting procedures for the brake master cylinder. Follow the sequence of illustrations, being careful to read the caption under each one. Also be sure to read any accompanying text.

HINTS & TIPS

• Remember, not all master cylinders are rebuildable. Before beginning work, check with accessory shops or dealer parts departments for parts availability and prices. Rebuilt master cylinders are available on an exchange basis, which makes this job quite easy, and much less time consuming.

Removal

If fitted, unplug the electrical connector from the fluid level sensor

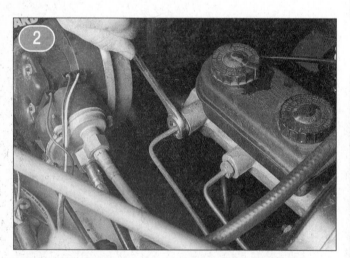

Place rags under the brake pipe fittings and prepare caps or plastic bags to cover the ends of the pipes once they're disconnected. Caution: Brake fluid will damage paint. Cover all painted surfaces and avoid spilling fluid during this procedure. Slacken the union nuts at the end of the pipes where they enter the master cylinder. To prevent rounding off the flats on these nuts, a split ring spanner, which wraps around the nut, should be used. Pull the brake pipes away from the master cylinder slightly and plug the ends to prevent contamination. Also plug the openings in the master cylinder

Remove the master cylinder mounting nuts (arrowed). Remove the master cylinder from the vehicle, being careful not to spill any fluid on the vehicle's paint. Remove the reservoir caps, or cover and gasket, then discard any fluid remaining in the reservoir

Overhaul

Note: *When disassembling the master cylinder, lay out all of the components in order. If the overhaul kit contains piston seals rather than entire piston assemblies, renew the seals on one piston at a time. Before disassembling a piston, make a sketch, noting the location of all seals, washers, springs, retainers, etc. Most importantly, pay attention to the direction the seal lips face. Refer to the accompanying illustrations to familiarise yourself with the master cylinder components (see illustrations).*

> **Warning:** *It's essential that you obtain the correct rebuild kit for the master cylinder you're servicing. Be sure to state the year, make and model of the vehicle when buying a kit. If you're still unsure, take the master cylinder with you when buying parts. DO NOT try to use the rebuild kit for a cast iron master cylinder in an aluminium unit, or vice versa. And don't open a new parts kit until you've compared the contents to the old parts you're removing from the master cylinder you intend to rebuild. Always verify parts availability before beginning a master cylinder rebuild.*

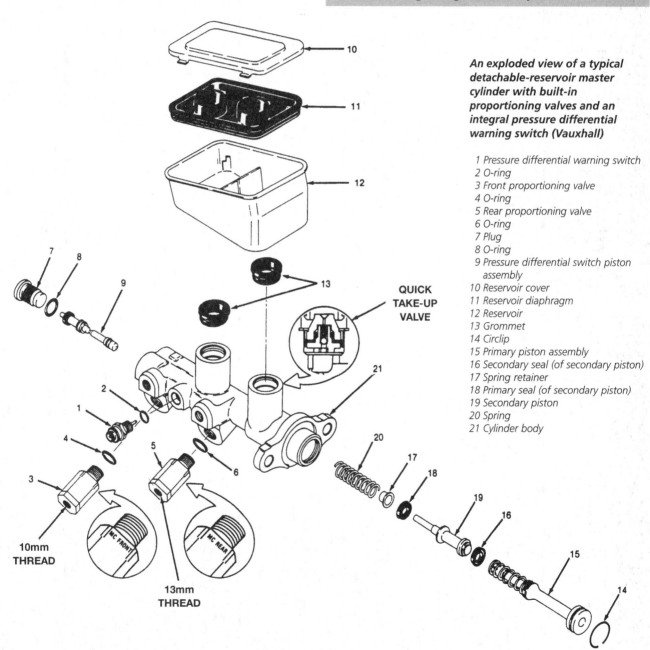

An exploded view of a typical detachable-reservoir master cylinder with built-in proportioning valves and an integral pressure differential warning switch (Vauxhall)

1 Pressure differential warning switch
2 O-ring
3 Front proportioning valve
4 O-ring
5 Rear proportioning valve
6 O-ring
7 Plug
8 O-ring
9 Pressure differential switch piston assembly
10 Reservoir cover
11 Reservoir diaphragm
12 Reservoir
13 Grommet
14 Circlip
15 Primary piston assembly
16 Secondary seal (of secondary piston)
17 Spring retainer
18 Primary seal (of secondary piston)
19 Secondary piston
20 Spring
21 Cylinder body

QUICK
TAKE-UP
VALVE

10mm
THREAD

13mm
THREAD

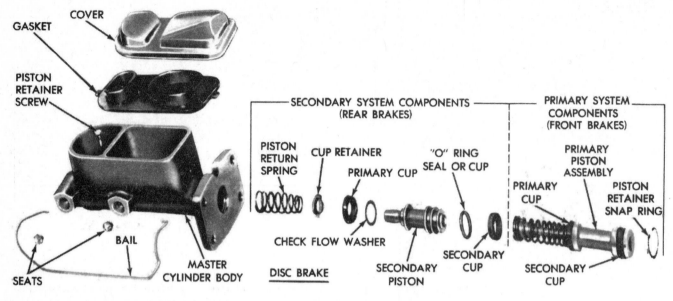

An exploded view of a typical cast iron master cylinder

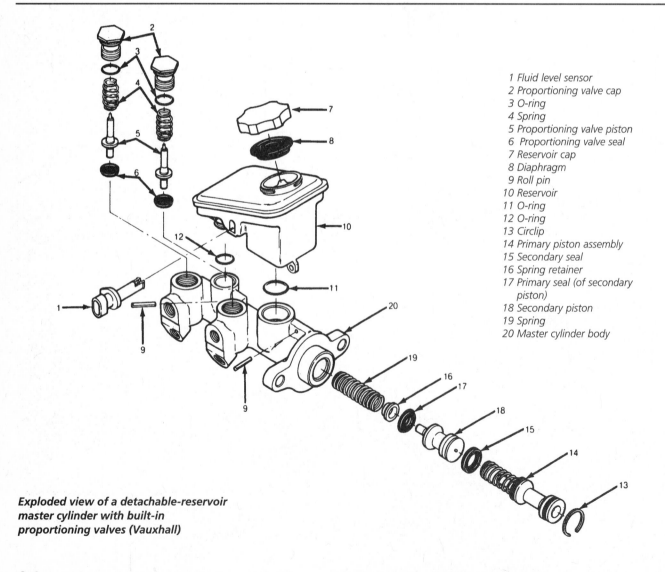

1 Fluid level sensor
2 Proportioning valve cap
3 O-ring
4 Spring
5 Proportioning valve piston
6 Proportioning valve seal
7 Reservoir cap
8 Diaphragm
9 Roll pin
10 Reservoir
11 O-ring
12 O-ring
13 Circlip
14 Primary piston assembly
15 Secondary seal
16 Spring retainer
17 Primary seal (of secondary piston)
18 Secondary piston
19 Spring
20 Master cylinder body

Exploded view of a detachable-reservoir master cylinder with built-in proportioning valves (Vauxhall)

Remove the reservoir (detachable reservoir models only)

Some reservoirs are secured by a retaining screw (arrowed). Remove the screw and carefully pull the reservoir off the master cylinder body

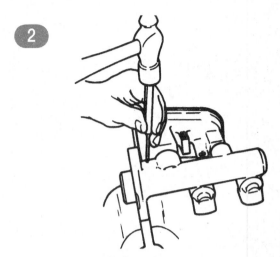

On some master cylinders, the reservoir is attached with a pair of roll pins which can be removed with a hammer and a small punch. Once the pins are removed, pull the reservoir off

If the reservoir sticks in the grommets, carefully prise it off

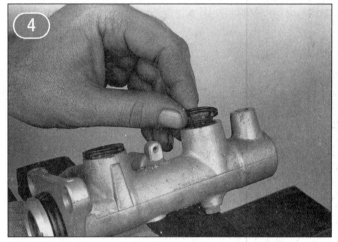

Remove the grommets from the master cylinder body

Some detachable reservoirs are retained by a large bolt in the centre of the reservoir. Remove the bolt ...

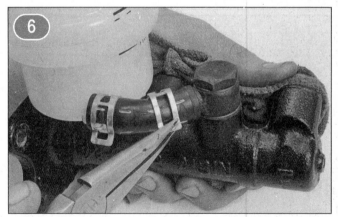

... then slide the hose clamp back on the hose and detach the hose from the fitting. If the sealing washers on the fitting bolt have been leaking, leave the hose attached and remove the fitting bolt and sealing washers, instead

Chapter 6

Remove the master cylinder pistons

Note: *Mount the master cylinder in a vice, with the jaws of the vice clamping on the cylinder mounting flange. Use soft jaws or a rag to prevent damage to the flange mounting surface.*

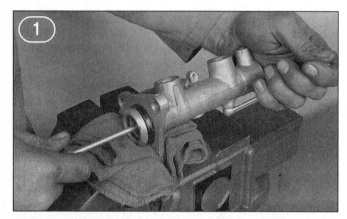

Using a cross-head screwdriver, depress the pistons, then remove the piston stop bolt or screw (be sure to use a new sealing washer on the stop bolt when you're reassembling the master cylinder). Note: Not all master cylinder have a stop bolt or screw

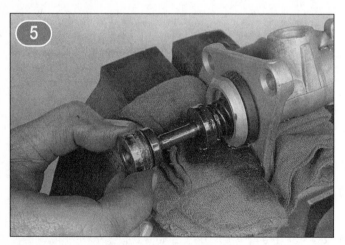

Depress the pistons again and remove the circlip or retainer

Remove the primary piston assembly from the master cylinder ...

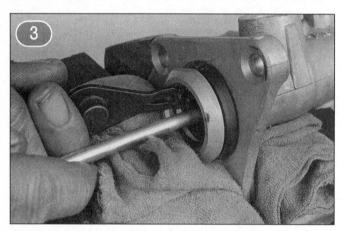

On some master cylinders, the piston stop is a screw or pin which is accessed from the inside of the reservoir

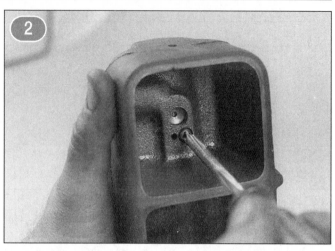

Some master cylinders use a stopper cap like this instead of a circlip. Depress the pistons and use a hooked tool to bend the tang up, then remove the stopper cap

... followed by the secondary piston assembly. If the piston is stuck inside the bore, remove the cylinder from the vice and tap it against a wood block. Pull the piston straight out - the bore could be damaged if the piston becomes cocked. Note: Some (although very few) manufacturers call this piston the primary piston, and one removed previously the secondary piston

Inspect and prepare the master cylinder

Clean the cylinder bore with brake system cleaner and inspect the bore for scoring and pitting. **Warning:** *DO NOT, under any circumstances, use petroleum-based solvents to clean brake parts.* Light scratches and corrosion on the cylinder bore walls can be usually be removed with crocus cloth or with a hone. However, deep scratches or score marks mean the cylinder must be replaced with a new unit. **Warning:** *Never attempt to hone an aluminium master cylinder.* If the pistons or bore are severely corroded, renew the master cylinder. Always use new piston cups and seals (or piston assemblies) when overhauling a master cylinder.

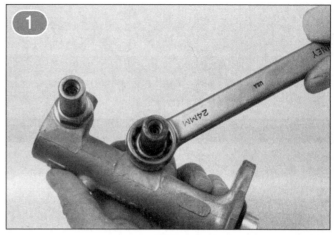

If equipped, unscrew the proportioning valve from the master cylinder

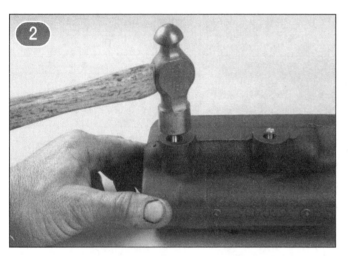

If you have a cast iron unit and you received new tube seats in the overhaul kit, screw a self-tapping screw into each seat ...

... then use a prybar as a pivot and remove the tube seats by levering them out with a pair of pliers. The best way to drive the new seats into place is with a spare section of brake pipe (a flared end) with the union fitting. Place the flared portion of the pipe over the seat, slide the union into place and thread it into the outlet. Tighten the fitting to push the seat into place

Overhaul the pistons

Note 1: *Some master cylinder rebuild kits come with all of the seals for each piston. Others come with the seals for one of the pistons (usually the secondary piston) and an entire new piston assembly. Some kits simply furnish two new piston assemblies. Use all of the parts in the overhaul kit. The following portion of this sequence depicts typical seal renewal procedures for a variety of master cylinders - it may differ slightly from the pistons in your master cylinder. As you disassemble your pistons, BE SURE to note how the components are arranged (make a sketch if necessary). Ignore any steps which don't apply to your pistons.*

Note 2: *A few manufacturers have named the pistons exactly opposite that of most manufacturers - they call the piston nearest the front of the vehicle the primary piston, and the piston nearest the brake servo (or bulkhead) the secondary piston.*

Chapter 6

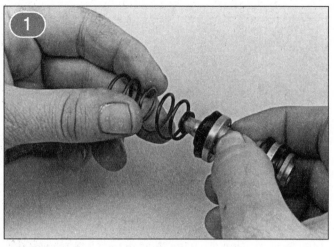

Begin overhaul of the secondary piston assembly by removing the spring, which can be pulled straight off

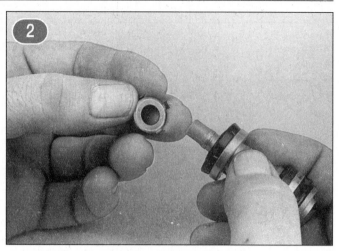

Remove the piston inner seal retainer, followed by the seal

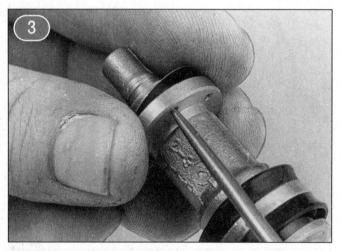

Remove the seal protector, if fitted, by inserting a thin instrument through one of the holes in the piston

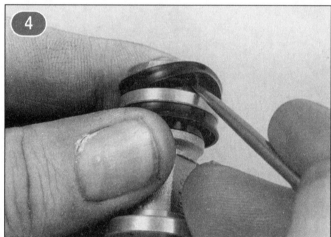

Prise the remaining piston seals off the piston

Lubricate the new seals with clean brake fluid and fit them onto the piston, making sure all of the components of the piston are situated in the right place, and the seal lips are facing the proper direction (the two outer seals must face the ends of the pistons. If there are three seals, the one in the centre faces the spring end). When fitting the seals, use your fingers only, or you may damage them

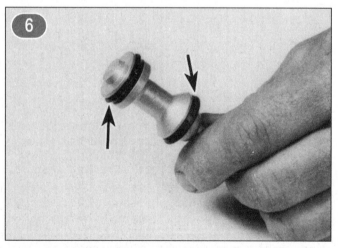

Some secondary pistons only have two seals (arrowed) - the seal lips must face the ends of the pistons

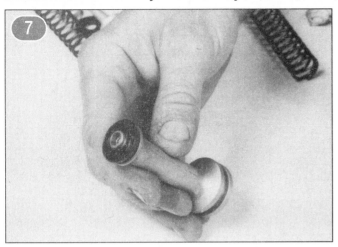

The seals on the primary piston are removed in the same manner as the seals on the secondary piston were. When fitting the primary seal on the end of the primary piston, the lip must face away from the centre of the piston. Remember, lubricate the seals with clean brake fluid before fitting them

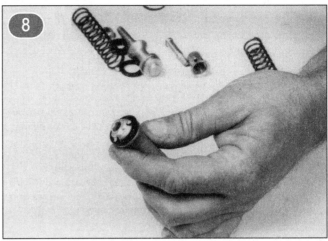

Fit the seal guard over the seal ...

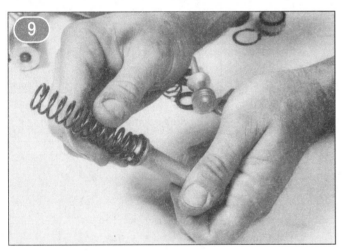

... then push the spring onto the end of the piston

Insert the spring retainer into the spring

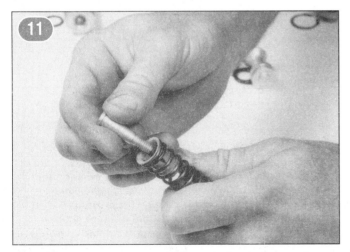

Insert the spring retaining bolt through the retainer and spring and thread it into the piston. Tighten it securely

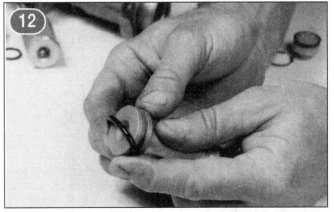

Lubricate the O-ring with clean brake fluid and fit it on the piston. Some primary pistons use a secondary seal instead of an O-ring (some use both) - the seal lip should face the spring end of the piston (the same way the lips of the primary seal face)

Chapter 6

Overhaul the proportioning valve and/or the pressure differential warning switch

Note: *This portion of the overhaul procedure only applies to master cylinders with an integral pressure differential warning switch and/or integral proportioning valves.*

Unscrew the proportioning valves from the master cylinder body. Disassemble the valves (one at a time), then lubricate the seals with clean brake fluid and fit the new components, making sure the seal lips are pointing in the right direction. Refit the valves and tighten the caps securely

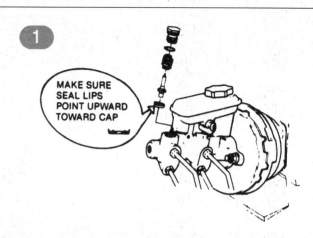

MAKE SURE SEAL LIPS POINT UPWARD TOWARD CAP

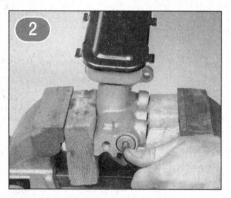

Remove the pressure differential warning switch from the side of the master cylinder, then mount the cylinder in a vice (use wood blocks as shown). Unscrew the switch piston plug

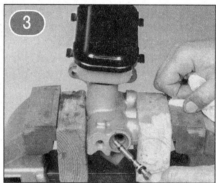

Pull out the switch piston assembly. Remove the components from the piston

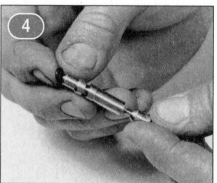

Lubricate the small O-ring with clean brake fluid and fit in on the switch piston

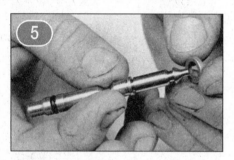

Fit the metal retainer on the switch piston

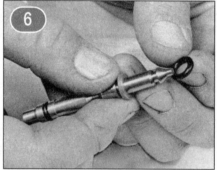

Lubricate the large O-ring with clean brake fluid and fit it on the switch piston

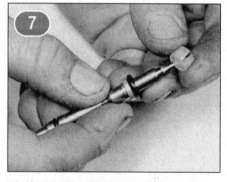

Fit the plastic retainer on the switch piston

Lubricate the switch piston assembly and fit it into its bore in the master cylinder body. Remove the master cylinder from the vice, then push the piston in until the small-diameter portion of the piston is visible through the pressure differential warning switch hole. Fit the pressure differential warning switch (using a new O-ring) and tighten it securely. Fit a new O-ring on the switch piston plug (be sure to lubricate it with clean brake fluid) and fit the plug, tightening it securely

Fit the piston assemblies and reservoir

Note 1: *Lubricate all components with lots of clean brake fluid before refitting them into the master cylinder.*

Note 2: *A few manufacturers have named the pistons exactly opposite that of most manufacturers - they call the piston nearest the front of the vehicle the primary piston, and the piston nearest the brake servo (or bulkhead) the secondary piston.*

Fit the secondary piston ...

... followed by the primary piston. Depress the pistons and install the circlip or retainer as previously shown, then depress the pistons again and install the piston stop bolt or pin. Be sure to use a new sealing washer on the stop bolt or screw

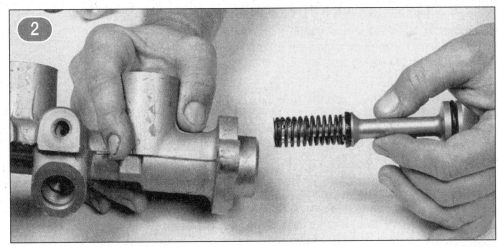

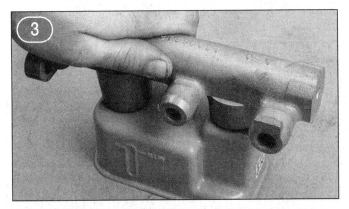

On models with detachable reservoirs, lubricate the new reservoir grommets with clean brake fluid and fit them in the openings in the master cylinder. Lay the reservoir face down on a bench and push the master cylinder straight down over the reservoir fittings with a rocking motion. If equipped, fit the retaining screw or roll pins. If your reservoir is retained by a large bolt, use new sealing washers, if applicable

Fit the reservoir diaphragm in the cover, if applicable

Chapter 6

Bench bleed

Whenever the master cylinder is removed, the entire hydraulic system must be bled. The time required to bleed the system can be reduced if the master cylinder is filled with fluid and bench bled before it's fitted on the vehicle. Since you'll have to apply pressure to the master cylinder piston, the master cylinder should be mounted in a vice, with the jaws of the vice clamping on the mounting flange.

Bleeder tube method

If available, attach a pair of master cylinder bleeder tubes to the outlet ports of the master cylinder *(see illustration)*. These can be made up using scrap brake pipe and unions. Fill the reservoir with fluid, then slowly push the pistons into the master cylinder (a large cross-head screwdriver can be used for this) - air will be expelled from the pressure chambers and into the reservoir. Because the tubes are submerged in fluid, air won't be drawn back into the master cylinder when you release the pistons. Repeat the procedure until no more air bubbles are present.

Remove the bleed tubes, one at a time, and refit plugs in the open ports to prevent fluid leakage and air from entering. Fit the reservoir cover or cap.

Alternative methods

An alternative to the bleed tube method is to insert threaded plugs into the brake pipe outlet holes and snug them down so that air won't leak past them - but not so tight that they can't be easily loosened. Fill the reservoir with brake fluid of the recommended type.

Remove one plug and push the pistons into the bore to expel the air from the master cylinder. A large cross-head screwdriver can be used to push on the piston assembly.

To prevent air from being drawn back into the master cylinder, the plug must be replaced and lightly tightened down before releasing the pressure on the piston.

Repeat the procedure until only brake fluid is expelled from the brake pipe outlet hole. When only brake fluid is expelled, repeat the procedure at the other outlet hole and plug. Be sure to keep the master cylinder reservoir filled with brake fluid to prevent the introduction of air into the system.

Since high pressure isn't involved in the bench bleeding procedure, an alternative to the removal and renewal of the plugs with each stroke of the piston assembly is available. Before pushing in on the piston assembly, remove one of the plugs completely. Before releasing the piston, however, instead of replacing the plug, simply put your finger tightly over the hole to keep air from being drawn back into the master cylinder. Wait several seconds for brake fluid to be drawn from the reservoir into the bore, then depress the piston again, removing your finger as brake fluid is expelled. Be sure to put your finger back over the hole each time before releasing the piston, and when the bleeding procedure is complete for that outlet, refit the plug and tighten it before going on to the other port.

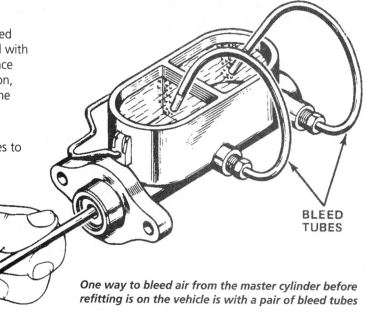

One way to bleed air from the master cylinder before refitting is on the vehicle is with a pair of bleed tubes

BLEED TUBES

Refitting

Refit the master cylinder by reversing the removal procedure. Don't tighten the mounting nuts until after the unions on the hydraulic pipes have been threaded into the ports by hand. This will allow you to wiggle the master cylinder back and forth, if necessary, to connect the pipes without cross-threading the unions.

If air entered the master cylinder after the bench bleeding procedure (or if you didn't bench bleed it), bleed the cylinder on the vehicle. To do this, have an assistant push the brake pedal to the floor and hold it there. Loosen the union nut (start with the one closest to the servo or bulkhead) to allow air and fluid to escape, then tighten the nut. Repeat this procedure on all unions until the fluid is clear of bubbles *(see illustration)*. **Note:** *Some master cylinders have bleed valves, making it unnecessary to loosen the brake pipe fittings.*

Bleed the entire brake system as described later in this Chapter.

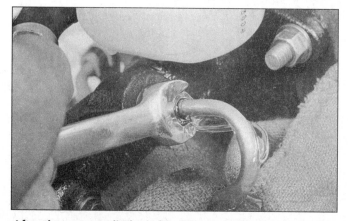

After the master cylinder is fitted, it can be bled by slackening the unions (one at a time) and applying the brakes

3 Brake servos

Vacuum-operated servos

Check

Perform the brake servo checking procedures described in Chapter 7. If a defective servo is not diagnosed from those checks, inspect the check valve. To do this, disconnect the vacuum hose where it connects to the metal pipe or the intake manifold (don't disconnect it at the servo). Apply pressure and suction to the end of the hose, to be sure air only flows away from the servo. If it flows in both directions or if there is no airflow at all, renew the check valve. On some vehicles the check valve is located inside the hose, requiring renewal of the hose.

If the check valve is functioning properly and the hose doesn't have a leak, the engine may be the culprit. If the engine is old and tired, if the ignition timing is way off or if there's a large vacuum leak, it may not be producing enough vacuum to enable the servo to give satisfactory power assist. A restricted exhaust system or defective vacuum pump (diesel models) could also be the cause of low vacuum.

Connect a vacuum gauge to the servo hose and start the engine. Allow the engine to reach normal operating temperature, then look at the gauge - there should be at least 15 in-Hg indicated at idle. If not, diagnose and repair the cause of low vacuum before condemning the brake servo.

HINTS & TIPS

- Some engines, including most Diesel engines, are fitted with vacuum pumps which help generate vacuum to power the brake servo and other accessories. A defective vacuum pump will often make a loud rapping sound that rises and falls with engine speed. You can also test the operation of the vacuum pump as outlined in the engine vacuum check in the next paragraph.

Removal

Note: *Brake servo units should not be disassembled. They require special tools not normally found in most service stations or garages. They are fairly complex and because of their critical relationship to brake performance it is best to renew a defective servo unit with a new or remanufactured one.*

Unbolt the master cylinder from the servo and pull it forward off the mounting studs, being careful not to kink the brake pipes. This will usually provide enough room for servo removal. If you can't do this on your vehicle, remove the master cylinder completely.

Disconnect the vacuum hose where it attaches to the brake servo.

Working under the dash, disconnect the brake pedal return spring, then remove the clip (and clevis pin on most vehicles) to disconnect the pushrod from the brake pedal *(see illustrations)*. On some vehicles it may be necessary to

To disconnect the brake servo pushrod from the brake pedal, remove the retaining clip (right arrow) and pull out the clevis pin (left arrow)

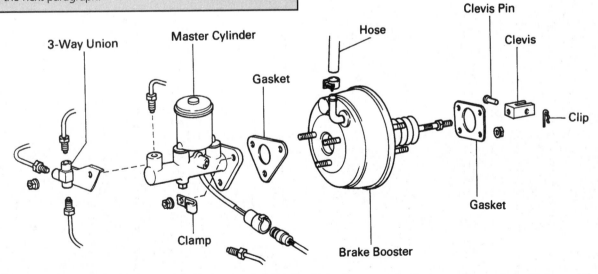

Fitting details of a typical vacuum-operated brake servo (not all vehicles have a gasket between the master cylinder and the servo)

Most vehicles have four servo mounting nuts (arrowed), accessible from under the facia

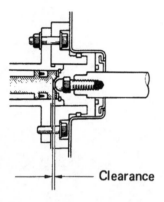

Ideally, there should be zero clearance between the servo pushrod and the master cylinder pushrod, but there shouldn't be any interference either - if there is any interference, the brakes may drag; if there's much clearance, brake pedal travel will be excessive

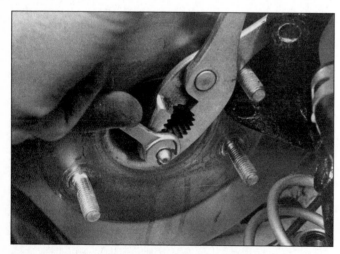

Turn the adjusting nut on the end of the brake pushrod to change the clearance - hold the pushrod with pliers to keep it from turning

remove a panel from under the dash, and maybe even an air conditioning or heater duct, for access to the pedal.

Remove the mounting nuts and withdraw the servo from the engine compartment *(see illustration)*. The mounting nuts on most vehicles are located under the dash. On some vehicles, however, the mounting nuts are removed from the engine compartment, directly behind the servo. Also, it may be necessary on some vehicles to remove one or more support braces.

Refitting

Refitting procedures are basically the reverse of those for removal. Tighten the servo mounting nuts securely. If a split pin was used to secure the clevis pin in the pushrod clevis, be sure to use a new one.

If the brake servo is being replaced, the clearance between the master cylinder and the pushrod in the servo must be measured and, if necessary, adjusted (this applies only to servos with adjustable pushrods) *(see illustration)*. Using a depth micrometer or vernier calipers, measure the distance from the piston seat (recessed area) in the master cylinder to the master cylinder mounting flange. Next, using a hand-held vacuum pump, apply 20 in-Hg of vacuum and measure the distance from the end of the vacuum servo pushrod to the mounting face of the servo (including the gasket, if any) where the master cylinder mounting flange seats. The measurements should be the same (indicating zero clearance). If not, subtract one measurement from the other - a slight amount of clearance is acceptable (approximately 0.10 to 0.40 mm). An interference fit is not acceptable because this means the servo pushrod would be depressing the master cylinder pistons slightly, even at rest.

If it is necessary to adjust the length of the pushrod, turn the adjusting screw on the end of the pushrod until the clearance is within the desired range *(see illustration)*.

Check the operation of the brakes before returning the vehicle to normal service.

Hydraulically operated servos

Check

Refer to Chapter 7 for the servo checking procedures. Checks that are any more involved than the ones described there require special testing equipment. Take the vehicle to a dealer or suitable equipped specialist for further diagnosis, if necessary.

Removal and refitting
Power steering fluid-operated servo

With the engine off, depress and release the brake pedal several times (at least 20 times) to discharge all pressure from the accumulator. Unbolt the master cylinder from the servo and pull it gently forward without straining the brake pipes.

Disconnect the hydraulic pipes from the servo unit. Plug all pipes and openings to prevent excessive fluid loss and contamination.

Working inside the vehicle, above the brake pedal, disconnect the servo pushrod from the pivot lever, then remove the nuts securing the servo to the bulkhead *(see illustration)*.

Refitting is the reverse of removal. Be sure to tighten the pipe fittings securely and bleed the power steering system.

To bleed the power steering system, begin by checking the fluid level in the power steering fluid reservoir. Add fluid if necessary, until the level is at the Cold mark on the dipstick.

Start the engine and allow it to run at fast idle. With the wheels in the straight ahead position recheck the fluid level, adding more, if necessary, to reach the Cold mark.

Bleed the system by turning the steering wheel from side-to-side without hitting the stops. This will work the air out of the system. Keep the reservoir full of fluid as this is done. You'll know when the system is fully bled, as the steering wheel action will feel smooth and all strange noises coming from the power steering pump will cease.

Check the operation of the brakes. The brake pedal should not feel "hard" when depressed, and should feel smooth, not jerky.

Electro-mechanical type servo

Warning: *Failure to fully depressurise the hydraulic unit before starting this procedure could result in bodily injury and damage to the painted surfaces of the vehicle. Wear eye protection when performing this procedure.*

Make sure the ignition key is in the Off position, then disconnect the cable from the negative terminal of the battery. Depressurise the system by firmly pushing the brake pedal down a minimum of 10 times. Cover the wing and the area surrounding the brake master cylinder/brake servo unit.

Disconnect the electrical connectors at the pressure switch and the hydraulic pump. Using a split ring spanner, disconnect the brake pipes from the unit *(see illustration)*.

Working under the dash, disconnect the pushrod from the brake pedal. Remove the mounting nuts that secure the unit to the bulkhead.

Carefully remove the servo /master cylinder unit from the engine compartment. **Note:** *The master cylinder portion of the unit should be bench-bled before refitting the unit.*

Refitting is the reverse of removal, but the system must be bled of air. Fill both sides of the reservoir to the Full marks with the recommended brake fluid. Turn the ignition switch to the On position. With the servo pump running, the brake fluid level in the servo side should decrease as the accumulator is pressurised. Watch the level and don't let the reservoir run dry.

Note: *The pump must shut off after 20 seconds. If not, turn the ignition key off after 20 seconds. Perform the*

Mounting details of a hydraulically operated brake servo

1 Nuts	4 Nut
2 Master cylinder	5 Gasket
3 Servo unit	

following steps if the fluid in the servo side of the reservoir does not drop:

a) *Loosen the servo pipe fitting at the casting boss, directly below the accumulator.*

b) *Wait for brake fluid to gravity bleed from the loosened fitting.*

c) *When fluid starts to flow, tighten the fitting. Check for leaks or flow back to the reservoir.*

Refit the reservoir cover. Make sure the ignition is Off, then depress the pedal ten times. Remove the reservoir cover and add fluid, if necessary. Repeat the bleeding procedure again and check the fluid level. Check the operation of the brakes before returning the vehicle to normal service.

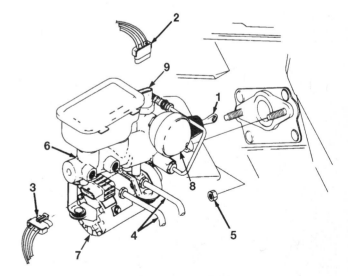

Fitting details of an electro-hydraulic brake servo

1 Pushrod	6 Master cylinder
2 Electrical connector	7 Electro-hydraulic pump
3 Electrical connector	8 Accumulator
4 Brake lines	9 Pressure switch
5 Nut	

4   Brake caliper

The following procedure depicts the removal, overhaul and refitting procedures for the brake caliper. If an overhaul is indicated (usually because of fluid leaks, a stuck piston or broken bleed screw) explore all options before beginning this procedure. New and factory rebuilt calipers are available on an exchange basis, which makes this job quite easy, and much less time consuming. Before beginning work, check with accessory shops and dealer parts departments for parts availability and prices. In some cases, rebuilt calipers are actually cheaper than rebuild kits.

Removal

> **(!)** *Warning: Dust created by the brake system may contain asbestos, which is harmful to your health. Never blow it out with compressed air and don't inhale any of it. An approved filtering mask should be worn when working on the brakes. Do not, under any circumstances, use petroleum-based solvents to clean brake parts. Use brake system cleaner only.*

Note: *Always rebuild or renew the calipers in pairs - never rebuild just one of them.*

Loosen the front wheel nuts, raise the vehicle and support it securely on axle stands. Remove the front wheels.

On models where the brake hose threads directly into the caliper, disconnect the brake pipe fitting from the brake hose (refer to "Hoses and pipes" in this Chapter, if necessary), then unscrew the hose from the caliper. (If the caliper is only being removed for access to other components, don't disconnect the hose.) On brake hoses with banjo fittings, unscrew the fitting bolt and detach the hose. Discard the two copper sealing washers on each side of the fitting and use new ones during refitting. Wrap a plastic bag around the end of the hose to prevent fluid loss and contamination.

To remove a fixed caliper, remove the bolts that attach the caliper assembly to the hub carrier. To remove a floating or sliding caliper, refer to the first few steps of the appropriate brake pad renewal sequence in Chapter 2 (caliper removal is the first part of the brake pad renewal procedure for those calipers).

Remove the brake pads from the caliper, also by referring to the appropriate sequence in Chapter 2.

Clean the caliper assembly with brake system cleaner. DO NOT use paraffin, petrol or petroleum-based solvents. And while you've got the caliper off, be sure to check the pads as well and renew them if necessary.

Overhaul

Fixed caliper

On some fixed calipers the pistons are a fairly loose fit in their bores. Try to work the pistons out by hand. If you can't, you'll have to use air pressure to force the pistons out. On most calipers this can be accomplished by removing the bolts holding the caliper halves together, separate the halves, then setting the pistons face-down on the workbench and applying pressurised air to the fluid inlet fitting. However,

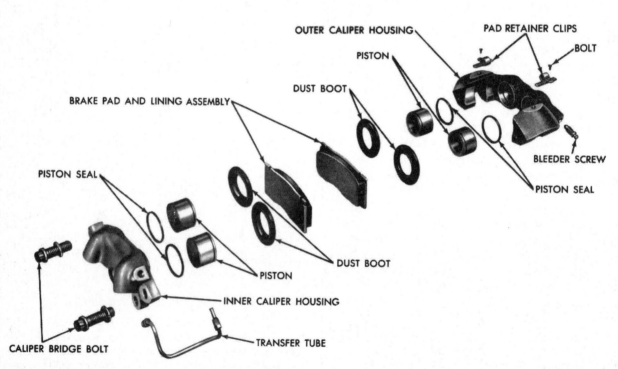

An exploded view of a fixed brake caliper - this type uses a transfer tube to deliver fluid from one half of the caliper to the other

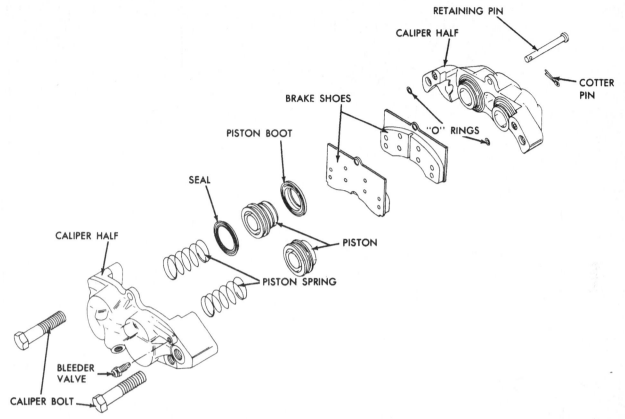

This fixed brake caliper doesn't have a transfer tube - instead, internal passages, sealed with O-rings where caliper halves meet, deliver fluid from one half of the caliper to the other

some manufacturers expressly state NOT to remove the bolts that hold the caliper halves together. These calipers are designed with short pistons which can be removed without separating the halves.

To find out if your caliper is the kind that should not be disassembled, place several rags in the middle of the caliper and apply air pressure to the fluid inlet port. **Warning:** *Wear eye protection, and never place your fingers in front of the pistons in an attempt to catch or protect them when applying pressurised air, as serious injury could occur. Apply only enough air pressure to ease the pistons out. The pressure from a foot pump is usually enough.* One piston may have to be fully depressed in its bore to provide enough space to remove the other piston. If the pistons can be removed without separating the caliper halves, go ahead and remove them (also, ignore any references in this procedure related to disassembling the caliper halves). If they are too long and can't be removed, you have the kind of caliper that is OK to disassemble.

Remove the transfer tube, if equipped. Use a split ring spanner, if available *(see illustrations)*.

Mount the caliper assembly in a bench vice lined with wood or equipped with soft protector jaws. **Caution:** *Clamp on the caliper mounting lugs, NOT the caliper itself!* Remove the bridge bolts that hold the two halves of the caliper together. Separate the two caliper halves.

Peel the dust boot out and away from the caliper housing and out of the piston groove *(see illustration)*.

Place each caliper-half face down (pistons facing down) on top of a block of wood and, while holding the caliper-half down against the wood with one hand, plug the hole for

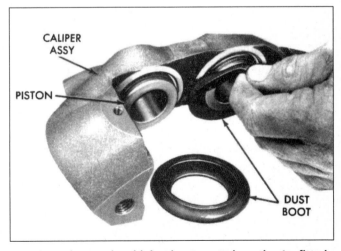

As you peel away the old dust boots, note how they're fitted over both the caliper housing retainer and into the piston groove - that's exactly how the new boots must be fitted during reassembly

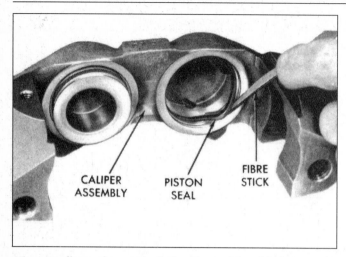

Use a small wooden or plastic tool to peel the old piston seals out of the piston bores - don't use a metal tool or you might damage the bores

the brake hose, apply a brief burst of pressurised air through the hole for the transfer tube and pop out the pistons. **Warning:** *Keep your fingers away from the pistons while doing this.* The outer caliper-half also has another hole, for the bleed screw, which must be fitted during this procedure, or the air will go in one hole and out the other, instead of pushing out the pistons. If a piston becomes cocked in its bore during removal, don't try to jerk it out with a pair of pliers, or you will damage the piston and the bore. Instead, carefully tap the piston back into its bore until it's square and try again.

Remove the pistons, noting which bore each of them

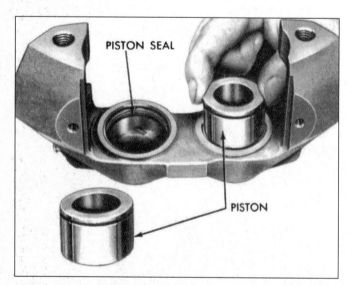

When you fit the pistons into their caliper halves, coat them with fresh brake fluid, double-check the new seals to make sure they're properly seated into their grooves in the piston bores walls and make sure the pistons are square to the bores

belongs to - they should be returned to the same bores. If there are springs behind the pistons, remove them.

Using a small pointed wooden or plastic tool, remove the piston seals from the groove in the cylinder bore *(see illustration)*. Discard the old seals. And be careful! Don't scratch or gouge the piston bore or the seal groove.

Clean everything with brake system cleaner and allow the parts to dry. Inspect the piston bores in both housings for scratches, scoring and pitting. Black stains in the bore walls are caused by the piston seals and are harmless. Light scratches, scoring and pitting can be cleaned up with crocus cloth. If the damage is deeper, the caliper should be replaced (rebuilt units are available). Light honing is permissible on cast iron calipers, but NEVER attempt to hone an aluminium caliper.

The pistons should be similarly inspected and cleaned up as necessary. If a piston is severely damaged - pitted, scored or the chrome plating worn off - renew the caliper.

Clamp the mounting lugs of the inner half of the caliper in a bench vice with soft jaws. Dip the new piston seals in clean brake fluid and fit them in the caliper grooves. Position each seal into its groove at one spot and gently work it around the piston bore with your finger until it's properly seated. **Warning:** *Do NOT use old seals!*

Coat the outside diameter of the pistons with clean brake fluid and refit them in the cylinder bores with the open end of each piston facing away from the caliper *(see illustration)*. If the caliper is equipped with springs behind the pistons don't forget to refit them first. Position the piston squarely in the bore and apply a slow, steady pressure until the piston is fully seated. If you encounter resistance, remove the piston and make sure the seal is properly fitted.

Fit the new dust boots into their grooves in the caliper and the pistons. Make sure the dust boots are properly seated.

Remove the inner caliper-half from the bench vice and mount the outer caliper-half the same way. Fit the seals, pistons and dust boots using the same method.

If your caliper does not have a transfer tube, fit new O-ring seals in the counterbore(s) around the fluid passage(s).

Refit the inner caliper-half onto the outer caliper-half that's still clamped into the vice, refit the bridge bolts and tighten. Refit the transfer tube (if applicable) and tighten the fittings securely. Refit the bleed screw, if removed. Refit the caliper.

Floating and sliding calipers (except opposed-piston calipers) - front (and rear on models with "drum-in-disc" handbrakes)

If your caliper has an integral torque plate on which the caliper floats, remove the bolts that secure the caliper halves, then separate the halves and remove the inner portion from the torque plate *(see illustrations)*.

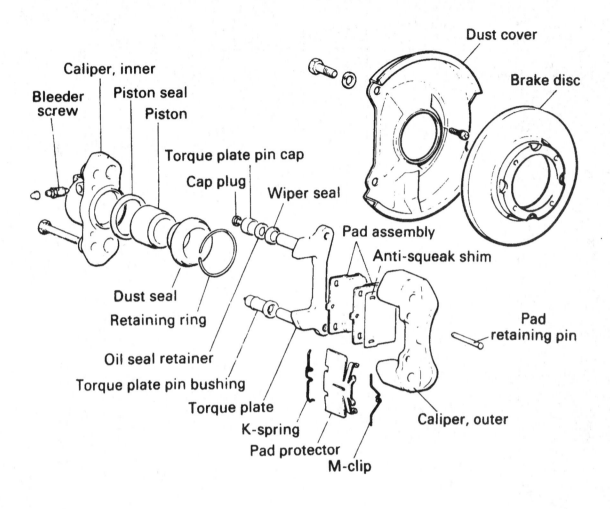

Bleeder screw

Caliper, inner

Piston seal

Piston

Torque plate pin cap

Cap plug

Wiper seal

Dust cover

Brake disc

Pad assembly

Anti-squeak shim

Pad retaining pin

Dust seal

Retaining ring

Oil seal retainer

Torque plate pin bushing

Torque plate

K-spring

Pad protector

M-clip

Caliper, outer

Exploded view of a floating caliper with an integral torque plate (mounting)

With the caliper held in a vice, remove the bolts that secure the inner and outer halves of the caliper frame together, then separate them (caliper with integral torque plate) ...

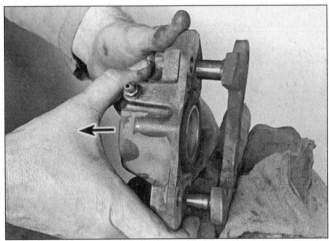

... then slide the inner half of the caliper off the torque plate

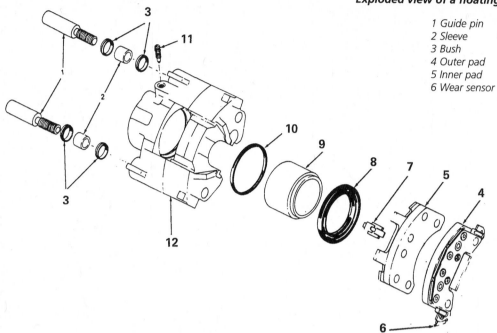

Exploded view of a floating brake caliper (Vauxhall)

1 Guide pin	7 Pad retainer
2 Sleeve	8 Dust boot
3 Bush	9 Piston
4 Outer pad	10 Piston seal
5 Inner pad	11 Bleed screw
6 Wear sensor	12 Caliper housing

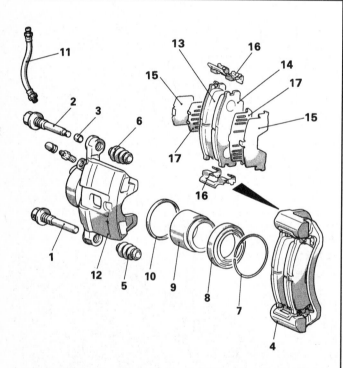

Exploded view of a single-piston floating caliper (Mitsubishi)

1 Guide pin	9 Piston
2 Lock pin	10 Piston seal
3 Bush	11 Brake hose
4 Torque plate (caliper mounting bracket)	12 Caliper body
5 Guide pin boot	13 Inner brake pad
6 Lock pin boot	14 Outer brake pad
7 Retaining ring	15 Shim
8 Dust boot	16 Anti-rattle shim
	17 Shim

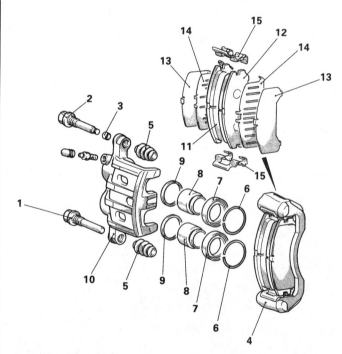

Exploded view of a dual-piston floating brake caliper (Mitsubishi)

1 Guide pin	8 Piston
2 Lock pin	9 Piston seal
3 Bush	10 Caliper body
4 Torque plate (mounting bracket)	11 Inner brake pad
5 Dust boot	12 Outer brake pad
6 Retaining ring	13 Shim
7 Piston dust boot	14 Shim
	15 Anti-rattle shim

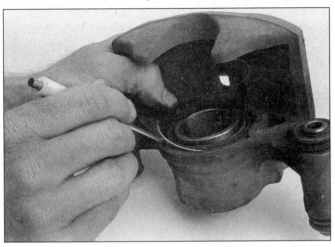

Remove the boot retaining ring with a small screwdriver - be careful not to gouge or scratch the piston or the bore

If the piston dust boot is held in place by a retaining ring, remove the ring and pull the dust boot out *(see illustrations)*.

Place several rags or a block of wood in the centre of the caliper to act as a cushion (unless the caliper halves have already been separated), then use pressurised air, directed into the fluid inlet, to remove the piston *(see illustration)*. If you separated the caliper halves to remove the torque plate, place the caliper on the workbench, piston facing down, and direct the pressurised air into the fluid inlet *(see illustration)*. Use only enough air pressure to ease the piston out of the bore. If the piston is blown out, even with the cushion in place, it may be damaged. **Warning:** *Never place your fingers in front of the piston in an attempt to catch or protect it, as serious injury could occur.*

Remove the dust boot from the caliper bore. Some types of dust boots have to be prised out *(see illustration)*. Now, using a wood or plastic tool, remove the piston seal from the groove in the caliper bore *(see illustration)*. Metal tools may cause bore damage.

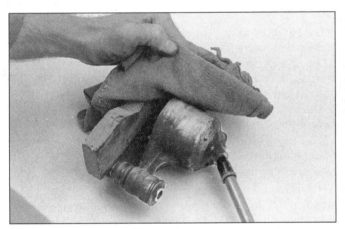

With the caliper padded to catch the piston, use pressurised air to force the piston out of its bore - make sure your fingers aren't between the piston and the caliper

On calipers with integral torque plates, place the caliper piston-side down and direct pressurised air into the brake hose inlet port to eject the piston

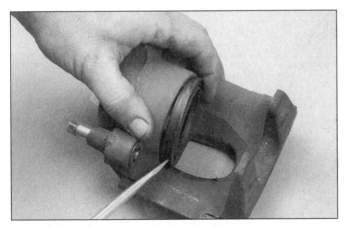

If the dust boot has a rigid casing, carefully prise it out of the caliper

To remove the seal from the caliper bore, use a plastic or wooden tool - a pencil will do the job

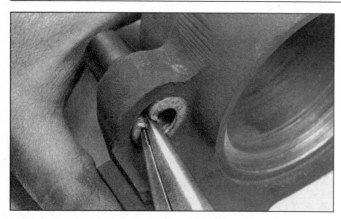

To remove a caliper pin boot, grab it with a pair of pliers, twist and push it through the caliper body

Remove the bleed screw, then remove and discard the caliper pin (mounting bolt) bushings, sleeves and boots, if equipped (see illustration).

Clean the remaining parts with brake system cleaner. Allow the parts to air dry. Inspect the surfaces of the piston for nicks and burrs and loss of plating. **Note:** *Some pistons are made of a plastic-like material called phenolic. If your caliper contains this kind of piston, be sure to check it for cracks,*

Position the new seal in the cylinder groove - make sure it isn't twisted

On calipers with dust boots that have rigid casings (or boots that use a retaining ring), slip the boot over the piston ...

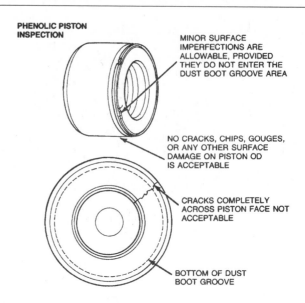

PHENOLIC PISTON INSPECTION

MINOR SURFACE IMPERFECTIONS ARE ALLOWABLE, PROVIDED THEY DO NOT ENTER THE DUST BOOT GROOVE AREA

NO CRACKS, CHIPS, GOUGES, OR ANY OTHER SURFACE DAMAGE ON PISTON OD IS ACCEPTABLE

CRACKS COMPLETELY ACROSS PISTON FACE NOT ACCEPTABLE

BOTTOM OF DUST BOOT GROOVE

Phenolic pistons must be carefully inspected for signs of damage, as shown

chips and other surface irregularities (see illustration). If surface defects are present, the caliper must be replaced. Check the caliper bore in a similar way. Light polishing with crocus cloth is permissible to remove slight corrosion and stains. Light honing is also permissible on cast iron calipers, but NEVER attempt to hone an aluminium caliper. Discard the caliper pins if they're severely corroded or damaged.

Lubricate the new piston seal with clean brake fluid and position the seal in the cylinder groove using your fingers only (see illustration).

If the dust boot on your caliper is held in place by a retaining ring, or if it has a hard casing around its outer diameter which seats in the caliper, fit the new dust boot in the groove in the end of the piston (see illustration). Dip the piston in clean brake fluid and insert it squarely into the cylinder. Depress the piston to the bottom of the cylinder bore (see illustration). Seat the boot in the caliper

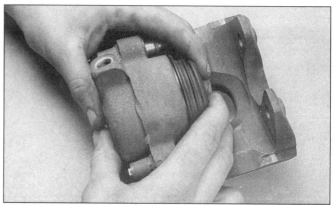

... then push the piston straight into the cylinder - make sure it doesn't become cocked in the bore

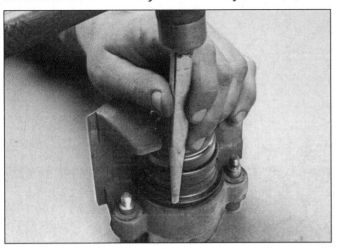

If you don't have a boot refitting tool, gently seat the boot with a punch

On calipers that use retaining rings, seat the boot in its groove, then fit the retaining ring

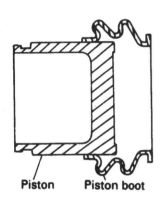

Piston   Piston boot

On calipers where the flange of the boot fits into a groove in the caliper, place the piston boot onto the bottom of the piston ...

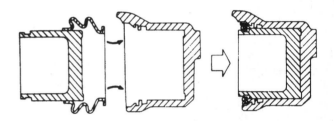

... then tuck the fluted portion of the boot into the upper groove of the caliper bore and bottom the piston in the bore

counterbore using a boot refitting tool or a blunt punch *(see illustration)*, or refit the retaining ring *(see illustration)*, depending on design.

If the dust boot on your caliper has a lip or flange at the bottom which seats in the upper groove in the caliper bore, refit the boot on the bottom (closed end) of the piston *(see illustration)*. Lower the piston and boot assembly into the caliper bore and work the flanged portion (the lip) into its groove in the bore *(see illustration)*. If you have trouble seating the lip of the dust boot in its groove, try this alternative method:

a) *Take the boot off the piston and refit the flanged portion of the boot into its groove in the caliper bore (see illustration). Coat the cylinder bore and the walls of the piston with clean brake fluid.*

b) *Place the caliper in a vice, with the jaws of the vice clamping onto one of the caliper mounting ears. Place the piston against the end of the new dust boot, apply a small burst of pressurised air (make sure it's filtered and unlubricated) to the caliper bore to inflate the boot, then*

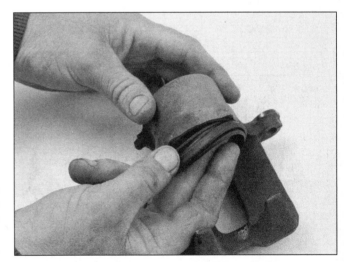

If you're having trouble refitting the piston and boot as previously described, fit the big end of the dust boot into the caliper, making sure the fluted portion is completely seated in its groove in the caliper bore ...

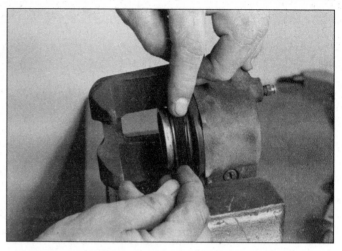

... then place the piston against the open end of the new dust boot. Apply a small burst of pressurised air to the fluid inlet to inflate the boot. Push the piston through the small end of the boot as the boot inflates ...

... as soon as the piston is in the boot, release the pressurised air and push the piston far enough into the bore to seat the ridge on the boot into its groove in the piston. Push the piston the rest of the way into the bore

push the piston through the boot opening as the boot inflates *(see illustration)*. **Warning:** *Once the piston has been inserted into the boot, stop applying pressurised air. Also, don't place your fingers between the piston and the*

caliper frame. Although it's possible to push the piston through the boot without applying pressurised air, it's extremely difficult and may damage the boot.

c) Continue to push the piston into the bore, then seat the dust boot into its groove near the outer end of the piston *(see illustration)*.

Fit the new mounting pin bushings and sleeves *(see illustrations)*. Be sure to lubricate the sleeves with silicone grease.

If your caliper has an integral torque plate on which the caliper floats, lubricate the torque plate pins with silicone grease and refit the torque plate to the inner half of the caliper *(see illustration)*. Attach the outer half of the caliper to the inner half, refit the bolts and tighten them.

Refit the bleed screw.

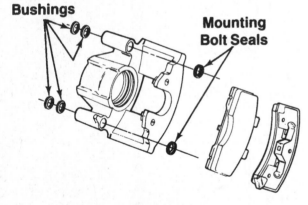

Caliper bush and seal details (Vauxhall)

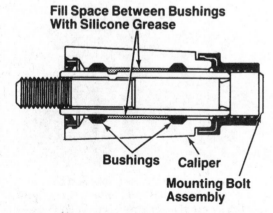

Be sure to lubricate the caliper bushes

On calipers with integral torque plates, lubricate the pins with silicone-based grease, then assembly the plate and the inner portion of the caliper - the caliper halves can now be bolted together

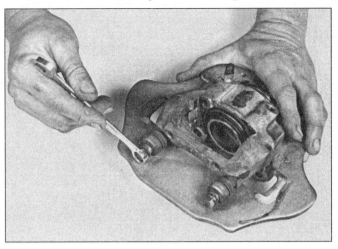

Remove the yoke-to-caliper bolts ...

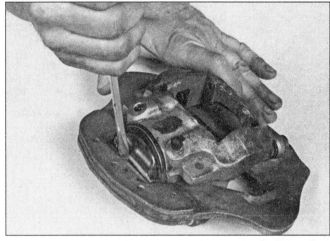

... then, using a screwdriver, prise the yoke holder off the yoke

On sliding calipers, clean the sliding surfaces of the caliper and the caliper adapter. Refer to Chapter 2 for the caliper refitting procedure.

Opposed-piston calipers - front

Remove the two bolts that attach the caliper to the yoke, then prise the yoke holder off the yoke *(see illustrations)*.

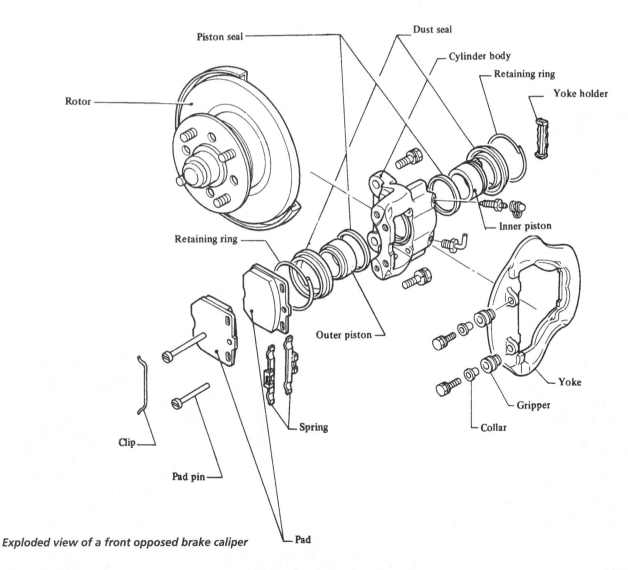

Exploded view of a front opposed brake caliper

Remove the retaining ring from the inner piston dust boot ...

... then remove the retaining ring from the outer piston dust boot

This disengages the piston from the yoke. The caliper can now be detached from the yoke.

Remove the yoke holder from the inner piston, then remove the dust boot retaining rings from each piston *(see illustrations)*.

Pull the dust boots off the pistons, then push both pistons out of the caliper from the pad side *(see illustration)*. The piston seals can now be removed *(see illustration)*. If you can't remove the seals with your fingers, use a wood or plastic tool - metal tools can cause bore damage.

Remove the grippers and collars from the yoke.

Clean everything with brake system cleaner and allow the parts to dry. Inspect the piston bore for scratches, scoring and pitting. Black stains in the bore walls are caused by the piston seals and are harmless. Light scratches, scoring and pitting can be cleaned up with crocus cloth. If the

damage is deeper, the caliper should be replaced (rebuilt units are available). NEVER attempt to hone an aluminium caliper.

The pistons should be similarly inspected and cleaned up as necessary. If a piston is severely damaged - pitted, scored or the chrome plating worn off - renew the caliper.

Check the yoke for cracks, excessive wear or other damage and renew it if necessary.

Lubricate the piston seals with clean brake fluid and fit them into their grooves in the caliper bore, making sure they seat correctly and aren't twisted. Lubricate the walls of the pistons with clean brake fluid (or silicone grease, if it was supplied in the rebuild kit). Refit the pistons into their respective ends of the bore. Don't refit them like you removed them (both pistons through the same side of the caliper).

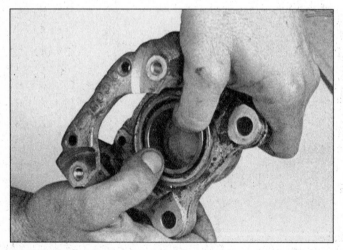

Both pistons are removed from the caliper by pushing on the outer piston

Remove the piston seals from the caliper bore

Press the outer piston into the bore so that the inner edge of the piston seal groove is in line with the inner edge of the caliper seal grooves *(see illustration)*. Apply silicone grease to the inside of the dust boots, then refit the dust boots and retaining rings *(see illustrations)*. Make sure the boots seat properly into the grooves in the pistons and the grooves in the caliper.

Press the yoke holder into its groove on the inner piston face, then position the caliper body in the yoke, making sure the yoke holder is aligned with the yoke *(see illustration)*. Place the entire assembly so the outer piston is facing up, then apply pressure to the outer piston to press the yoke holder onto the yoke *(see illustration)*.

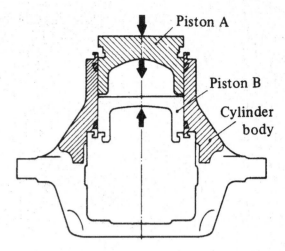

The pistons should be positioned like this when refitting the dust boots

Apply silicone grease to the inside of the dust boots prior to refitting

Fit the outer piston dust boot ...

... followed by the dust boot retaining ring

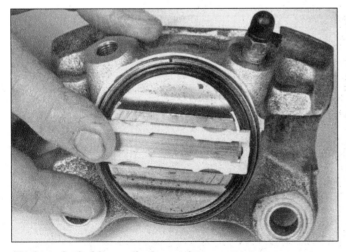

Fit the yoke holder on the inner piston

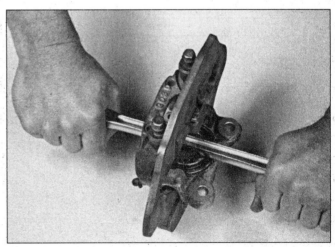

To seat the yoke holder on the yoke, place a tool across the outer piston and push down

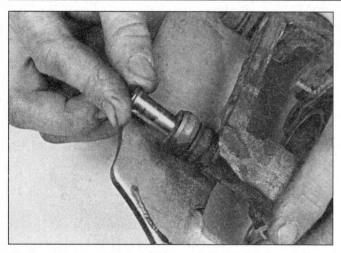

Fit the bushes and boots (collars and grippers), lubricating them with silicone grease

Refit the grippers and collars into their holes in the yoke *(see illustration)*. Be sure to lubricate the collars with silicone grease.

Once the yoke holder is pressed onto the yoke, refit the two mounting bolts that retain the yoke to the caliper housing, tightening them securely.

Refit the calipers.

Floating and sliding calipers (except opposed-piston calipers) - rear (calipers with integral handbrake mechanisms)

Note: *If you're not sure what type of rear caliper you have, refer to the component descriptions in Chapter 1. Also, the following procedures are typical for the type of caliper designs they represent. There may be some differences between the calipers shown and the ones on your vehicle. Whenever disassembling a rear brake caliper, make sketches of the relationship of the components and lay the parts out in order as they are removed.*

As stated in the beginning of this Section, it may actually be more cost effective to purchase factory-rebuilt calipers rather than buy a rebuild kit and overhaul them yourself.

Calipers with an actuator screw-type parking brake mechanism

Remove the sleeves and bolt boots from the ends of the caliper, then remove the pad retainer (if equipped) from the end of the piston by rotating the retainer until the inside tabs line up with the notches in the piston *(see illustration)*.

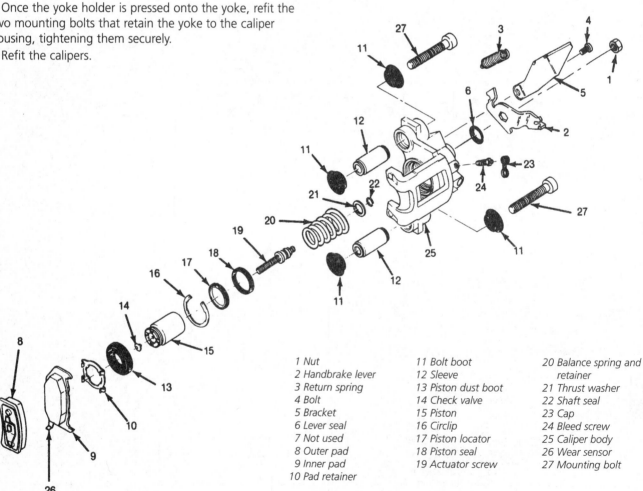

1 Nut	11 Bolt boot	20 Balance spring and
2 Handbrake lever	12 Sleeve	retainer
3 Return spring	13 Piston dust boot	21 Thrust washer
4 Bolt	14 Check valve	22 Shaft seal
5 Bracket	15 Piston	23 Cap
6 Lever seal	16 Circlip	24 Bleed screw
7 Not used	17 Piston locator	25 Caliper body
8 Outer pad	18 Piston seal	26 Wear sensor
9 Inner pad	19 Actuator screw	27 Mounting bolt
10 Pad retainer		

Exploded view of a rear brake caliper with an actuator screw-type handbrake mechanism (Vauxhall)

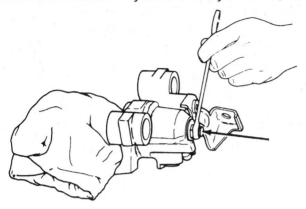

Rotate the actuator screw (arrowed) to remove the piston

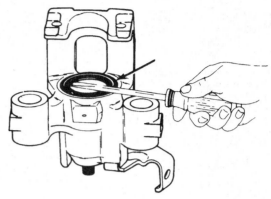

Carefully prise the dust boot out of the body, taking care not to scratch the surface of the bore

Remove the handbrake lever nut, lever and seal. Place rags between the piston and the caliper frame, then turn the actuator screw with a spanner to work the piston out of the bore *(see illustration)*. Remove the balance spring then push on the handbrake lever end of the actuator screw to remove it. Remove the shaft seal and thrust washer from the actuator screw.

While being careful not to scratch the housing bore, remove the boot *(see illustration)*.

Using circlip pliers, remove the circlip, followed by the piston locator. Using a plastic or wooden tool, remove the piston seal from the caliper bore.

Remove the bleed valve. Clean all parts not included in the repair kit with brake system cleaner. Allow the parts to dry. Inspect all parts for wear, damage and corrosion. **Note:** *It is okay to remove minor corrosion from the caliper bore using emery cloth.*

Lubricate all of the internal parts with clean brake fluid. Fit a new piston seal into its groove in the caliper bore.

Fit a new piston locator on the piston. Fit the thrust

washer on the actuator screw with the greyish side toward the caliper housing and the copper side toward the piston assembly. Fit the shaft seal on the actuator screw, then refit the actuator screw onto the piston assembly.

Fit the piston assembly with the actuator screw and balance spring into the lubricated bore of the caliper. Push the piston into the caliper bore so the locator is past the retainer groove in the caliper bore. **Note:** *A pair of adjustable pliers might be necessary to press the piston into the caliper. Fit the circlip using circlip pliers.*

With the inside of the boot in the piston groove and boot fold toward the end of the piston that contacts the brake pad, refit the caliper boot onto the piston. Use a seal driver to seat the caliper boot into the cylinder counterbore *(see illustration)*. If a seal driver isn't available, use a blunt punch and carefully tap around the outer circumference of the seal to seat it. Fit the pad retainer on the piston.

Lubricate the outside diameter of the mounting bolt sleeves and the caliper sleeve cavities with silicone grease. Fit one sleeve boot into a groove of the sleeve cavity *(see illustration)*. Fit a sleeve

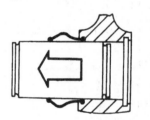

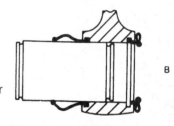

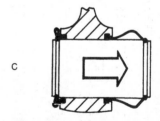

Sleeve boot refitting procedure
A *Fit the sleeve boot into the groove in the sleeve bore, then push the sleeve into the boot*
B *Fit the other boot into the groove in the other side of the bore*
C *Push the sleeve back and seat both boots into the grooves in the ends of the sleeve*

Use a seal driver, if available, to seat the boot in the caliper body

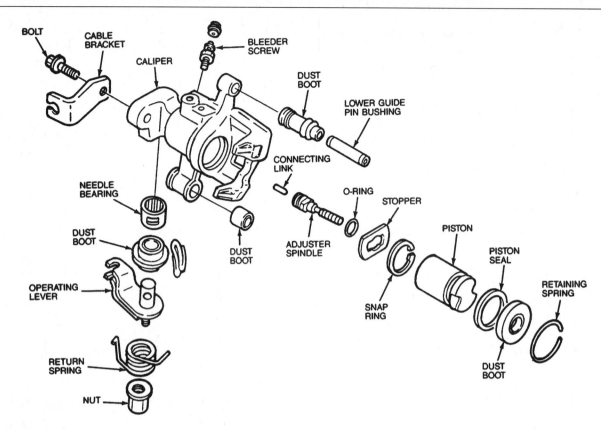

Exploded view of a rear caliper with an actuator-spindle handbrake mechanism

through the opposite side of the sleeve cavity and continue pushing the sleeve until the boot lip seats in the sleeve groove.

Fit the boot in the opposite side of the sleeve cavity groove

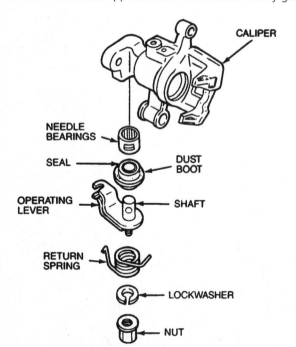

Exploded view of the handbrake lever assembly

and push the sleeve through the cavity far enough for that boot to slip into the remaining groove of the sleeve. Repeat the sleeve boot refitting procedure to the remaining sleeve.

Refit the caliper.

Calipers with an actuator spindle-type handbrake mechanism

Remove the caliper guide bush and dust boots *(see illustration)*. Discard all rubber parts. Clean the exterior of the caliper with brake system cleaner.

Prise the retaining ring off the dust boot with a screwdriver. Discard the boot.

Rotate the piston anti-clockwise using a brake piston turning tool (see Chapter 2) or a pair of needle-nose pliers, and remove the piston from the adjuster spindle.

Using a wood or plastic tool, remove the piston seal from the caliper bore groove. Metal tools may cause bore damage.

Remove the caliper bleed screw.

Using a pair of circlip pliers, remove the circlip above the stopper. Remove the adjuster spindle, stopper and connecting link. Separate the adjuster spindle from the stopper. Remove the O-ring from the adjuster spindle. Discard the O-ring.

Remove the return spring from the operating lever of the handbrake mechanism *(see illustration)*. Remove the operating lever nut and lockwasher. Mark the relationship

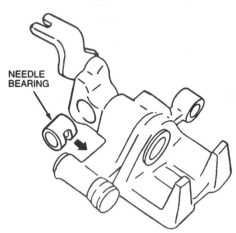

Align the opening in the needle bearings with the bore in the caliper body

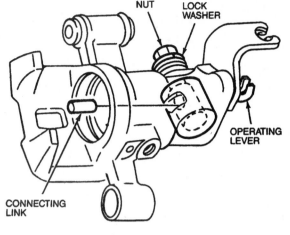

When you refit the operating lever, be sure to align the marks you made before disassembly

between the operating lever and the shaft. Remove the operating lever from the shaft.

Remove the seal from the caliper housing. Also remove the shaft and the needle bearing.

Carefully examine the piston for nicks and burrs and loss of plating. If surface defects are evident, renew the caliper assembly. Inspect the caliper bore for similar damage and wear. You can lightly polish the bore with crocus cloth to remove light corrosion and stains. If that fails to clean up the damage, renew the caliper. Inspect the mounting bolt - if it's corroded or damaged, discard it. Also inspect the guide pin bushings for wear. If they're worn or corroded, renew them.

Lubricate the needle bearings with multi-purpose grease. Align the opening in the needle bearings with the bore in the caliper housing *(see illustration)*. Fit the needle bearings.

Fit the operating shaft into the caliper housing. Fit the operating lever *(see illustration)*. Align the marks made during removal. Fit the lockwasher nut.

Insert the connecting link into the operating lever shaft. Fit the O-ring onto the adjuster spindle. Position the stopper onto the adjuster spindle so the pins will align with the caliper housing *(see illustration)*. Fit the adjuster spindle and the stopper into the caliper.

Fit the stopper retaining circlip. Be sure the operating lever and adjuster spindle move freely. Fit the handbrake return spring.

Before reassembling the caliper, lubricate the piston bore and O-ring with clean brake fluid. Fit the O-ring into its groove in the caliper bore. Make sure it isn't twisted.

Lubricate the piston with clean brake fluid, then insert it into the caliper bore. Rotate the piston clockwise using a brake piston turning tool or a pair of needle-nose pliers, to refit it onto the adjusting spindle. Screw the piston in fully. Align the notches in the piston with the opening in the caliper.

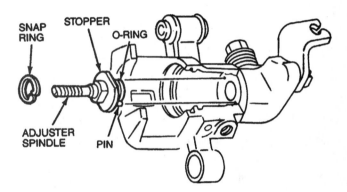

Exploded view of the adjuster spindle and stopper assembly

Fit a new dust boot in the piston groove with the fold toward the open end of the piston. Seat the boot in the caliper bore. Fit the retaining ring.

Fit the dust boots for the guide pin bushings *(see illustration)*. Fit the caliper guide pin bush.

Refit the caliper.

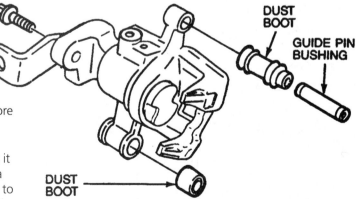

Exploded view of the guide pin (mounting bolt) bushings and dust boots

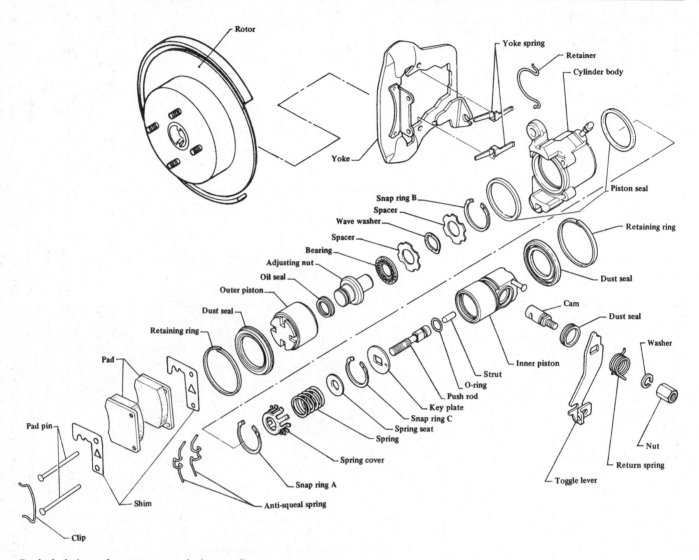

Exploded view of a rear opposed-piston caliper

Remove the anti-squeal clamps from the yoke

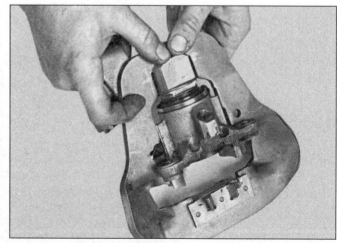

Separate the caliper from the yoke by pushing outward on the inner piston

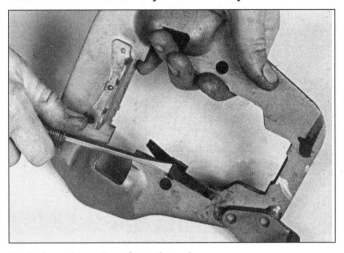

Push the yoke springs from the yoke

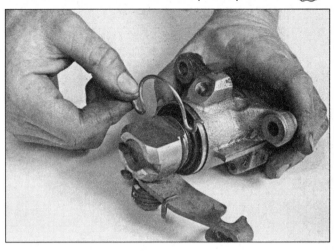

Remove the caliper retaining clip

Remove the retaining rings from both piston dust boots ...

... and peel the dust boots from the caliper

Push the pistons out of the caliper

Opposed-piston calipers - rear

Unclip the two anti-squeal clamps and detach them from the yoke, then separate the caliper from the yoke and remove the yoke springs *(see illustrations)*.

Remove the caliper retainer clip *(see illustration)*.

Remove the inner and outer dust boot retaining rings, then remove the dust boots and push the pistons from the caliper *(see illustrations)*. Remove the piston seals from the grooves in the caliper bore.

Remove the outer piston from the inner piston by rotating it anti-clockwise *(see illustration)*. Remove the circlip from the

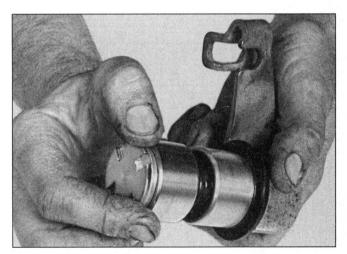

Separate the pistons by turning the outer piston anti-clockwise

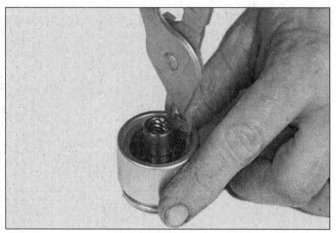

Using circlip pliers, remove the circlip from the outer piston ...

... then remove the contents of the piston and lay the components out in order

outer piston, then lift out the components for inspection *(see illustrations)*.

Remove the dust boot from the inner piston *(see illustration)*. Remove the outer circlip from the inner piston. Lift off the spring cover and spring. Remove the inner circlip from the inner piston. Turn the inner piston upside-down and remove the spring seat and key plate.

Pull the pushrod out of the piston and remove the strut and O-ring. Disengage the return spring from the toggle lever *(see illustration)*. Remove the toggle lever and cam assembly by pulling it out of the inner piston. Remove the toggle lever lip seal from the inner piston.

Use a screwdriver to carefully prise out the seal and bearing retainer from the inner piston.

Check the outer surfaces of the inner and outer pistons for scoring, nicks, rust or other damage. If light rust or scoring is present, it can be removed with crocus cloth. If damage is deep, the piston must be replaced. Check the threads on the pushrod. Make sure they are in good condition and renew the rod if necessary. Inspect the inner surface of the caliper

bore for any nicks, scoring, rust or other damage. Again, if light rust or scoring is present, it can be removed using crocus cloth, but the caliper will have to be replaced if the damage is deeper.

Inspect the needle bearing inside the outer piston for freedom of movement. If any of the rollers are binding, the bearing will have to be replaced by prising it out.

Apply a light coat of silicone-based grease to the needle bearings.

Fit the seal and bearing retainer by gently tapping it into place with a plastic-head hammer. Fit a new lip seal onto the retainer.

Carefully insert the toggle lever and cam assembly into the outer piston.

Lubricate both ends of the strut with silicone-based grease and refit it into the pushrod. Lightly lubricate the pushrod O-ring with silicone-based grease and refit it into its groove on the pushrod. Insert the strut and pushrod into the piston.

Fit the key plate over the pushrod. Be sure the pushrod is aligned so that the locating pin in the key plate is properly

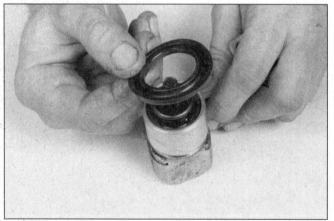

Remove the dust boot from the inner piston

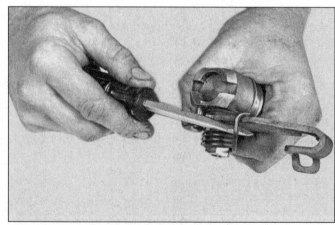

Use a screwdriver to remove the return spring from the toggle lever

The seal on the outer piston adjusting nut should be fitted like this

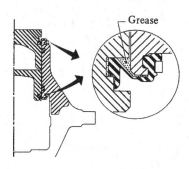

The pistons should be positioned like this when refitting the dust boots. Apply silicone grease to the boots before refitting them

fitted into its hole in the piston. Fit the inner circlip into its groove in the piston.

Fit the spring seat, spring and spring cover then place an appropriately sized socket over the pushrod, so that it sits on the spring cover. Place the assembly in a vice and tighten the vice until the spring is compressed enough for the outer circlip to be fitted in its groove. Be careful that the spring cover is properly centred in the bore so that the tangs don't get damaged.

Fit a new lip seal onto the adjusting nut. Be sure the lip is facing in the proper direction *(see illustration)*. Lubricate the lip seal with silicone-based grease.

Place the adjusting screw into the bore in the outer piston. Place the bearing spacer, wave washer and spacer, in that order, over the adjusting nut. Fit the circlip into the outer piston. Fit the outer piston onto the pushrod.

Apply a light coat of silicone-based grease to the cylinder bore. Fit the new piston seals into their grooves inside the bore. Lightly lubricate the seals with silicone-based grease.

Apply a light coat of silicone-based grease to the seal groove on the inner piston. Wipe off any residual grease that may have got onto the exterior surface of the piston. Fit a new dust boot into position on the inner piston, then refit the retaining ring.

Apply a light coat of silicone-based grease to the outer surfaces of both pistons. Apply a light coat of silicone-based grease into the two dust boot grooves on either side of the caliper housing. Carefully insert the pistons into the caliper bore. Align the inner piston so the inner edge of its boot groove is in line with the inner edge of the caliper boot groove, then pull the boot into position on the caliper.

Align the outer piston in a similar fashion to the inner piston so that the inner edge of the dust boot groove is in line with the inner edge of the caliper seal groove *(see illustration)*. Fit the outer piston dust boot and retaining ring.

Place the caliper retainer into its groove.

Fit the yoke springs into position on the yoke *(see illustration)*.

Apply a light film of high-temperature grease to the indicated surfaces *(see illustration)*.

Fit the caliper into the yoke, then refit the anti-squeak clamps onto the yoke.

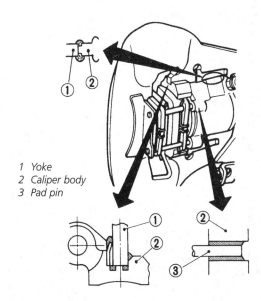

1 Yoke
2 Caliper body
3 Pad pin

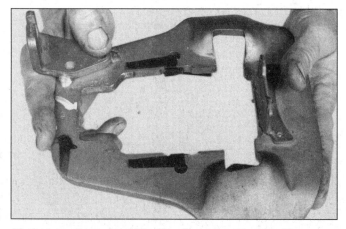

The yoke springs should be fitted prior to attaching the caliper to the yoke

The friction surfaces of the yoke and caliper and pad pin holes should be lubricated with the high-temperature grease prior to refitting the caliper to the yoke

Refitting

If you're servicing a fixed caliper, refit the caliper assembly and the caliper mounting bolts, then tighten the bolts, then refit the brake pads (see Chapter 2). If you're servicing a floating or sliding caliper, caliper refitting is a part of brake pad refitting in Chapter 2. Make sure you tighten the caliper pins/bolts.

On models where the brake hose threads directly into the caliper, connect the brake hose to the caliper and tighten it securely. Position the other end of the hose in its bracket and connect the brake pipe fitting. Tighten the fitting securely. On models that use banjo fittings, connect the hose to the caliper using new sealing washers. Tighten the banjo bolt securely.

Bleed the brakes as outlined in later in this Chapter.

Fit the wheels and wheel nuts/bolts. Lower the vehicle and tighten the wheel nuts/bolts securely.

After the job has been completed, firmly depress the brake pedal a few times to bring the pads into contact with the disc. Check the operation of the brakes before driving the vehicle in traffic.

5   Wheel cylinders

Note: *If an overhaul is indicated (usually because of fluid leakage or sticky operation) explore all options before beginning the job. New wheel cylinders are available, which makes this job quite easy. If you decide to rebuild the wheel cylinder, make sure a rebuild kit is available before proceeding. Never overhaul only one wheel cylinder. Always rebuild both of them at the same time.*

Removal

Remove the brake shoes (see Chapter 3). Unscrew the brake pipe union from the rear of the wheel cylinder *(see illustration)*. If available, use a split ring spanner to avoid rounding off the corners on the union. Don't pull the metal pipe out of the wheel cylinder - it could bend, making refitting difficult.

Remove the bolt(s) or clip securing the wheel cylinder to the brake backing plate *(see illustration)*. Remove the wheel cylinder. Plug the end of the brake pipe to prevent the loss of brake fluid and the entry of dirt.

Unscrew the brake pipe union from the rear of the wheel cylinder with a split ring spanner, then remove the bolts (arrowed) securing the cylinder to the back plate

On wheel cylinders that aren't retained by bolts, a pair of screwdrivers can be used to remove the cylinder retainer

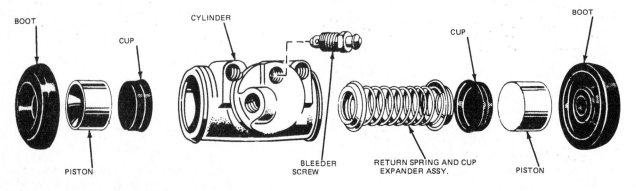

Exploded view of a typical wheel cylinder

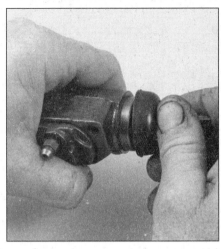

Remove the wheel cylinder dust boots

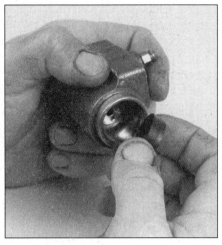

Fit the pistons seals with their open ends facing in, towards the seal expanders

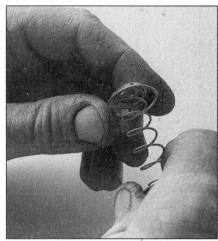

Attach the seal expanders to the spring ...

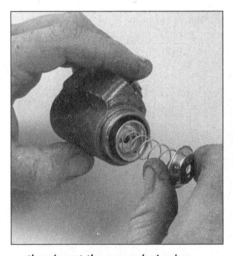

... then insert the expander/spring assembly into one end of the wheel cylinder housing (some wheel cylinders don't use expanders - they only have springs)

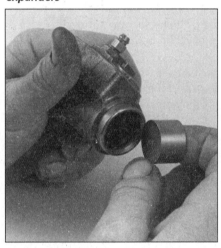

Fit the piston into each end of the wheel cylinder housing

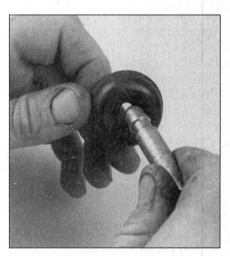

Insert the wheel cylinder pushrods into the new dust boots, then fit the dust boots and pushrods onto both ends of the wheel cylinder (not all cylinders have pushrods)

Overhaul

To disassemble the wheel cylinder, remove the rubber dust boot from each end of the cylinder, then push out the two pistons, the cups (seals) and the expander/spring assembly *(see illustrations)*. Discard the rubber parts and use new ones from the rebuild kit when reassembling the wheel cylinder.

Inspect the pistons for scoring and scuff marks. If present, the pistons should be replaced with new ones. Examine the inside of the cylinder bore for score marks and corrosion. If these conditions exist, the cylinder can be honed slightly to restore it, but renewal is recommended. If the cylinder is in good condition, clean it with brake system cleaner. **Warning:** *DO NOT, under any circumstances, use petrol or petroleum-based solvents to clean brake parts!*

Remove the bleed screw and make sure the hole is clean.

Lubricate the cylinder bore with clean brake fluid, then insert one of the new rubber cups into the bore *(see illustration)*. Make sure the lip on the rubber cup faces in.

Fit the cup expanders, if equipped, onto the ends of the spring, insert the expander/spring assembly into the opposite end of the bore and push it in until it contacts the rear of the rubber cup *(see illustrations)*. Fit the remaining cup in the cylinder bore.

Fit the pistons *(see illustration)*. Insert the pushrods (if equipped) into the boots *(see illustration)*, then refit the boots and pushrods.

Refitting

Refitting is the reverse of removal. Attach the brake pipe to the wheel cylinder before refitting the mounting bolt(s) or clip and tighten the pipe union after the wheel cylinder mounting bolt(s) have been tightened or the clip has been fitted. If available, use a split ring spanner to tighten the pipe union.

Fit the brake shoes and brake drum (see Chapter 3).

Bleed the brakes following the procedure described later in this Chapter. Don't drive the vehicle in traffic until the operation of the brakes has been thoroughly tested.

6 Hoses and pipes

Note: *Refer to Chapter 7 for the brake hose and pipe inspection procedures.*

Flexible hose renewal

Clean all dirt away from the ends of the hose. Disconnect the metal brake pipe from the hose fitting *(see illustration)*. You'll need a second spanner on some fittings. Be careful not to bend the frame bracket or pipe. If necessary, soak the connections with penetrating oil. Remove the U-clip (lock) from the female fitting at the bracket and remove the hose from the bracket.

On models that use banjo fittings, unscrew the banjo bolt and disconnect the hose from the caliper, discarding the sealing washers on either side of the fitting. On models where the brake hose threads directly into the caliper, unscrew the hose from the caliper.

Using new sealing washers, attach the new brake hose to the caliper (models that use banjo fittings). Tighten the banjo bolt. On models where the brake hose threads directly into the caliper, tighten the hose fitting securely.

Pass the female fitting through the frame or frame bracket. With the least amount of twist in the hose, secure the fitting in this position. **Note:** *The weight of the vehicle must be on the suspension, so the vehicle should not be raised while positioning the hose. If this is not possible, raise the suspension with a floor jack to simulate normal ride height.*

Fit the U-clip (lock) in the female fitting at the frame bracket. Attach the brake pipe to the hose fitting using another spanner to counterhold the fitting. Tighten the fitting securely.

Carefully check to make sure the suspension or steering components don't make contact with the hose. Have an assistant push on the vehicle and also turn the steering wheel lock-to-lock during inspection.

Bleed the brake system as described later in this Chapter.

Metal brake pipes

When replacing brake pipes, be sure to use the correct parts. Don't use copper tubing for any brake system components. Purchase steel brake pipes from a dealer parts department or accessory shop.

When fitting the new pipe make sure it's well supported in the brackets and has plenty of clearance between moving or hot components. Make sure you tighten the fittings securely.

To disconnect a brake hose from the brake pipe union, place a spanner on the union (A) and slacken the union (B) with a split ring spanner. Remove the U-clip (C) to detach the hose from the bracket

After refitting, check the master cylinder fluid level and add fluid as necessary. Bleed the brake system and test the brakes carefully before placing the vehicle into normal operation.

7 Brake system bleeding

Warning: Wear eye protection when bleeding the brake system. If the fluid comes in contact with your eyes, immediately rinse them with water and seek medical attention. Never use old brake fluid. It contains moisture and contaminants which will deteriorate the brake system components and could cause the fluid to boil when braking temperatures rise. This can lead to complete loss of pressure in the hydraulic system.

Note: *Bleeding the brake system is necessary to remove any air that's trapped in the system when it's opened during removal and refitting of any hydraulic component.*

Models without an Anti-lock Brake System (ABS)

Standard (two-person) bleeding procedure

It will probably be necessary to bleed the system at all four brakes if air has entered the system due to low fluid level, or if the brake pipes have been disconnected at the master cylinder. If a brake pipe was disconnected only at a wheel, then only that caliper or wheel cylinder must be bled. If a brake pipe is disconnected at a fitting located between the master cylinder and any of the brakes, that part of the system served by the disconnected pipe must be bled. If you suspect air in the master cylinder, begin by bleeding the master cylinder on the vehicle *(see page 6•12)*.

Remove any residual vacuum from the brake servo (if equipped) by applying the brake several times with the engine off. Remove the master cylinder reservoir cover and fill the reservoir with brake fluid. Reinstall the cover. **Note:** *Check the fluid level often during the bleeding operation and add fluid as necessary to prevent the fluid level from falling low enough to allow air bubbles into the master cylinder.*

Have an assistant on hand, as well as a supply of new brake fluid, an empty clear plastic container, a length of 6 mm plastic, rubber or vinyl tubing to fit over the bleed valve and a spanner to open and close the bleed valve.

The order of bleeding depends on the design of the brake system. It is worthwhile finding out the vehicle manufacturer's recommended sequence - refer to the appriopriate Service and Repair Manual. Generally, the caliper or wheel cylinder farthest away from the master cylinder is bled first, then the other caliper or wheel cylinder, in the same half of the circuit just bled, would be bled of air.

If the hydraulic system in the vehicle being bled is split front-to-rear, as is the case with most rear-wheel drive vehicles, you would bleed the brakes in the following order on a right-hand drive vehicle:

Left rear -> Right rear -> Left front -> Right front

If the hydraulic system is diagonally split, as is the case with most smaller front-wheel drive vehicles, you would bleed the brakes in this order on a right-hand drive vehicle:

Left rear -> Right front -> Right rear -> Left front

Warning: *Regardless of the order used to bleed the brake hydraulic system, the vehicle should NOT be driven unless a satisfactory, firm brake pedal is obtained.*

Beginning at the first wheel cylinder or caliper to be bled, loosen the bleed screw slightly, then tighten it to a point where it's snug but can still be loosened quickly and easily. Place one end of the tubing over the bleed screw fitting and submerge the other end in brake fluid in the container *(see illustration)*.

Have the assistant depress the brake pedal slowly to get pressure in the system, then hold the pedal firmly depressed. While the pedal is held depressed, open the bleed screw just enough to allow a flow of fluid to leave the valve. Watch for air bubbles to exit the submerged end of the tube. When the fluid flow slows after a couple of seconds, tighten the screw and have your assistant release the pedal.

Repeat this procedure until no more air is seen leaving the tube, then tighten the bleed screw and proceed to the next wheel cylinder or caliper in the bleeding sequence, and perform the same procedure. Be sure to check the fluid in the master cylinder reservoir frequently. **Note:** *On the rear brakes of some drum brake systems, only the wheel cylinder on one side of the vehicle is equipped with a bleed screw. Both wheel cylinders are bled through the cylinder that has the bleed screw.*

Refill the master cylinder with fluid at the end of the operation. Check the operation of the brakes. The pedal

When bleeding brakes, a hose is connected to the bleed screw at the caliper or wheel cylinder and then submerged in brake fluid - air will be seen as bubbles in the tube and container (all air must be expelled before moving to the next wheel)

should feel solid when depressed, with no sponginess. If necessary, repeat the entire process. Bleed the height (or load) sensing proportioning valve, if equipped.

Warning: *Do not operate the vehicle if you are in doubt about the effectiveness of the brake system.*

Alternative methods

Vacuum bleed method

Several companies manufacture brake bleeding kits that use hand-held vacuum pumps to suck the air out of the hydraulic circuit. The pump is connected to a reservoir, which is connected to the bleed screw. When the bleed screw is opened and the vacuum pump is operated, fluid (and any air bubbles) will collect in the reservoir *(see illustration)*. The pump itself does not come in contact with the fluid. The normal bleeding sequence can be used.

The vacuum-operated brake bleeding method is a convenient way to bleed the brakes, and you don't need a helper to do it! Just connect the hose from the container to the bleed valve, connect the hand-held vacuum pump to the container, open the bleed valve and apply vacuum. Fluid and air will be sucked out and will collect in the container

This type of brake bleeding set-up also allows you to bleed the brakes alone. Just attach the hose to the bleed screw and insert the other end into the container partially filled with fluid. Open the bleed screw and slowly pump the brake pedal - fluid and air will be expelled from the caliper, but the one-way valve in the hose prevents anything from being sucked back in

This is a very convenient method which only requires one person, but it has a couple of potential drawbacks. Since the cups in the wheel cylinder depend on pressure to seal against the walls of the cylinder, negative pressure can cause air to be drawn around the lips of the seal and into the hydraulic circuit. This may not happen in every case, but is more likely if the cups in the wheel cylinder are old or the hydraulic system has not been maintained properly. Air can also be drawn past the bleed screw threads when the screw is loosened.

One-person method

In addition to the vacuum bleed method, which is also a one-person method, another single-handed bleeding method exists. A number of one-person bleeding kits are available, and your local accessory shop will almost certainly stock one of them.

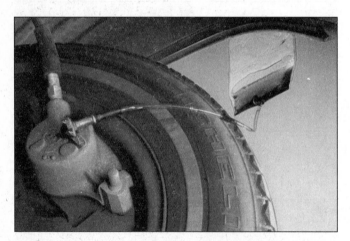

Another type of one-person brake bleeder is this bag-type. In operation it works similar to the set-up shown above, but it doesn't have a one-way valve. Air bubbles rise up into the bag, but they can't flow back into the hose. It is important to pump the pedal slowly in order for this method to be effective

The most common type of one-person bleeder kit is really nothing more than a hose with a one-way valve in it, and a container to collect the fluid *(see illustration)*. All you have to do is connect the bleed hose to the bleed screw, put the other end of the hose into the container (which must be partially filled with brake fluid) loosen the bleed screw and slowly pump the brake pedal. Fluid and air will be forced out of the circuit, past the one-way valve and into the container. The one-way valve prevents old fluid or air from being sucked back into the system.

HINTS & TIPS

- If you just can't seem to bleed all of the air out of a circuit, there are a couple of things you can try. Always keep in mind that air rises to the high points in an enclosed system.
  a) Make sure the master cylinder is free of air. Re-bleed it if necessary.
  b) Try raising the end of the vehicle being bled. This will help any air trapped in the system to find its way to the bleeder screw, which should be located at the highest point in its caliper or wheel cylinder.
  c) Lightly tap the caliper or wheel cylinder with a hammer. This can dislodge air bubbles that cling to the walls of the hydraulic cylinder.
  d) Follow the brake lines from the master cylinder, bleeding each line at each connection by loosening the fitting. Work from the closest fitting to the master cylinder to the farthest.
  e) Try one of the alternative bleeding methods.

Another type of one-man bleeding kit consists of a hose connected to a bag, which must be suspended above the level of the bleed screw *(see illustration)*. Connect the hose to the bleed screw, open the bleed screw and slowly pump the brake pedal. The old fluid and air will be forced from the caliper or wheel cylinder and into the bag. Since air rises, the bubbles that have been pushed into the bag can't be sucked back into the system.

Gravity bleeding

Gravity bleeding is exactly what it sounds like - the force of gravity pulls the brake fluid through the pipes to the bleed screw, and any air trapped in the pipes flows out of the bleed screw with it. This procedure can't be used in systems incorporating residual pressure check valves, because the check valves prevent the flow of fluid. When using this procedure you have to be sure to check the fluid level from time-to-time, since the procedure can take an hour or even more. This method might, however, be the answer to a hydraulic system that just can't seem to be purged of air.

To start the gravity bleeding procedure, raise both ends of the vehicle and support it securely on axle stands. Attach a length of clear plastic hose to the bleed screw at each wheel and direct the end of each hose into a container. Open each bleed screw one full turn, making sure fluid flows from each hose. **Note:** *If fluid does not flow, it may be necessary to* start a siphon. **Warning:** *Don't do this by mouth - use a hand-held vacuum pump to start the siphon! Remember, don't let the fluid in the master cylinder reservoirs drop too low.*

Allow the fluid to drain until the fluid in each hose is free of bubbles. Tighten the bleed screws and check the operation of the brakes. Top up the fluid level in the master cylinder reservoir.

Pressure bleeding

This is the method most garages use to bleed brake systems. It's quick, easy, and probably the most effective way to bleed a hydraulic system.

With this method, an adapter is attached to the top of the master cylinder reservoir. A hose is connected between the adapter and the pressure bleeder unit. Air pressure is connected to the bleeder unit also. (The professional systems use air from a compressor. There is a DIY version which uses air pressure from the spare tyre.) This forces pressurised fluid through the system - all you have to do is open the bleed valve at each wheel until the flow of fluid is free of air bubbles.

When using a pressure bleeder on some vehicles you'll have to use a metering valve override tool, which defeats the hold-off function of the metering valve so pressure can be directed to the front brakes *(see illustration)*. On some metering valves a plunger must be pulled out and held in the extended position - on others a button on the valve must be depressed. Special spring tools are available for this purpose. **Caution:** *Never use a rigid clamp or wedge to depress or pull out the valve plunger, since this can damage the metering valve internally. Either way, the tool must be removed after the bleeding process is complete.* **Note:** *It isn't necessary to defeat the metering valve when bleeding brakes manually, since the pressure created in the system is greater than the hold-off point of the valve (approximately 10 to 11 bar). It also isn't necessary to defeat the valve when using vacuum or gravity bleeding methods, since there basically is no pressure generated in the system.*

There are drawbacks, though. Pressure bleeding outfits are quite expensive and require special adapters to fit different master cylinder reservoirs. Also, great care must be taken to ensure that all pressure in the fluid reservoir is bled off before removing the adapter. If it isn't, brake fluid will "explode" everywhere, possibly causing damage to the vehicle's paint and injury to anyone nearby.

Models with an Anti-lock Brake System (ABS)

Warning: *Consult the appropriate Service and Repair Manual before carrying out any service operations other than brake pad or shoe renewal.*

It is possible to bleed ABS hydraulic systems using the methods outlined previously. However, If the master cylinder or modulator assembly has been disturbed, specialist equipement to operate the solenoid valves in the correct

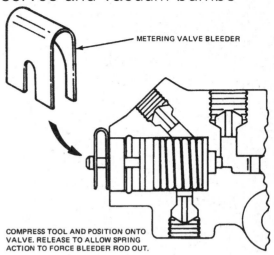

COMPRESS TOOL AND POSITION ONTO VALVE. RELEASE TO ALLOW SPRING ACTION TO FORCE BLEEDER ROD OUT.

When using a pressure bleeder, you may have to fit a metering valve bypass tool to defeat the metering valve. Otherwise, no fluid will flow to the front brakes

sequence may be required to puge the air from the modulator - refer to the appropriate Service and Repair Manual. In the vast amjority of cases, providing the hoses have been clamped, or the pipe openings plugged, bleeding the system after removal of the calipers, wheel cylinders or hoses/pipes should not be a problem.

8   Vacuum pumps

On most diesel engines, the air entering the engine is not throttled. This means there is no vacuum in the inlet manifold, which could be used to power a brake servo. Consequently, a vacuum pump is commonly fitted to supply the servo. The pump maybe driven by the camshaft, or by an auxiliary shaft driven by the timing belt, or may even be integral with the alternator and therefore driven by the auxiliary belt *(see illustrations)*.

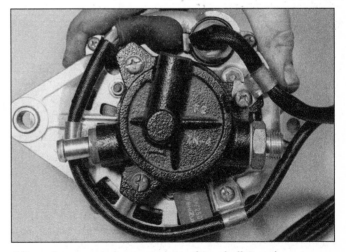

Alternator mounted vacuum pump (Vauxhall Corsa)

Camshaft driven vacuum pump (Vauxhall Astra)

Auxiliary shaft driven vacuum pump (arrowed) (Seat Ibiza)

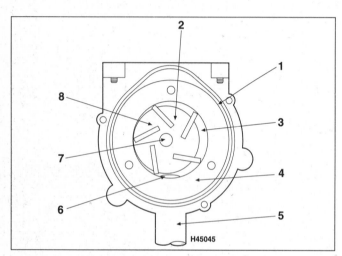

Typical vane-type vacuum pump

1 Outlet passage   5 Brake servo connection
2 Vane   6 Inlet passage
3 Cells   7 Pump shaft
4 Housing   8 Race

Tandem pump fitted to VW Pump Injector engines

1 Brake servo hose   3 Fuel return hose
2 Fuel supply hose   4 Tandem pump

The vane pump is the most common type. Here, as the central shaft rotates the vanes sweep the internal chamber(s) evacuating air and passing it through a non-return valve *(see illustration)*. This evacuation results in a vacuum to which the servo is connected. The vacuum source may also be used to supply various other components (EGR valve, Wastegate control actuator, etc.).

In almost all cases, apart from renewing the O-ring seals between the pump and the engine, it is not possible to overhaul the pumps - check in the appropriate Service and Repair manual.

Removal

Camshaft driven pump

Remove any engine covers as necessary to gain access to the pump, which is normally mounted on the end of the cylinder head, at the opposite end to the timing belt/chain.

Disconnect the pipe leading to the servo. Often this pipe is secured by a quick release coupling. If there is more than one pipe connected to the pump, label them to aid refitment. **Note**: *On VW Pump Injector engines, the vacuum is generated by a camshaft driven tandem pump, which also supplies fuel at low pressure to the injectors - be prepared for fuel spillage when disconnecting the pipes (see illustration).*

Undo the bolts/nuts securing the pump to the cylinder head, and remove the pump. Discard the O-ring seals, new ones must be fitted *(see illustration)*.

Auxiliary shaft driven pump

Remove any engine covers as necessary to gain access to the pump, which is normally mounted on the front face of the engine block, adjacent to the transmission mounting plate.

Release any retaining clips and disconnect the hose from the top of the pump.

Remove the bolt securing the pump clamp to the engine

Undo the vacuum pump mounting bolts (arrowed) (Peugeot 307 1.4 HDi)

Vacuum pump retaining bolt (arrowed) (Seat Ibiza)

block, and with draw the pump. Discard the sealing ring, a new one must be fitted *(see illustration)*.

Alternator driven pump

This pump is normally fitted to the rear of the alternator. Consequently, access is gained from under the vehicle. Jack up the front of the vehicle and support it securely on axle stands. Remove the engine undershield (where fitted) to gain access to the alternator. Alternatively, it may be preferable to remove the alternator as described in the appropriate Service and Repair Manual.

Disconnect the oil supply, return and vacuum hoses from the pump *(see illustrations)*.

Undo the bolts and detach the pump from the alternator. Discard the O-ring seal, a new one must be fitted *(see illustration)*.

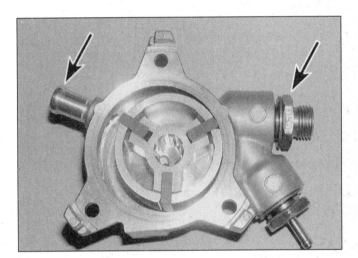

Disconnect the oil supply (A) and return hoses (B) ...

... and the vacuum hose (arrowed)

Undo the bolts and detach the pump from the alternator

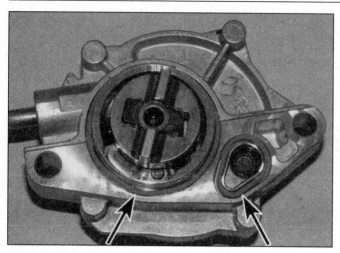

Always renew the pump O-rings (arrowed)

Align the pump drive lug with the slot in the end of the camshaft (arrowed)

Overhaul

As no parts appear to be available, overhaul of these units is not possible. If defective, renewal is the only course of action.

Refitting

Refitting these pumps is a reversal of removing them, with the exception of the alternator mounted pump. Prior to refitting this pump, pour 5 cc of clean engine oil into the oil feed aperture.

On all pumps, ensure the mating faces are clean, and always renew the seals. Align the drive lug of the pump with the slot in the end of the camshaft/auxiliary shaft - where applicable *(see illustrations)*.

Check the operation of the braking system before venturing out into traffic.

Maintenance 7

Inspection and maintenance procedures   3

Introduction   1

Maintenance schedule   2

1   Introduction

The key objective of this Chapter is to establish a preventive maintenance program to minimise the chances of brake trouble or system failure. This is done by maintaining a constant awareness of the condition of the entire braking system and by correcting defects or replacing worn-out parts before they become serious problems. The majority of the operations outlined in this Chapter are nothing more than inspections of the various components that make up the brake system.

Secondly, this preventive maintenance program should cause most, if not all, maintenance and repairs to take place by intent, hopefully eliminating all "unscheduled maintenance." By doing so, all brake system repairs that may become necessary can be performed when and where you choose. Not only will it save you money by catching worn-out brake pads and shoes before they cause serious damage, it'll also save you money by avoiding body shop repair bills, recovery, ambulance and hospital fees, lawsuits, etc!

The following brake maintenance schedule is very simple, as are the checking procedures that go with it. The maintenance intervals are based on normal operating conditions for a normal passenger vehicle. If a particular vehicle is subjected to more severe usage, the intervals should be shortened and the inspection procedures performed more often. Vehicles that tow trailers, carry heavy loads, are driven in a lot of stop-and-go traffic or in mountainous regions are going to wear out parts and need service more often than vehicles that enjoy mostly traffic-free motorway trips. Mileage isn't always a factor - the important thing is to perform the inspections routinely. If your vehicle is operated under severe conditions, it would be a good idea to at least perform the disc and/or drum brake inspections twice as frequently as outlined below, until you develop a feel for the rate at which your vehicle wears down the brake linings.

The maintenance schedule is basically an outline for the actual inspection and maintenance procedures. The individual procedures are then described in detail. Some of the items on the schedule may be listed at a shorter interval than recommended by some manufacturers, and some of the items listed may not even appear on the maintenance schedules of some manufacturers, but that's OK - it's better to be safe than sorry.

If you're experiencing a specific problem with the brake system, refer to Chapter 8, Fault Finding, for the proper course of action to take.

2 Maintenance schedule

Every 250 miles or weekly, whichever comes first

☐ Check the tyres and tyre pressures
☐ Check the wheel nut/bolt tightness
☐ Check the brake fluid level and condition
☐ Check the brake pedal "feel" and travel (master cylinder check)
☐ Check the brake servo, if equipped
☐ Check the operation of the brake lights and the brake warning light

Every 6000 miles or 6 months, or whichever comes first

☐ Check the front brakes
☐ Check the brake hoses and pipes

Every 12,000 miles or 12 months, whichever comes first

All items listed above, plus:
☐ Check the rear brakes
☐ Check and, if necessary, adjust the handbrake
☐ Check the brake pedal pivot bush and bracket

Every 30,000 miles or 2 years, whichever comes first

All items listed above, plus:
☐ Renew the brake fluid
☐ Check the master cylinder for leakage past the primary piston seals

Every 80,000 miles, or 5 years, whichever comes first

☐ Rebuild or renew the master cylinder, calipers and wheel cylinders (here's an item that most manufacturers don't specifically recommend, but it can prevent a myriad of problems. Master and wheel cylinder cups (seals) and caliper pistons and seals don't last forever, so to overhaul or renew them before they pose a problem makes sense).

3 Inspection and maintenance procedures

Preliminary checks

Tyres and tyre pressures

The first step in a brake system inspection should be of the tyre condition and pressures. If the tyres aren't inflated properly, or if they're in bad shape, there's no way the vehicle is going to stop in a straight line.

Check to see how much tread is left on the tyres. Tread wear can be monitored with a simple, inexpensive device known as a tread depth indicator (see illustration).

Note any abnormal tread wear. Tread pattern irregularities such as cupping, flat spots and more wear on one side than the other are indications of front end alignment and/or balance problems. If any of these conditions are noted, take the vehicle to a tyre specialist to correct the problem.

Look closely for cuts, punctures and embedded nails or tacks. Sometimes a tyre will hold air pressure for a short time or leak down very slowly after a nail has embedded itself in the tread. If a slow leak persists, check the valve stem core to make sure it's tight (see illustration). Examine the tread for an object that may have embedded itself in the tyre. If a puncture is suspected, it can be easily verified by spraying a solution of soapy water onto the puncture area (see

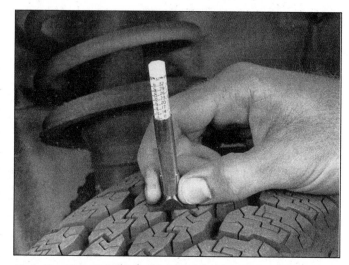

Use a tyre tread depth indicator to monitor tyre wear - they're widely available and inexpensive

If a tyre loses air on a steady basis, check the valve core first to make sure it's tight (special tools for doing this are also widely available and inexpensive)

If the valve core is tight, raise the corner of the vehicle with the low tyre and spray a soapy water solution onto the tread as the tyre is turned slowly - leaks will cause small bubbles to appear

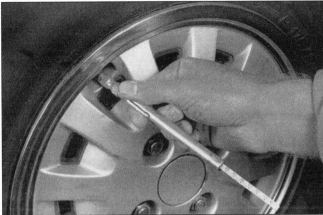

To extend tyre life, check the air pressure at least once a week with an accurate gauge (don't forget the spare!)

illustration). The soapy solution will bubble if there's a leak. Unless the puncture is unusually large, a tyre specialist can usually repair the tyre.

Carefully inspect the inner sidewall of each tyre for evidence of brake fluid leakage. If you see any, inspect the brake hoses, calipers and/or wheel cylinders immediately.

Correct air pressure adds miles to the lifespan of the tyres, improves fuel consumption and enhances overall ride quality. Tyre pressure cannot be accurately estimated by looking at a tyre, especially if it's a radial. A tyre pressure gauge is essential. Keep an accurate gauge in the vehicle. The pressure gauges attached to the nozzles of air lines at garages are often inaccurate.

Always check tyre pressure when the tyres are cold. Cold, in this case, means the vehicle has not been driven over a mile in the three hours preceding a tyre pressure check. A pressure rise of 0.2 to 0.5 bar is not uncommon once the tyres are warm.

Unscrew the valve cap protruding from the wheel or hubcap and push the gauge firmly onto the valve stem *(see illustration).* Note the reading on the gauge and compare the figure to the recommended tyre pressure shown on the sticker on the driver's side door pillar or in the owner's handbook. Be sure to refit the valve cap to keep dirt and moisture out of the valve stem mechanism. Check all four tyres and, if necessary, add enough air to bring them up to the recommended pressure.

Wheel nut (or bolt) tightness

Loose wheel nuts (or bolts) present a very hazardous situation. Not only is the wheel in danger of falling off, but the brakes won't operate correctly and the vehicle won't come to a straight stop. It will pull to one side or the other, the pedal will pulsate, and there's a good chance the vehicle will go out of control.

If the vehicle that you're working on is equipped with hubcaps, remove them. Using a wheel nut spanner or a

socket and a long extension bar, check the tightness of all of the wheel nuts or bolts. None of them should be able to be tightened more than 1/8-turn. All vehicles have an actual torque specification for their wheel nuts or bolts (refer to the appropriate Service and Repair Manual), but the important thing here is that none are loose.

If you find any wheel nuts that are loose, be sure to check the wheel studs for damage, and the holes in the wheel for elongation. If any of the studs are damaged, renew them (don't attempt to clean up the threads with a die or thread file). The same goes for lug bolts. If any of the holes in the wheel are elongated, renew the wheel.

Brake fluid

The brake master cylinder is mounted in the upper right of the engine compartment, near the bulkhead, on most vehicles. On some models it's located on the passenger side of the engine compartment.

The fluid inside can be checked after removing the cover or cap *(see illustrations).* Before removing the cover, be sure

On vehicles with this type of reservoir cover, prise the clip off the cover with a screwdriver

This master cylinder has two caps - each one must be removed to check the fluid level of both hydraulic circuits

The brake fluid level in master cylinders with translucent plastic reservoirs is easily checked - the fluid level should be kept near the MAX mark

to wipe the top of the reservoir with a clean rag to prevent contamination of the brake system.

When adding fluid, pour it carefully into the reservoir to avoid spilling it on surrounding painted surfaces. Vehicles with translucent plastic reservoirs usually have maximum and minimum level marks - it isn't necessary to remove the cover or cap to check the fluid level *(see illustration)*. Be sure to keep the fluid level within this range. On models with integral reservoirs, add fluid until the level is within 6 mm from the top *(see illustration)*.

Most vehicles on the road use DOT 3 approved brake fluid, but it would be a good idea to check your owner's handbook - some models (notably many Citroëns) use a type of mineral oil instead of brake fluid. Mixing the brake fluid with the mineral oil in one of these systems would destroy all of the rubber components in the hydraulic system and cause brake failure.

Warning: *Brake fluid can harm your eyes and damage painted surfaces, so use extreme caution when handling or pouring it. Do not use brake fluid that has been standing open or is more than one year old. Brake fluid absorbs*

moisture from the air. Excess moisture can cause a dangerous loss of brake performance, because the moisture in the fluid can boil. If you get any fluid in your eyes, immediately flush your eyes with water and seek medical attention.

At this time, the fluid and master cylinder can be inspected for contamination. The system should be drained and refilled if deposits, dirt particles or water droplets are seen in the fluid.

After filling the reservoir to the proper level, make sure the cover or cap is on tightly to prevent fluid leakage. Make sure the rubber diaphragm, if equipped, is in good condition.

If, upon checking the master cylinder fluid level, you discover one or both reservoirs empty or nearly empty, fill the reservoirs with brake fluid, bleed the system and check the entire hydraulic system for leaks (including behind the master cylinder).

Brake servo (vacuum-operated)

Begin the servo check by depressing the brake pedal several times with the engine off to deplete any vacuum.

Now, depress the pedal and start the engine. If the pedal goes down slightly, operation is normal *(see illustration)*. Release the brake pedal and let the engine run for a couple of minutes.

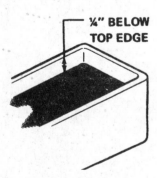

On master cylinders with integral, cast iron reservoirs, the brake fluid level should be kept at approximately 6 mm (1/4-inch) from the top

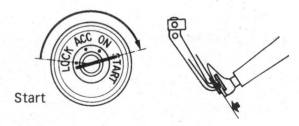

Push down on the brake pedal then start the engine - the brake pedal should go down slightly, indicating normal servo operation

Turn off the engine and depress the brake pedal several times slowly. If the pedal goes down farther the first time but gradually rises after the second or third depression, the servo is airtight (see illustration).

Start the engine and depress the brake pedal, then stop the engine with the pedal still depressed. If there is no change in the reserve distance (the distance between the pedal and the floor) after holding the pedal for about 30-seconds, the servo is airtight.

If the pedal feels "hard" when the engine is running, the servo isn't operating properly. Refer to Chapter 6 for more servo checking procedures.

Brake pedal freeplay, "feel," and travel (master cylinder check)

Using your hand, push down on the pedal and note how far the pedal travels until resistance is felt (see illustration). This is the pedal freeplay. It's important to have at least approximately 2 to 4 mm of freeplay, because this allows the pistons in the master cylinder to return to their at-rest positions when the brake pedal is released, ensuring that the compensating ports are uncovered and can equalise the pressure in the areas in front of the pistons.

Too much freeplay will result in a brake pedal that is too close to the floor under hard braking (it may even hit the floor). Generally, freeplay greater than 25 mm can be considered too much.

Pedal freeplay on some vehicles is adjusted at the master cylinder pushrod that protrudes from the servo. On other vehicles it's adjusted at the pushrod between the brake pedal and the servo.

If the vehicle is equipped with power brakes, start the engine. Slowly depress the brake pedal a few times. How does it feel? Is it firm or "spongy"? If it feels spongy or springy, chances are there's air in the hydraulic system, in which case it will be necessary to bleed the entire system (see Chapter 6). In addition, the entire system should be inspected for a fluid leak.

Now, with the engine still running, push the pedal down with a considerable amount of force. The pedal should come to a stop at some point and stay there. If the pedal slowly creeps towards the floor, check the entire hydraulic system for a fluid leak. If the pedal meets no resistance until it's 50 mm from the floor, there's a strong possibility that there's a problem with one of the hydraulic circuits. If there is no evidence of an external fluid leak, the seals in the master cylinder are bad, in which case it must be rebuilt or renewed. See Chapter 6 for master cylinder removal and refitting, as well as the overhaul procedure.

With the pedal firmly depressed, measure the distance between the pedal and the floor - this is the reserve distance (see illustration). This specification varies from vehicle to vehicle, but generally there should be at least 50 mm to spare. Any less than this and you run the risk of the pedal contacting the floor before the brakes are fully utilised.

Inadequate reserve distance can be caused by worn-out brake linings or by a problem in the hydraulic circuit.

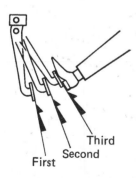

With the engine turned off, the pedal should build up with each pump if the servo is functioning properly

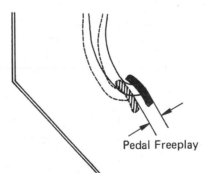

There must be at least 2 to 4 mm of freeplay in the brake pedal - if not, the master cylinder pistons won't be able to return all the way, which could result in a low pedal (because the pressure chambers in front of the pistons wouldn't fill up completely)

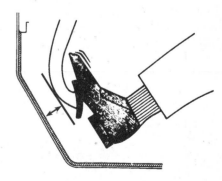

With your foot firmly pushing on the brake pedal, measure the distance between the bottom of the pedal and the floor (you may need an assistant) - there should be at least 50 mm of reserve travel left

Brake warning light

The brake warning light on the instrument panel rarely fails, but it is a very important component of the brake system. Although in service it will usually come on only when you're in the midst of a braking problem, it can warn you of some problems before they become catastrophic.

On some models the brake warning light doubles as the "handbrake on" warning light. Refer to the owner's handbook for your vehicle for details of brake warning light operation, including checking procedures if appropriate.

Some vehicles have float-operated switches in their master cylinder reservoirs. If the fluid level drops below a certain level, the switch will complete the circuit and turn the warning light on. If your vehicle is like this, make sure the fluid is at the proper level.

Another type of warning light is operated by a switch which senses a pressure difference in the brake hydraulic circuits. If this type of light comes on, it indicates that there may be air or a leak in one half of the hydraulic system. Check the entire system for leaks.

If the light doesn't come on when it should, check the fuses. If they're all OK, check the bulb. If there's still a problem, it must be in the switch or in the wiring.

Brake lights

Have an assistant stand behind the vehicle while you depress the brake pedal. All of the brake lights should come on (on some vehicles the ignition key must be turned to the On position). If any bulbs are burned out, renew them.

If none of the lights come on, refer to Chapter 8 for further diagnosis.

Front brakes

Since your front brakes do most of the work, you should inspect them twice as often as the rear. Before removing the wheels, however, the wheel bearings should be checked for proper adjustment. Loose wheel bearings can cause a host of problems, such as inconsistent pedal travel, brake chatter, pedal pulsation, and the vehicle pulling to one side or the other when the brakes are applied. For this inspection, refer to the section titled "Wheel bearing, check, repack and adjustment." Take note, however, that not all wheel bearings are adjustable - some are sealed units which will require renewal if the bearings are sloppy. This includes the front hub bearings on front-wheel drive vehicles.

Drum brakes

If your vehicle is equipped with front drum brakes, refer to the section referenced in the previous paragraph ("Wheel bearing check, repack and adjustment") to remove the hub nut, then slide the drum off. If it won't come off, the shoes have probably begun to wear ridges into the drum and will have to be retracted. For this procedure and the remainder of the drum brake inspection, refer to the Drum brakes inspection procedure, under Rear brakes, since the procedure is the same as for rear drum brakes. When the inspection is complete, refit the drum and wheel bearings and adjust the bearings as

described in the aforementioned section. **Note:** *Be sure to clean, inspect and repack the bearings if they appear somewhat dry, dirty, or if it has been more than 20,000 miles since the last time they were packed. Also, adjust the brake shoes as described in the section entitled Drum brake adjustment.*

While the wheels are off, be sure to check the brake hoses as described later in this Chapter.

Wheel bearing check, repack and adjustment

Note: *The wheel bearing repack and adjustment portions of this procedure do not apply to vehicles with sealed bearings or to the front axle of front-wheel drive or four-wheel drive vehicles, nor to the rear axle on vehicles with heavy-duty (full-floating) rear axles. If your vehicle falls into any of these categories, consult the appropriate Haynes Service and Repair Manual.*

In most cases the front wheel bearings will not need servicing until the brake pads are changed. However, the bearings should be checked whenever the front of the vehicle is raised for any reason.

Check

Chock the wheels at the opposite end of the vehicle being inspected, raise the appropriate end of the vehicle and support it securely on axle stands placed under the frame rails, subframe or the seam below the sills where the body is mated with the floorpan (Check in the Owners Handbook or Service and Repair Manual). Spin each wheel and check for noise, rolling resistance and freeplay.

Grasp the top of each tyre with one hand and the bottom with the other *(see illustration)*. Move the wheel in-and-out on the spindle. If there's any noticeable movement, the bearings should be checked and then repacked with grease or renewed if necessary. **Note:** *In the case of vehicles with sealed bearing assemblies, the bearings aren't adjustable. Some sealed bearings are integral with the wheel hub, requiring renewal of the entire hub. Others have the sealed bearing assembly pressed into the hub.*

Grasp the roadwheel top and bottom and check for bearing wear by trying to rock the wheel

Dislodge the dust cap by working around the outer circumference with a hammer and chisel

Remove the split pin and discard it - use a new one when the nut is refitted

Repack

Warning: *The dust created by the brake system may contain asbestos, which is harmful to your health. Never blow it out with compressed air and don't inhale any of it. An approved filtering mask should be worn when working on the brakes. Do not, under any circumstances, use petroleum-based solvents to clean brake parts. Use brake system cleaner only!*

Note: *This procedure applies to adjustable wheel bearing assemblies on the front wheels of rear-wheel drive vehicles and the rear wheels of front-wheel drive vehicles.*

Remove the wheel. You'll probably have to lower the vehicle to slacken the wheel nuts (or bolts). After that, raise the vehicle and support it on axle stands once again.

If the wheel you're working on is equipped with a disc brake, remove the brake caliper (see Chapter 2) and hang it out of the way on a piece of wire. A wood block can be slid between the brake pads to keep them separated, if necessary.

Prise the dust cap out of the hub using a screwdriver or hammer and chisel *(see illustration)*.

Straighten the bent ends of the split pin, then pull the split pin out of the nut lock *(see illustration)*. Discard the split pin and use a new one during reassembly.

Remove the nut lock, nut and washer from the end of the spindle *(see illustration)*.

Pull the hub/disc or drum assembly out slightly, then push it back into its original position. This should force the outer bearing off the spindle enough so it can be removed.

Pull the hub/disc or drum assembly off the spindle. If you're working on a drum brake and the drum won't pull off, the brake shoes will have to be retracted. Refer to the shoe retraction procedure described in the Drum brakes subheading under the Rear brakes section.

Use a screwdriver to prise the seal out of the rear of the hub *(see illustration)*. As this is done, note how the seal is refitted.

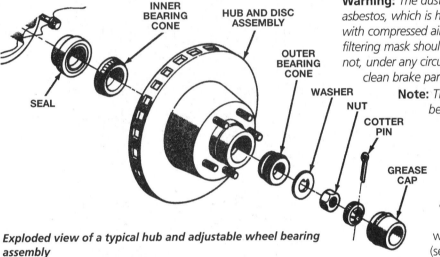

INNER BEARING CONE

HUB AND DISC ASSEMBLY

OUTER BEARING CONE

WASHER

NUT

COTTER PIN

SEAL

GREASE CAP

Exploded view of a typical hub and adjustable wheel bearing assembly

Use a large screwdriver to prise out the seal from the rear of the hub

Remove the inner wheel bearing from the hub.

Use solvent to remove all traces of the old grease from the bearings, hub and spindle. A small brush may prove helpful; however make sure no bristles from the brush embed themselves inside the bearing rollers. Allow the parts to air dry.

Carefully inspect the bearings for cracks, heat discolouration, worn rollers, etc. Check the bearing races inside the hub for wear and damage. If the bearing races are defective, the hubs should be taken to a workshop with the facilities to remove the old races and press new ones in. Note that the bearings and races come as matched sets and old bearings should never be fitted on new races.

Use high-temperature wheel bearing grease to pack the bearings. Work the grease completely into the bearings, forcing it between the rollers, cone and cage from the back side (see illustration).

Apply a thin coat of grease to the spindle at the outer bearing seat, inner bearing seat, shoulder and seal seat.

Put a small quantity of grease inboard of each bearing race inside the hub. Using your finger, form a dam at these points to provide extra grease availability and to keep thinned grease from flowing out of the bearing.

Place the grease-packed inner bearing into the rear of the hub and put a little more grease outboard of the bearing.

Place a new seal over the inner bearing and tap the seal evenly into place with a hammer and blunt punch until it's flush with the hub.

Carefully place the hub assembly onto the spindle and push the grease-packed outer bearing into position.

Adjustment

Note: *This is a general procedure which applies to most adjustable wheel bearing assemblies on the front wheels of rear-wheel drive vehicles and the rear wheels of front-wheel drive vehicles.*

Refit the washer and spindle nut. Tighten the nut only slightly (no more than 15 Nm).

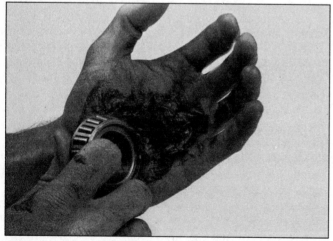

Work grease into the bearing rollers by pressing it against the palm of your hand (wear gloves!)

Spin the hub in a forward direction while tightening the spindle nut to approximately 24 Nm to seat the bearings and remove any grease or burrs which could cause excessive bearing play later.

Loosen the spindle nut 1/4-turn, then using your hand (not a spanner of any kind), tighten the nut until it's snug. Refit the nut lock and a new split pin through the hole in the spindle and the slots in the nut lock. If the nut lock slots don't line up, remove the nut lock and turn it slightly until they do. Ideally, when the wheel bearings are properly adjusted there should be no play in the bearings, but no preload either. You should be able to push the washer under the lock nut back and forth with a screwdriver (without prising), but you shouldn't be able to feel any slop in the bearing. **Note:** *If you do feel some play in the bearing, tighten the hub nut a little more than hand-tight, but don't exceed 4 Nm of preload. If there's still play, the wheel bearings may be excessively worn.*

Bend the ends of the split pin until they're flat against the nut. Cut off any extra length which could interfere with the dust cap.

Refit the dust cap, tapping it into place with a hammer.

On models with disc brakes, place the brake caliper near the disc and carefully remove the wood spacer. Refit the caliper (see Chapter 2).

Refit the wheel on the hub and tighten the wheel nuts/bolts.

Grasp the top and bottom of the tyre and check the bearings in the manner described earlier.

Lower the vehicle.

Disc brakes

Warning: *The dust created by the brake system may contain asbestos, which is harmful to your health. Never blow it out with compressed air and don't inhale any of it. An approved filtering mask should be worn when working on the brakes. Do not, under any circumstances, use petroleum-based solvents to clean brake parts. Use brake system cleaner only!*

Disc brakes are used on the front wheels of most vehicles. Extensive disc damage can occur if the pads are not renewed when needed.

Loosen the wheel nuts/bolts, raise the front of the vehicle and support it securely on axle stands placed under the frame rails, subframe or the seam below the sills where the body is mated with the floorpan (Check in your Owners Handbook or Service and Repair Manual). If not already done, chock the wheels at the opposite end of the vehicle to prevent it from rolling. The disc brake calipers, which contain the pads, are visible with the wheels removed. There is an outer pad and an inner pad in each caliper. All pads should be inspected.

Before inspecting the brakes, position a drain pan under the brake assembly, clean the entire brake with brake system cleaner and allow it to dry.

Most calipers have a "window" or opening to inspect the

Look through the caliper inspection window to inspect the brake pads (arrowed)

The pad lining which rubs against the disc (arrowed) can also be inspected by looking at each end of the caliper

pads. Check the thickness of the pad lining by looking into the caliper at each end and down through the inspection window at the top of the housing *(see illustrations)*. If the pad material has worn to the manufacturer's minimum recommended thickness, the pads should be renewed. Ideally, the pads should be changed before they become that thin. Some pads are equipped with metal wear sensors, consisting of a small, bent piece of metal which is attached to the backing plate of one of the brake pads. When the pad wears down to its specified limit, the metal sensor rubs against the disc and makes a squealing sound *(see illustration)*. If your vehicle is equipped with such sensors, and the tips of the sensors are nearing the disc surface, you might as well go ahead and renew the brake pads.

If you're unsure about the exact thickness of the remaining lining material, remove the pads for further inspection or renewal (see Chapter 2).

Make sure the caliper mounting bolts, guide pins or retaining plates (depending on caliper design) are secure. Also check the tightness of the caliper mounting (or anchor) bracket fasteners, if equipped.

Check around the area of the caliper piston bore(s) for wetness, which would indicate a leaking piston seal. On fixed calipers, check around the transfer tube fittings (if equipped) or at the seam where the caliper halves mate. If the caliper is leaking, refer to Chapter 6 and rebuild or renew the calipers.

If the brake pedal has been pulsating, the discs are probably warped. Refer to Chapter 2 and measure the disc runout with a dial indicator.

Before refitting the wheels, check for leakage and/or damage (cracks, splitting, etc.) around the brake hoses and connections, as described later in this Chapter.

Check the condition of the disc as described in Chapter 2.

The brake pad wear indicator (arrowed) will contact the disc and make a squealing noise when the pad is worn out

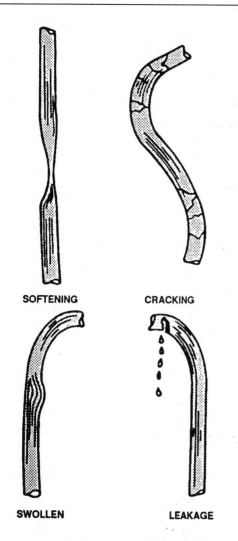

SOFTENING   **CRACKING**

SWOLLEN   **LEAKAGE**

Here are some samples of common brake hose defects

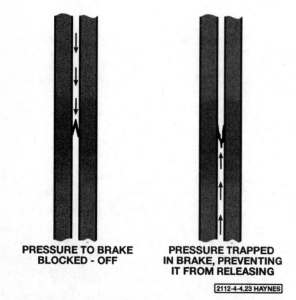

PRESSURE TO BRAKE BLOCKED - OFF

PRESSURE TRAPPED IN BRAKE, PREVENTING IT FROM RELEASING

2112-4-4.23 HAYNES

An internally split hose can be very difficult to diagnose

Brake hoses and pipes

About every six months, with the vehicle raised and supported securely on axle stands, the rubber hoses which connect the steel brake pipes with the front and rear brake assemblies should be inspected for cracks, chafing of the outer cover, leaks, blisters and other damage *(see illustration)*. These are important and vulnerable parts of the brake system and inspection should be complete. A light and mirror will be helpful for a thorough check. If a hose exhibits any of the above conditions, renew it.

Internally split brake hoses

Some of the trickiest brake problems to diagnose are caused by internally split brake hoses. This malady can restrict pressure from reaching a brake, or it can act like a one-way valve and cause the brake to lock up *(see illustration)*. This is not a common problem, and mostly affects older vehicles with neglected brake systems. It can also be caused by clamping a brake hose shut with locking pliers - something that should never be done.

If you're faced with a brake that won't release, which may be characterised by the vehicle pulling to one side or an overheated brake, open the bleed screw on that particular caliper or wheel cylinder. If the disc or drum now turns, suspect an internally split hose. Renew the hose and bleed the system (see Chapter 6).

Conversely, if one brake (or both rear brakes on models with a solid rear axle) will not apply but the rest do, there are two possibilities - a "seized" caliper (or wheel cylinder), or an internally split hose that refuses to pass fluid. Attach a bleed hose to the bleed screw on the brake that won't apply. Have an assistant depress the brake pedal while you crack open the bleed screw. If fluid flows out the bleed hose, the brake hose is OK - the caliper or wheel cylinder is malfunctioning. If no fluid flows out of the bleed hose, follow the brake hose to where it meets the metal brake pipe. Disconnect the pipe and have your helper push the brake pedal - if fluid squirts from the pipe, the problem is an internally split brake hose. Renew the hose and bleed the system.

The metal brake pipes should also be inspected. While they aren't subjected to the same punishment that the brake hoses are, they're still fair game to objects thrown up from the tyres, to vibration, and rust. Make sure all of the metal clips securing the pipes are in place. Check the pipes for twists, dents, crimping and kinks *(see illustration)*. Make sure none of the pipes travel too close to any hot or moving parts. If you find a damaged section of pipe, it should be renewed with a genuine factory renewal part, or equivalent, with the pipes pre-bent and the fittings already in place. Never attempt to repair a brake pipe with rubber hose, and never use substandard materials to fabricate a pipe. Brake pipes are made of high-quality seamless, double-thickness steel tubing. They are coated (usually with a copper-lead alloy) to prevent corrosion.

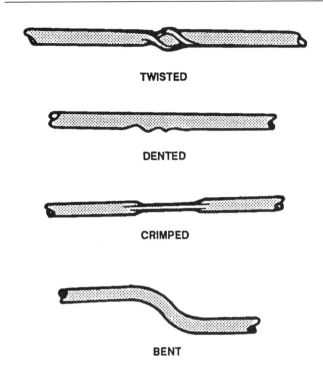

TWISTED

DENTED

CRIMPED

BENT

Typical metal brake pipe defects

Rear brakes

If you're working on a front-wheel drive vehicle, it's a good idea to check the rear wheel bearing adjustment before proceeding with the brake check. See the section entitled "Wheel bearing check, repack and adjustment" for this procedure.

Disc brakes

If your vehicle is fortunate enough to be equipped with rear disc brakes, refer to the disc brake inspection procedure under the Front brakes subheading. The procedures are identical.

Drum brakes

Warning: *The dust created by the brake system may contain asbestos, which is harmful to your health. Never blow it out with compressed air and don't inhale any of it. An approved*

filtering mask should be worn when working on the brakes. Do not, under any circumstances, use petroleum-based solvents to clean brake parts. Use brake system cleaner only!

Loosen the wheel nuts or bolts, raise the vehicle and support it securely on axle stands placed under the frame rails, subframe, the seam below the sills where the body is mated with the floorpan (refer to your Owners Handbook or Service and Repair Manual). If not already done, chock the wheels at the opposite end of the vehicle to prevent it from rolling. Release the handbrake.

Some vehicles are equipped with a rubber plug in the brake backing plate (or in the drum on some models) near the edge of the drum. When removed, the brake shoe lining is visible through the hole *(see illustration)*. This is sufficient for a quick check of the brake shoes, but for a thorough check, the drums must be removed.

Remove the brake drum. If you're working on the rear brakes of a front-wheel drive vehicle, or on a vehicle with front drum brakes, and the drum is integral with the hub, refer to the section entitled "Wheel bearing check, repack and adjustment" for the removal procedure. If the hubs on your vehicle are sealed, but retained by a lock nut, remove the nut and discard it (a new one should be used upon reassembly). If the drum is not integral with the hub, remove it by pulling it off the axle and brake assembly. **Note:** *Some brake drums are retained to the axle flange by two or three small screws.* If this proves difficult, make sure the handbrake is released, then squirt penetrating oil around the centre hub area and around the wheel studs. Allow the oil to soak in and try to pull the drum off again.

If the drum still cannot be pulled off, the brake shoes will have to be retracted. This is done by first removing the small rubber plug from the backing plate or brake drum. On some vehicles there is a cut-out in the backing plate or drum instead of a plug. If this is the case, knock the cut-out portion out with a hammer and chisel *(see illustration)* (you'll

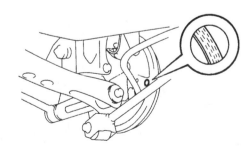

Some vehicles are equipped with holes in the backing plate (or in the brake drums) that allow you to view the brake lining thickness

Use a hammer and a chisel to remove the plug from the brake backing plate or brake drum

Push the self-adjusting lever aside and turn the star wheel

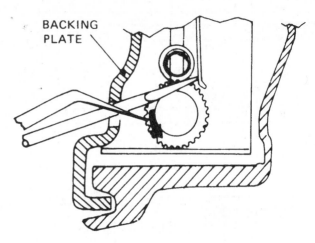

BACKING PLATE

Here's a cut-away view of the retracting procedure. The screwdriver is pushing the adjusting lever off the star wheel, while the adjusting tool (another screwdriver) turns the start wheel to reduce the length of the adjusting screw. This allows the shoes to move away from the drum, providing clearance for drum removal

retrieve it after the drum has been removed). **Note:** *Rubber plugs are available from a dealer service department or car accessory shop - be sure to fit one in the hole when you're done.*

With the plug removed, insert a thin screwdriver and lift or push the adjusting lever off the star wheel, then use an adjusting tool or screwdriver to back off the star wheel several turns *(see illustrations)*. This will move the brake shoes away from the drum. If the drum still won't pull off, tap around its inner circumference with a soft-face hammer.

With the drum removed, do not touch any brake dust (see the Warning at the beginning of this Section). Position a drain pan under the brake assembly, clean the entire brake with brake system cleaner and allow it to dry.

Observe the thickness of the lining material on both brake shoes. If the material has worn away to within 1.0 mm of

the recessed rivets or metal backing, the shoes should be renewed *(see illustrations)*. The shoes should also be renewed if they're cracked, glazed (shiny surface) or contaminated with brake fluid, grease or gear oil.

Make sure that all the brake assembly springs are connected and in good condition.

Check the brake components for any signs of fluid leakage. If the brake linings are wet, identify the source of the fluid. If it's gear oil, the rear axle seal is leaking and must be renewed. Carefully prise back the rubber dust boots on the wheel cylinders located between the brake shoes *(see*

The lining thickness of a brake shoe with bonded linings is measured from the outer surface of the lining to the metal shoe - be sure to check both ends and in the centre

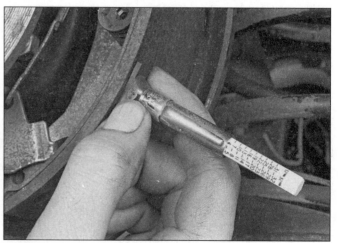

A tyre tread depth gauge works well for measuring the thickness or the remaining material on brake shoes with riveted linings

Carefully peel the wheel cylinder boot back and check for leaking fluid - any leakage indicates the cylinder must be replaced or overhauled

illustration). Any leakage is an indication that the wheel cylinders should be overhauled immediately (see Chapter 6). Check the brake hoses and connections for signs of leakage.

Clean the inside of the drum with brake system cleaner. Again, be careful not to breathe the dangerous asbestos dust.

Check the inside of the drum for cracks, score marks, deep scratches and hard spots, which will appear as small discolourations. If these imperfections cannot be removed with fine emery cloth, the drum must be taken to a engineering workshop equipped to resurface the drums.

If, after the inspection process all parts are in good working condition, refit the brake drum. If it was necessary to retract the brake shoes to get the drum off, adjust the brake shoes (see the section on drum brake adjustment). If your vehicle has sealed hubs retained by a locknut, tighten the nut securely (preferably you should consult a Haynes Service and Repair Manual that covers your particular vehicle).

Refit the wheels and lower the vehicle.

Drum brake adjustment

Most drum brakes are equipped with self-adjusters but some (mainly on older vehicles) are not, and will need periodic adjustment to compensate for wear. Even the brake shoes on self-adjusting drum brakes have to be adjusted when they are first fitted. This is because the self-adjusters maintain a specified clearance between the brake shoe lining and the drum, but won't compensate for a large gap (not until after many applications of the footbrake or handbrake, depending on design). Brakes that are out of adjustment will result a low pedal condition and can also cause the vehicle to pull to one side or the other when the brakes are applied.

Loosen the wheel nuts or bolts, raise the vehicle and support it securely on axle stands placed under the frame rails, subframe, the seam below the sills where the body is mated with the floorpan (refer to your Owners Handbook or Service and Repair Manual). If not already done, chock the wheels at the opposite end of the vehicle to prevent it from rolling. Release the handbrake if you're adjusting rear drum brakes.

Remove the adjustment hole plug(s) in the brake backing plate or drum, if applicable. Rotate the wheel and make sure that the handbrake isn't causing any brake drag. If there is any drag, back off the handbrake adjusting nut. Using a screwdriver or brake adjusting tool used in the correct location, turn the adjuster star wheel or the adjuster screw until the drum is locked in place *(see illustrations)*. Some brakes (leading/leading shoe brakes [see Chapter 1]) have two adjusters. If you are working on one of these kinds of brakes, adjust the shoes one at a time.

Now, back-off the star wheel or adjuster screw eight to ten notches, or just to the point where the drum rotates freely without the brake shoes dragging (if the shoes are allowed to drag they may get too hot and expand, causing the drum to bind). To accomplish this it will be necessary to disengage the adjusting lever from the star wheel by inserting a thin screwdriver through the hole in the backing plate or drum, pushing or pulling the lever off the star wheel

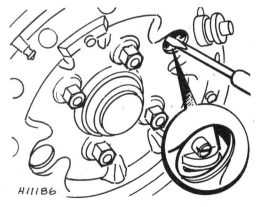

On some older vehicles, the adjuster is slotted and can be turned with a screwdriver - this turns an eccentric which spreads the shoes apart (or conversely, allows them to retract)

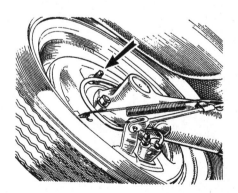

Other older vehicles also use eccentric adjusters, but the adjuster screw is a square-drive affair protruding from the backing plate (Austin Metro)

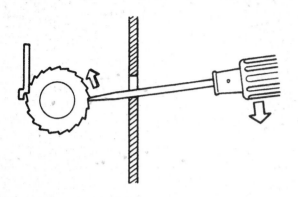

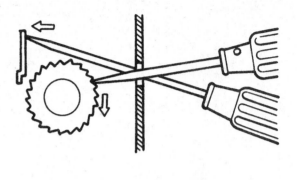

Here's the most common kind of adjuster set-up. Insert a screwdriver through the hole in the backplate (or brake drum) and turn the adjuster star wheel until the brake shoes drag on the drum ...

... then, using another screwdriver or adjusting tool, push (or pull) the lever off the adjuster wheel and back it off 8 to 10 clicks

(see illustrations). **Note:** *Leading/leading shoe brakes don't have adjuster levers - simply turn the star wheel in the other direction to back-off the shoes.*

If necessary, adjust the handbrake as described later in this Chapter.

Refit the wheels and lower the vehicle.

Handbrake

The handbrake or parking brake is lever, pullrod or pedal operated and, on most vehicles, is self-adjusting through the automatic adjusters in the rear brake drums (a very few manufacturers place the handbrake on the front wheels). However, supplementary adjustment may be needed in the event of cable stretch, wear in the linkage or after fitting of new components.

Check

Check the entire length of each handbrake cable for wear,

fraying, rust, kinks, etc. Apply multi-purpose grease to all friction areas and to the adjuster screw(s)

Many vehicles have a specification as to how many clicks the handbrake lever or pedal is supposed to ratchet, but the most obvious method to check the adjustment of the handbrake is to park the vehicle on a hill or on a steep driveway, apply the handbrake and place the transmission in Neutral (be sure to stay in the car during this check). The lever or pedal should ratchet anywhere between five and eight clicks or so. If the vehicle rolls, the handbrake should be adjusted.

Adjustment

If your handbrake is lever-actuated, look through the slot in the centre console or peel back the boot and look for the end(s) of the handbrake cable(s) and the adjusting nut(s). If your vehicle has this set-up, apply the handbrake two clicks and tighten the nut until the handbrake lever travel is within reason *(see illustration)*. It may be necessary to remove the centre console for access to the nut(s). If there are two cables, tighten each nut equally. If the handbrake is pullrod-actuated, look up under the dash for a wingnut-type adjuster *(see illustration)*. On other models, the equaliser (the point where the front cable meets the rear cables) is

On some vehicles, the handbrake cable is adjusted at the lever

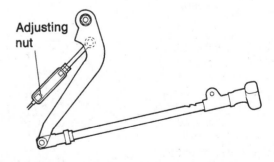

Adjusting nut

On some vehicles with pullrod-actuated handbrakes, the adjuster is located up under the dash

The handbrake adjuster on this vehicle is located beneath the centre console - once the console has been removed, the handbrake can be adjusted by tightening this nut (arrowed) at the equaliser

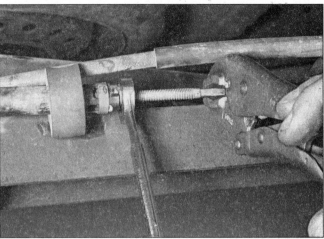

In this arrangement, then handbrake cable is located at the rear of the vehicle, where the left and right cables meet - to adjust, hold the threaded rod with a pair of pliers and turn the adjusting nut

located under the centre console, which will require removal of the console *(see illustration)*. Raise the rear of the vehicle, support it securely on axle stands and release the handbrake. Turn the wheels to confirm that the brakes are not dragging.

On many cars and vans the adjuster is located under the vehicle. Raise the rear of the vehicle (or the front on vehicles with the handbrake on the front wheels) until the wheels are clear of the earth, support it securely on axle stands and block the front wheels. Release the handbrake pedal or lever.

Locate the handbrake equaliser. Hold the rod from turning with locking pliers, then loosen the locknut, if equipped, and tighten the adjuster nut *(see illustrations)* until a slight drag is felt when the rear wheels are turned. **Note:** *If the threads appear rusty, apply penetrating oil before attempting adjustment.*

Loosen the adjuster nut until there's no longer any drag when the rear wheels are turned, then loosen the cable adjusting nut an additional two turns.

Tighten the locknut, then apply and release the handbrake several times. Confirm that the brakes do not drag. Lower the vehicle to the earth.

Handbrake shoe adjustment (vehicles with rear disc brakes containing a drum style handbrake)

This kind of handbrake set-up is almost identical to a full-size service drum brake assembly, only smaller, and its actuation is not hydraulic, but mechanical. It even has an adjuster screw with a star wheel. To adjust the shoes on this kind of handbrake (which will almost never need adjustment, unless you occasionally forget to release the handbrake before driving) refer to the section entitled "Drum brake adjustment."

On this type of handbrake cable equaliser, simply hold the threaded rod stationary and turn the nut to adjust the cable

Brake pedal and bracket

Rarely do problems develop in this area, but when they do they have the potential to be very serious. Therefore, it's a good idea to crawl under the dash periodically and inspect the pedal pivot and the support bracket.

Working under the dash, grasp the pedal and wiggle it from side-to-side. If there's any slop in the pedal bushes, the bushes should be renewed **(see illustration overleaf)** (refer to the appropriate Service and Repair Manual).

Also, be sure to check the pedal for distortion and fatigue.

Brake fluid renewal

Dirty, contaminated, moisture-laden fluid will deteriorate brake system components and, besides leaks, can cause dangerous problems like boiling fluid and loss of braking pressure.

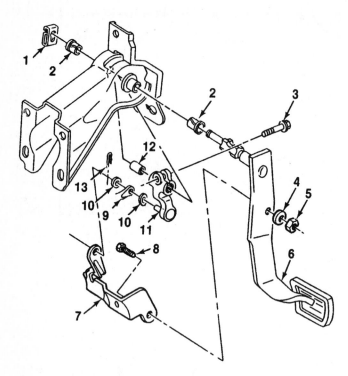

Typical brake pedal mounting details

1 Retaining clip
2 Bush
3 Pinch bolt
4 Washer
5 Nut
6 Brake pedal
7 Actuator

8 Bolt
9 Pushrod
10 Washer
11 Actuator lever
12 Spacer
13 Retaining clip

To renew the fluid in your hydraulic system, simply bleed the brakes at each wheel until clean, clear brake fluid flows out. If performed at the interval specified, this method is sufficient.

Master cylinder seal check

Unbolt the master cylinder (without disconnecting the pipes), pull it forward off the servo or bulkhead and check for leakage. You won't find this item on any manufacturer's maintenance schedule, but leaks can develop in the master cylinder and fluid can escape past the secondary cup or O-ring of the primary piston. This can go unnoticed for a long time. The dropping fluid level may at first be mistaken for normal brake pad wear, when in actuality it is leaking into the servo (which will damage the servo) or onto the floor in the driver's footwell (which will damage the driver's shoes).

Rebuild or renew the master cylinder if you find leakage (see Chapter 6).

Rebuild or renew the hydraulic cylinders (master cylinder, calipers and/or wheel cylinders)

This is a maintenance item that isn't recommended by all manufacturers. You might even think it sounds like a waste of money and time. But, it's a sure way to know that your hydraulic components are in top shape. Brake pads and shoes are easy to check, and you can gauge how they are wearing just by looking at them. You can't see inside of a master cylinder or caliper, though, so you really don't know what kind of shape they're in. Refer to Chapter 6 for the rebuilding or renewal procedures.

Reference

Glossary

A

ABS: Anti-lock Brake System.

Accumulator: A vessel that stores hydraulic fluid under pressure.

Adapter: See Caliper mounting bracket.

Air-suspended servo: A type of brake servo that contains atmospheric pressure in both chambers of the servo when the brake pedal is at rest. When the pedal is applied, the front chamber is opened to manifold/pump vacuum, causing the diaphragm of the servo to move toward the master cylinder which assists the driver in the application of the brakes.

Anaerobic locking compounds: Anaerobic locking compounds are used to keep fasteners from vibrating or working loose and cure only after refitting, in the absence of air. Medium strength locking compound is used for small nuts, bolts and screws that may be removed later. High-strength locking compound is for large nuts, bolts and studs which aren't removed on a regular basis.

Anchor: The stationary portion of a leading/trailing drum brake on which the heels of the brake shoes ride.

Anchor plate: See Caliper mounting bracket.

Anchor pin: The stationary portion of a duo-servo drum brake on which the tops of the brake shoes rest. The secondary shoe bears against the anchor pin when the brakes are applied and the vehicle is moving forward. Conversely, when the vehicle is reversing and the brakes are applied, the primary shoe bears against it.

Anti-lock brake system: A brake control system that monitors the rotational speeds of the wheels and reduces hydraulic pressure to any wheel it senses locking up.

Anti-seize compound: Anti-seize compound prevents seizing, galling, cold welding, rust and corrosion in fasteners. High-temperature anti-seize, usually made with copper and graphite lubricants. Often known as 'Copperslip'.

Arcing: A process where the brake shoes are ground to the proper curvature for the drums they are to be used with. Modern brake shoes are pre-arced.

Asbestos: A fibrous mineral used in the composition of brake friction materials. Asbestos is a health hazard and the dust created by brake systems should never be inhaled or ingested.

Asbestosis: An incurable lung disease caused by the inhalation of asbestos fibres.

Automatic adjusters: Brake adjusters that are actuated by the application of the handbrake or by normal brake operation, to compensate for lining wear.

B

Backing plate: The part of a drum brake to which the wheel cylinder(s) and the brake shoes are attached.

Banjo fitting: A type of hydraulic fitting, shaped like a banjo, through which a hollow bolt passes, allowing fluid transfer from a hydraulic line to a hydraulic component.

Bleed screw: The hollow screw that is loosened to open a bleed valve, allowing fluid and air bubbles to pass through during a bleeding procedure.

Reference

Bleed valve: A valve on a wheel cylinder, caliper or other hydraulic component that is opened to purge the hydraulic system of air.

Bonded linings: Brake linings that are affixed to the shoe or backing plate with high-temperature adhesive and cured under pressure and heat.

Brake adjuster: A mechanism used to adjust the clearance between the brake linings and the brake drum.

Brake balance: The ratio of front-to-rear braking force.

Brake caliper: The component of a disc brake that converts hydraulic pressure into mechanical energy.

Brake disc: The component of a disc brake that rotates with the wheels and is squeezed by the brake caliper and pads, which creates friction and converts the energy of the moving vehicle into heat.

Brake drum: The component of a drum brake that rotates with the wheel and is acted upon by the expanding brake shoes, which creates friction and converts the energy of the moving vehicle into heat.

Brake dust: The dust created as the brake linings wear down in normal use. Brake dust usually contains dangerous amounts of asbestos.

Brake fade: The partial or complete loss of braking power which results when the brakes are overheated and can no longer generate friction.

Brake lathe: The machine used to resurface the friction surfaces of brake discs or drums.

Brake lines: The rigid steel and flexible rubber hoses composing the portion of the hydraulic system that transfers brake fluid from the master cylinder to the calipers and/or wheel cylinders.

Brake lining: The friction material that is either riveted or bonded to the brake backing plates or brake pads.

Brake pads: The components of a disc brake assembly that are surfaced with brake lining and clamped against the brake disc to generate friction.

Brake shoes: The components of a drum brake assembly that are surfaced with brake lining and forced against the brake drum to generate friction.

Brake system cleaner: Brake system cleaner removes grease and brake fluid from brake parts like disc brake rotors, where a spotless surfaces is essential. It leaves no residue and often eliminates brake squeal caused by brake dust or other contaminants. Because it leaves no residue, brake cleaner is often used for cleaning other parts as well.

Breather port: The small passage between the master cylinder fluid reservoir and the area behind the primary cups of the pistons. This port allows fluid from the reservoir to fill the area behind the primary cups of the pistons, preventing a vacuum from being formed behind the cups when the brakes are applied, which prevents air bubbles from travelling around the lips of the primary cups as the brakes are released.

Bridge bolts: High-strength bolts used to fasten together the halves of a split brake caliper.

Bulkhead: The partition between the passenger compartment and the engine compartment. Sometimes referred to as a firewall.

Burnish: The process of "running-in" new brake pads or shoes so the linings conform to the disc or drum friction surfaces.

C

Caliper: See Brake caliper.

Caliper mounting bracket: The component that connects a brake caliper to the steering knuckle, hub carrier or rear axle.

Cam: An eccentric shaped device mounted on a shaft that raises and lowers the component in contact with it. Some brake adjuster designs use a cam (or cams) to set the clearance between the brake shoes and the brake drum.

Clevis: A U-shaped device with a pin or bolt passing through it used for attaching the master cylinder or servo pushrod to the brake pedal. Clevises are sometimes used in other parts of the brake system, for instance for attaching the handbrake cable to the handbrake lever at the rear brakes.

Coefficient of friction: A numerical value indicating the amount of work required to slide one surface against another. The coefficient of friction equals the side force acting on the object divided by the weight of the object.

Combination valve: A hydraulic valve usually incorporating a pressure differential warning switch, a metering valve and a proportioning valve. Not all combination valves contain all of these control valves.

Compensating port: The small passage between the master cylinder fluid reservoir and the pressure chamber (the area in front of the primary seals of both pistons) that allows fluid to flow in or out as necessary, depending on requirements.

Component Anti-lock Brake System: A type of Anti-lock Brake System in which the hydraulic control unit is not part of the master cylinder/power servo assembly.

Crocus cloth: A very fine abrasive paper

Cup: A type of lip seal used on hydraulic pistons.

D

Degreasers: Degreasers are heavy-duty solvents used to remove grease from the outside of the engine and from chassis components. They're usually sprayed or brushed on. Depending on the type, they're rinsed off either with water or solvent. **Warning**: *Never wash brake system components with petroleum-based solvents.*

Diaphragm: A flexible partition used to separate two chambers or elements.

Discard diameter: The diameter at which a worn brake drum should be renewed.

Discard thickness: The thickness at which a worn brake disc should be renewed.

Disc: See Brake disc.

Disc brake: A brake design incorporating a flat, disc-like rotor onto which brake pads containing lining material are squeezed, generating friction and converting the energy of a moving vehicle into heat.

Dished brake disc: A disc that has worn thinner at the inner part of its friction surface. This is an abnormal form of wear.

Double anchor drum brake: See Leading/trailing drum brake.

Drum brake: A brake design incorporating a drum with brake shoes inside that expand to contact the drum, creating friction and converting the energy of the moving vehicle into heat.

Dual circuit brake system: A brake hydraulic system composed of two separate hydraulic circuits.

Duo-servo drum brake: A type of self-energising drum brake that has servo action in both forward and reverse.

Dust boot: A rubber diaphragm-like seal that fits over the end of a hydraulic component and around a pushrod or end of a piston, not used for sealing fluid in but keeping dust out.

E

EBA: Emergency Brake Assist. A system pioneered by Mercedes Benz, whereby the ABS ECU recognises an attempted emergency stop and applies the brakes to the limit of tyre grip.

Electrical contact cleaner: Electrical contact cleaner removes oxidation, corrosion and carbon deposits from electrical contacts, restoring full current flow.

Electro-hydraulic pump: An electrically powered hydraulic pump used to create pressure in certain portions of the brake system. Typically found in hydraulically operated power brake servos and in ABS hydraulic control units.

Electronic Control Unit (ECU): The "brain" of an ABS system. The ECU reads impulses from the wheel speed sensors to determine if anti-lock braking needs to take place. If so, the ECU controls the cycling of the solenoid valves in the hydraulic control unit.

Emergency brake: Another term for the handbrake.

Equaliser: A bracket or cable connector which balances tension equally on the cables to the handbrakes.

F

Filler port: See breather port.

Fixed caliper: A caliper containing one or more pistons on each side of the brake disc that is bolted to the steering knuckle, hub carrier or rear axle and is incapable of movement.

Flare-nut spanner: A spanner designed for loosening hydraulic fitting tube nuts (flare-nuts) without damaging them. Flare-nut spanners are like a six-point ring spanner with one of the flats missing, which allows the spanner to pass over the tubing but still maintain a maximum amount of contact with the nut. Also called a split ring spanner.

Floating caliper: A caliper that rides on bushes, has one or more pistons only on one side of the caliper and moves laterally as the piston pushes on the inner brake pad, which pulls the outer pad against the brake disc.

Four-wheel ABS: An anti-lock brake system that operates on all four wheels.

Free play: The amount of travel before any action takes place. In a brake pedal it is the distance the pedal moves before the pistons in the master cylinder are actuated.

Friction: Surface resistance to relative motion.

G

Glazed lining: A brake lining that has been overheated and become smooth and glossy.

Grinding: The process of resurfacing a brake disc or drum on a brake lathe using a power-driven abrasive stone.

Grommet: A round rubber seal which fits into a hole or recess, intended to seal or insulate the component passing through it.

Guide pin: A caliper mounting bolt used for fastening a floating caliper to its mounting plate.

H

Handbrake: The mechanically actuated portion of a drum brake or disc brake caliper, used to prevent the vehicle from rolling when it is parked, usually applied by a lever, or rod. Also called an emergency brake or parking brake.

Hard spots: Shiny bluish/brown glazed areas on a brake drum or disc friction surface, caused by extreme heat. Hard spots can usually be removed by resurfacing.

Hat: The portion of a detachable brake disc that comes in contact with the wheel hub.

Heat checking: Small cracks on a brake disc or drum friction surface caused by heat. Heat checks can usually be removed by resurfacing.

Hold-down pin, spring and retainer: The most common method of retaining a brake shoe to the backing plate. The pin passes through the backing plate and brake shoe. The spring and retainer are fastened to the pin, which holds the shoe against the backing plate.

Hold-off valve: See Metering valve.

Hydraulically operated servo: A brake servo that uses hydraulic pressure to assist the driver in the application of the brakes. This hydraulic pressure comes from a belt-driven pump or an electro-hydraulic pump.

Hydraulic control unit: The portion of an anti-lock brake system that houses the solenoid valves and electro-hydraulic pump.

Hydraulic modulator: See Hydraulic control unit.

Hydroplane: The action that takes place when an accumulation of water builds up in front of a tyre, causing the tyre to ride on a layer of water instead of on the pavement.

Hygroscopic: The tendency to attract or absorb moisture from the air.

I

Inboard brakes: Disc or drum brakes not mounted out at the wheels, but near the differential. Rarely found on modern vehicles.

Inertia: The tendency of a body at rest to remain at rest, and a body in motion to remain in motion.

Integral Anti-lock Brake System: An anti-lock system that incorporates the master cylinder and servo into the hydraulic control unit.

K

Kinetic energy: The energy of a body in motion.

Knockback: The action of a brake disc with excessive runout pushing back the brake pads when the brakes are not applied.

L

Lateral runout: Side-to-side warpage of the brake disc friction surfaces.

Leading shoe: The shoe in a leading/trailing drum brake assembly which is self-energised by the rotation of the brake drum.

Leading/trailing drum brake: A drum brake design in which both brake shoes are attached to an anchor plate, and only one of the shoes is self-energised.

Load Sensing Proportioning Valve (LSPV): A hydraulic system control valve that works like a proportioning valve, but also takes into consideration the amount of weight carried by the rear axle.

M

Manual adjuster: A type of brake adjuster that must be adjusted from time-to-time, with the use of a hand tool.

Master cylinder: The component in the hydraulic system which generates pressure for the calipers and/or wheel cylinders.

Metering valve: A hydraulic control valve placed in the circuit to the front brakes, designed to restrict pressure to the front brake calipers until the rear brake shoes overcome the tension of the retracting springs.

N

Non-servo drum brake: A drum brake design in which the application of one shoe has no effect on the other.

O

Organic linings: Brake lining material using asbestos as its main ingredient.

Out-of-round: The condition of a brake drum when it has become distorted and is no longer perfectly round. In many cases an out-of-round brake drum can be salvaged by resurfacing on a brake lathe.

P

Pad wear indicators: Mechanical or electrical devices which warn the driver when the lining material on the brake pads has worn to the point that they should be renewed.

Parallelism: The relationship between one friction surface of a brake disc and the other.

Parking brake: See Handbrake.

Pascal's Law: The law of physics stating that "pressure, when applied to a confined liquid, is transmitted undiminished." Discovered by Blaise Pascal (1623 - 1662).

Penetrating lubricants: Penetrating lubricants loosen and lubricate seized, rusted and corroded fasteners and prevent future rusting or freezing.

Pressure bleeder: A device that forces brake fluid under pressure into the master cylinder, so that by opening the bleeder screws all air will be purged from the hydraulic system.

Pressure differential warning switch: A component of the brake hydraulic system that warns the driver of a failure in one of the circuits.

Primary shoe: The shoe in a duo-servo drum brake that transfers part of its braking force to the secondary shoe.

Proportioning valve: A hydraulic control valve located in the circuit to the rear wheels which limits the amount of pressure to the rear brakes to prevent wheel lock-up during panic stops.

R

Replenishing port: See Breather port.

Reservoir: A container attached to the master cylinder, either directly or by hoses, that stores extra brake fluid for the hydraulic system.

Residual pressure: Pressure remaining in a hydraulic circuit after the brakes have been released.

Residual pressure check valve: A small valve, usually located in the outlet port(s) of the master cylinder, which maintains a certain amount of pressure in the hydraulic circuit(s) when the brakes are released. Used only in drum brake hydraulic circuits to keep the lips of the wheel cylinder cups sealed against the walls of the cylinder.

Resurfacing: The process of machining a brake drum or disc on a brake lathe to remove surface imperfections from the friction surface.

Riveted linings: Brake linings that are riveted to the pad backing plate or brake shoe.

Rotor: *See Brake disc.*

Runout: Side-to-side warpage of the brake disc friction surfaces.

S

Scoring: Grooves or deep scratches on a friction surface caused by metal-to-metal contact (worn-out brake pads or shoes) or debris caught between the friction material and the friction surface.

Secondary shoe: The shoe in a duo-servo drum brake assembly that is acted upon by the primary shoe. It provides more stopping power than the primary shoe (by about 70 percent).

Select-low principle: The method by which the rear brake application of an ABS brake system is monitored and controlled, based on the rear wheel with the least amount of traction.

Self-energising action: The action of a rotating brake drum that increases the application pressure of the brake shoe(s).

Semi-metallic lining: Brake lining incorporating a high-percentage of metal in its composition.

Servo: A device using vacuum or hydraulic power to assist the driver in the application of the brakes.

Servo-action drum brake: See Duo-servo drum brake.

Sliding caliper: Similar to a floating caliper, but instead of riding on guide pins and bushes, the caliper slides on machined "ways" and is retained by keys or spring plates.

Solid brake disc: A brake disc that is solid metal between its friction surfaces.

Split ring spanner: See Flare nut spanner.

Star wheel: The portion of a brake adjuster that turns the adjuster screw.

T

Toothed signal rotor: The component of an ABS system that rotates with the hub, driveshaft, axle or ring gear, used along with the wheel speed sensors for generating impulses to be rear by the ABS Electronic Control Unit (ECU). The ECU counts these impulses and determines if a wheel is decelerating too rapidly.

Torque: A turning or twisting force imposed on a rotating part.

Torque plate: See Caliper mounting bracket.

Traction: The amount of adhesion between the tyre and earth.

Trailing shoe: A shoe in a drum brake assembly that is not self-energised.

Two-wheel ABS: An anti-lock brake system that only operates on two wheels.

Tyre slip: The difference between the speed of the vehicle and the speed between the tyre and the earth, expressed in a percentage.

U

Uni-servo drum brake: A servo-action drum brake that only has servo action when the vehicle is braked in a forward direction.

V

Vacuum: As an automotive term, vacuum is any pressure less than atmospheric pressure.

Vacuum pump: An engine driven device to provide a vacuum source for the brake servo - normally fitted only to diesel engines.

Vacuum-operated servo: A servo that uses engine manifold vacuum to assist the driver in the application of the brakes.

Vacuum-suspended servo: A type of servo that contains vacuum in both chambers of the servo when the brake pedal is at rest. When the pedal is applied, the rear chamber is vented to the atmosphere, causing the diaphragm of the servo to move toward the master cylinder which assists the driver in the application of the brakes.

Vapour lock: The abnormal condition that occurs when brake fluid contains too much moisture and is overheated, causing the moisture in the fluid to boil. Gas bubbles are formed in the fluid, which causes a spongy brake pedal or a complete loss of hydraulic pressure.

Vented brake disc: A brake disc that has cooling passages cast or drilled between its friction surfaces.

Viscosity: The property of a fluid that resists the force tending to cause the fluid to flow.

W

Ways: Machined abutments on which a sliding brake caliper rides.

Wheel bearing grease: Wheel bearing grease is a heavy grease that can withstand high loads and friction, and is used in wheel bearings, balljoints, track rod ends and universal joints.

Wheel cylinder: The component in a hydraulic system that converts hydraulic pressure into mechanical force to apply the brake shoe(s).

Wheel speed sensor: The component of an anti-lock brake system that picks up the impulses of the toothed signal rotor, sending these impulses to the ABS ECU.

Fault finding

This section provides an easy reference guide to the more common problems which may occur in just about any kind of automotive brake system. **Note:** *Although the problems included here do apply to the wheel brakes and, to an extent, the hydraulic system of ABS-equipped vehicles, malfunctions that pertain solely to the anti-lock portion of such systems aren't dealt with here. For a description of Anti-lock Brake Systems (ABS) and general fault finding procedures, refer to Chapter 5.*

Remember that successful fault finding is not a mysterious "black art" practised only by professional mechanics. It's simply the result of a bit of knowledge combined with an intelligent, systematic approach to the problem. Always work by a process of elimination, starting with the simplest solution and working through to the most complex. If necessary, refer to Chapter 1 and remind yourself of the basic braking system principles.

If you keep a close eye on the condition of your brakes and perform routine inspections as described in Chapter 7, you might not ever need the following fault finding information. Brakes work hard, though, probably harder than any other system in your car. They're subjected to lots of abuse. Unexpected problems do occur, and a

straightforward, logical analysis of the disorder will save you time and unnecessary expense.

Before assuming that a brake problem exists, make sure the tyres are in good condition and properly inflated. Also, the steering and suspension must be in proper alignment and the vehicle must not be loaded with weight in an unequal manner.

If, after using this fault finding guide, you are still unable to resolve the problem, seek advice from a professional mechanic. If necessary, have the vehicle towed to a garage. Don't drive a vehicle with defective brakes.

Warning: The dust created by the brake system may contain asbestos, which is harmful to your health. Never blow it out with compressed air and don't inhale any of it. An approved filtering mask should be worn when working on the brakes. Do not, under any circumstances, use petroleum-based solvents to clean brake parts. Use brake system cleaner only!

Brake judder

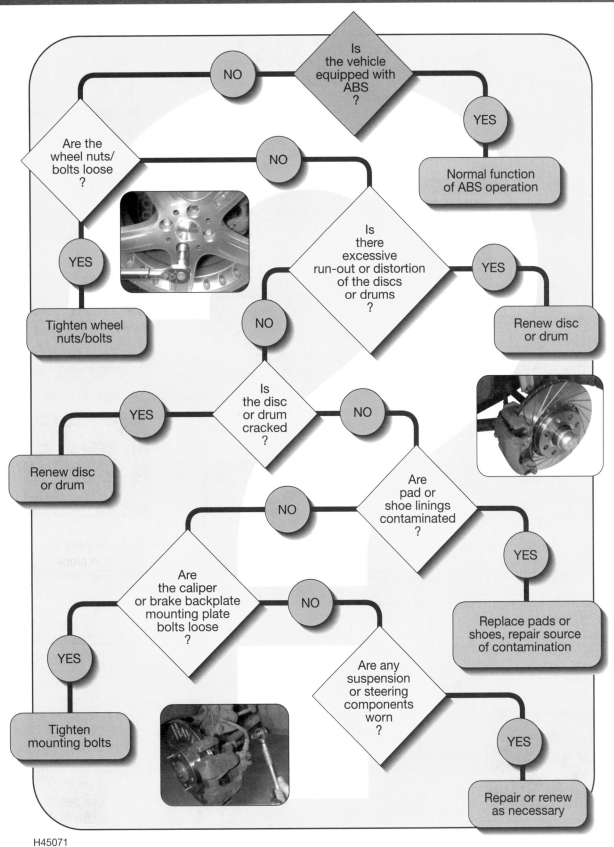

Is the vehicle equipped with ABS ?

NO → Are the wheel nuts/bolts loose ?

YES → Normal function of ABS operation

YES (wheel nuts/bolts loose) → Tighten wheel nuts/bolts

NO → Is there excessive run-out or distortion of the discs or drums ?

YES → Renew disc or drum

NO → Is the disc or drum cracked ?

YES → Renew disc or drum

NO → Are pad or shoe linings contaminated ?

YES → Replace pads or shoes, repair source of contamination

NO → Are the caliper or brake backplate mounting plate bolts loose ?

YES → Tighten mounting bolts

NO → Are any suspension or steering components worn ?

YES → Repair or renew as necessary

H45071

Brakes binding

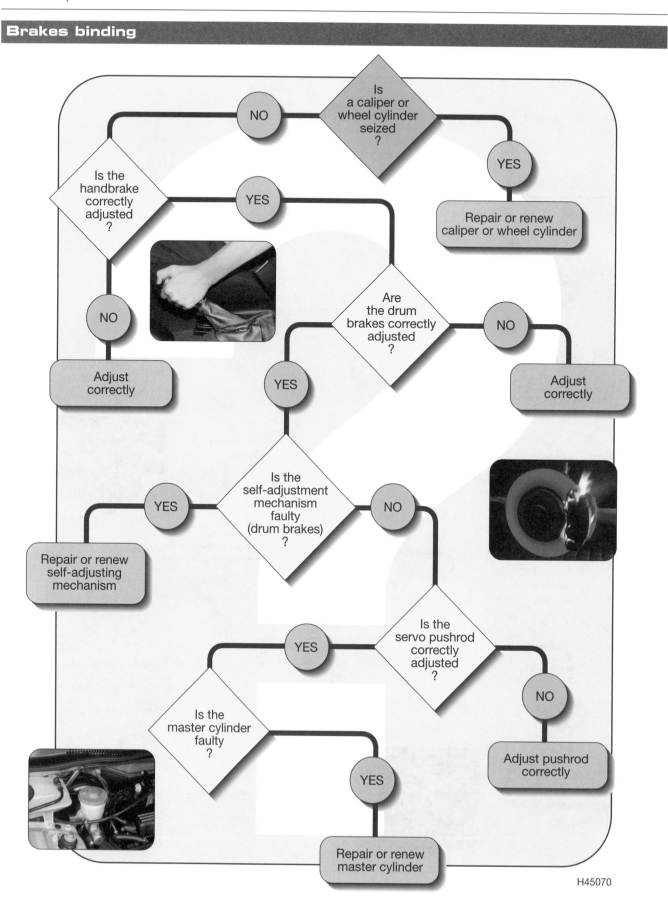

Is a caliper or wheel cylinder seized ?

NO

YES

Is the handbrake correctly adjusted ?

NO

Adjust correctly

YES

Repair or renew caliper or wheel cylinder

Are the drum brakes correctly adjusted ?

NO

Adjust correctly

YES

Is the self-adjustment mechanism faulty (drum brakes) ?

YES

Repair or renew self-adjusting mechanism

NO

Is the servo pushrod correctly adjusted ?

YES

NO

Adjust pushrod correctly

Is the master cylinder faulty ?

YES

Repair or renew master cylinder

H45070

Handbrake ineffective

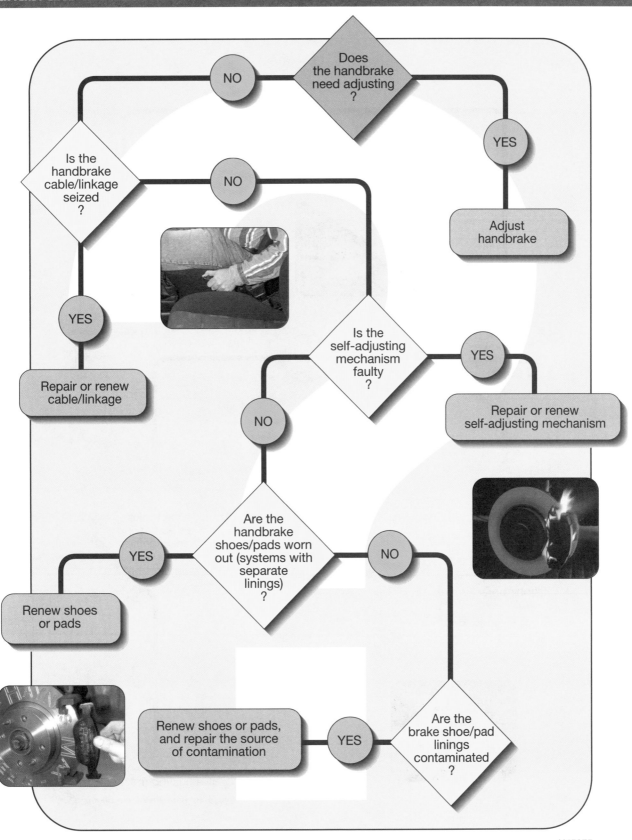

Does the handbrake need adjusting?

NO

Is the handbrake cable/linkage seized?

YES

Adjust handbrake

NO

Is the self-adjusting mechanism faulty?

YES

Repair or renew cable/linkage

Repair or renew self-adjusting mechanism

NO

Are the handbrake shoes/pads worn out (systems with separate linings)?

YES

NO

Renew shoes or pads

Renew shoes or pads, and repair the source of contamination

YES

Are the brake shoe/pad linings contaminated?

H45075

Handbrake will not release

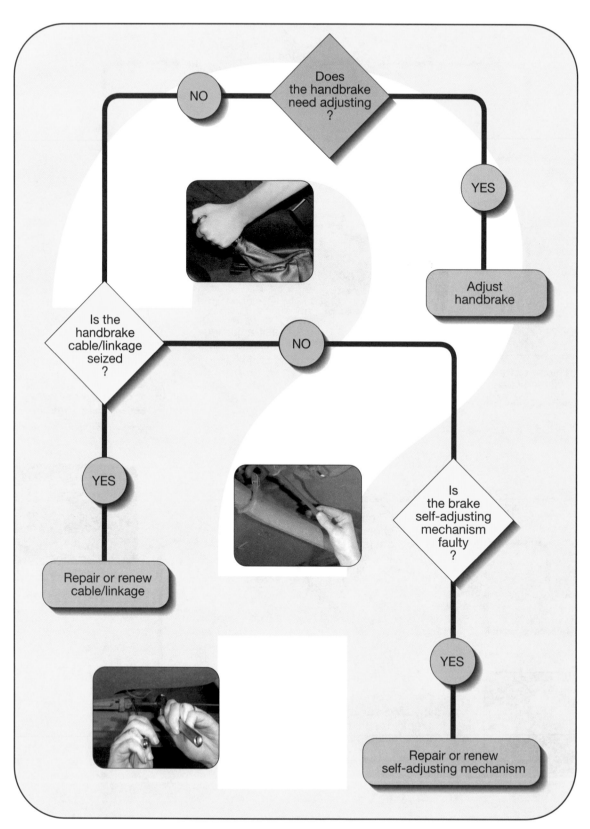

Does the handbrake need adjusting ?

NO

YES

Adjust handbrake

Is the handbrake cable/linkage seized ?

NO

YES

Is the brake self-adjusting mechanism faulty ?

Repair or renew cable/linkage

YES

Repair or renew self-adjusting mechanism

H45079

Rear wheels lock under normal braking

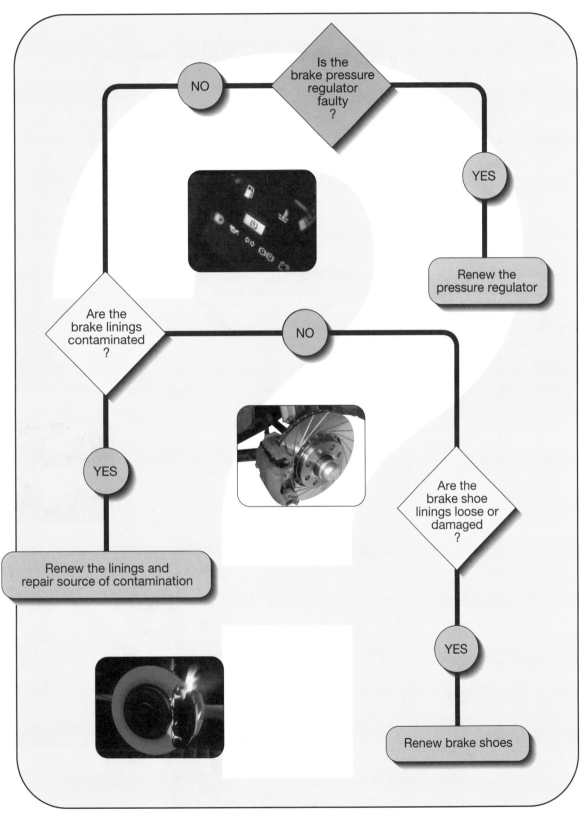

Is the brake pressure regulator faulty?

NO

YES

Renew the pressure regulator

Are the brake linings contaminated?

NO

YES

Renew the linings and repair source of contamination

Are the brake shoe linings loose or damaged?

YES

Renew brake shoes

H45080

Noisy brakes

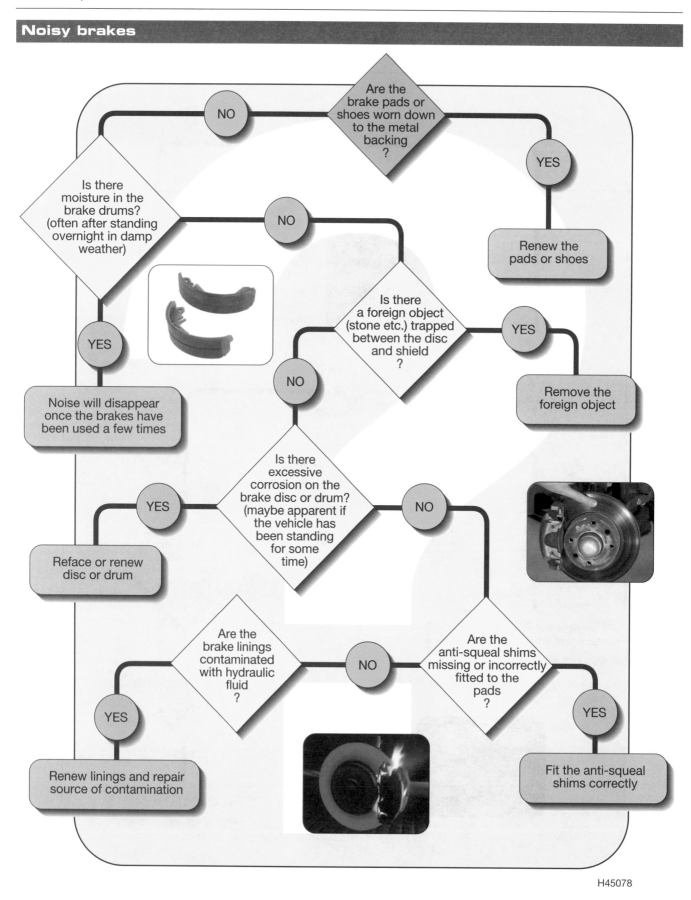

Are the brake pads or shoes worn down to the metal backing?

NO / **YES**

YES → Renew the pads or shoes

Is there moisture in the brake drums? (often after standing overnight in damp weather)

NO

YES → Noise will disappear once the brakes have been used a few times

Is there a foreign object (stone etc.) trapped between the disc and shield?

NO / **YES**

YES → Remove the foreign object

Is there excessive corrosion on the brake disc or drum? (maybe apparent if the vehicle has been standing for some time)

YES → Reface or renew disc or drum

NO

Are the brake linings contaminated with hydraulic fluid?

NO

YES → Renew linings and repair source of contamination

Are the anti-squeal shims missing or incorrectly fitted to the pads?

YES → Fit the anti-squeal shims correctly

H45078

Excessive brake pedal travel

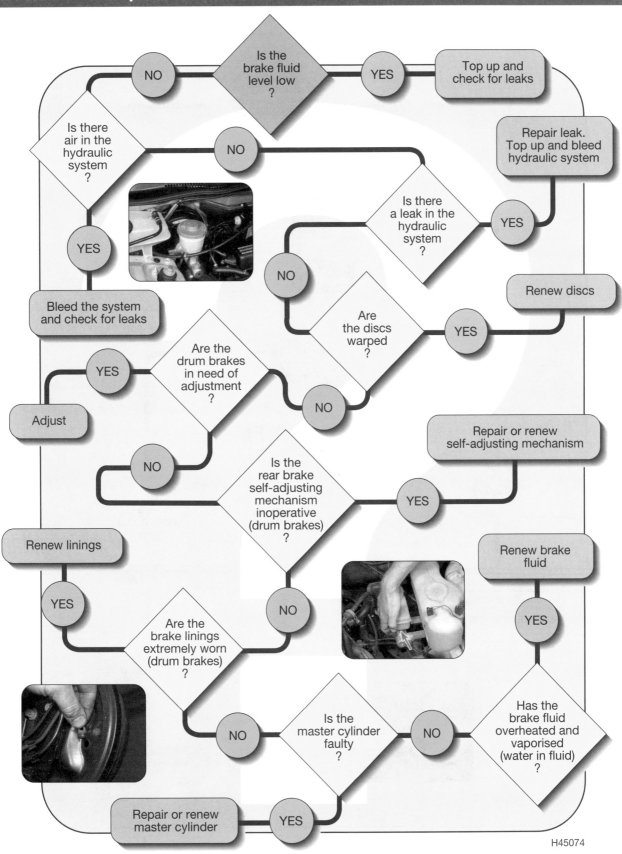

Is the brake fluid level low ?

NO

YES → Top up and check for leaks

Is there air in the hydraulic system ?

NO

Is there a leak in the hydraulic system ?

YES → Repair leak. Top up and bleed hydraulic system

YES → Bleed the system and check for leaks

NO

Are the discs warped ?

YES → Renew discs

NO

Are the drum brakes in need of adjustment ?

YES → Adjust

NO

Is the rear brake self-adjusting mechanism inoperative (drum brakes) ?

YES → Repair or renew self-adjusting mechanism

NO

Renew linings

YES

Are the brake linings extremely worn (drum brakes) ?

NO

Is the master cylinder faulty ?

NO

Has the brake fluid overheated and vaporised (water in fluid) ?

YES → Renew brake fluid

YES → Repair or renew master cylinder

H45074

8•13

No brake lights

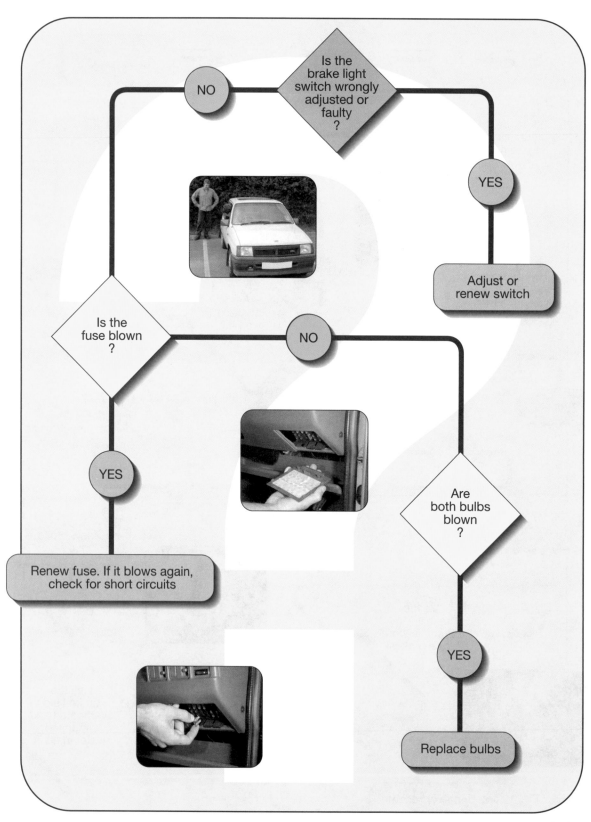

Is the
brake light
switch wrongly
adjusted or
faulty
?

NO

YES

Adjust or
renew switch

Is the
fuse blown
?

NO

YES

Renew fuse. If it blows again,
check for short circuits

Are
both bulbs
blown
?

YES

Replace bulbs

H45076

Brake light won't go out

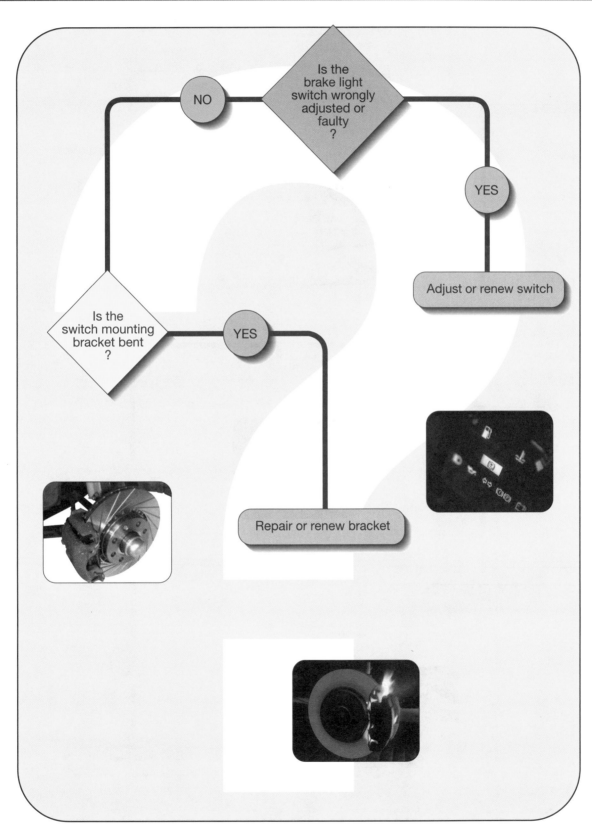

NO

Is the brake light switch wrongly adjusted or faulty ?

YES

Adjust or renew switch

Is the switch mounting bracket bent ?

YES

Repair or renew bracket

H45082

One brake light defective

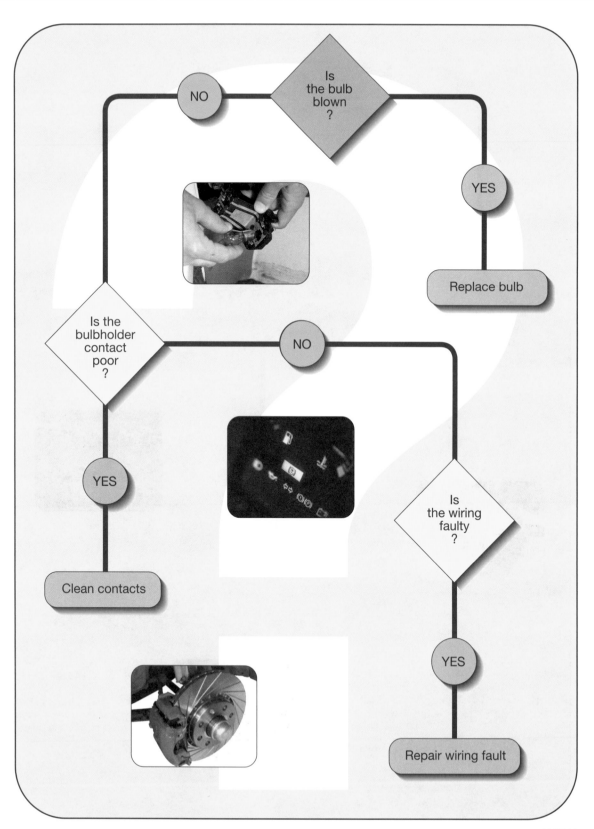

Is the bulb blown?

NO

YES → Replace bulb

Is the bulbholder contact poor?

NO

YES → Clean contacts

Is the wiring faulty?

YES → Repair wiring fault

H45081

Brake pedal feels spongy when pressed

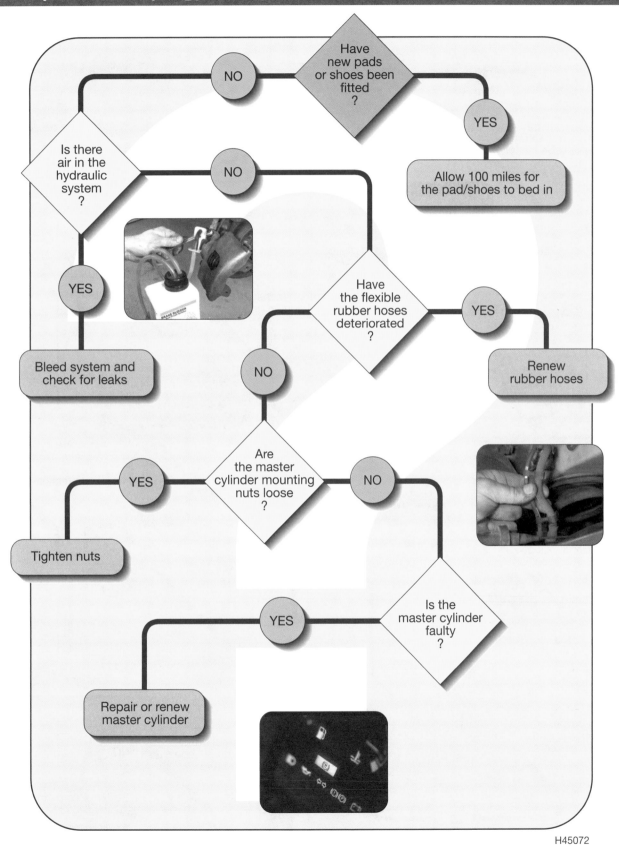

Have new pads or shoes been fitted ?

NO

YES

Allow 100 miles for the pad/shoes to bed in

Is there air in the hydraulic system ?

NO

YES

Bleed system and check for leaks

Have the flexible rubber hoses deteriorated ?

YES

Renew rubber hoses

NO

Are the master cylinder mounting nuts loose ?

YES

NO

Tighten nuts

Is the master cylinder faulty ?

YES

Repair or renew master cylinder

H45072

Excessive brake pedal effort required to stop vehicle

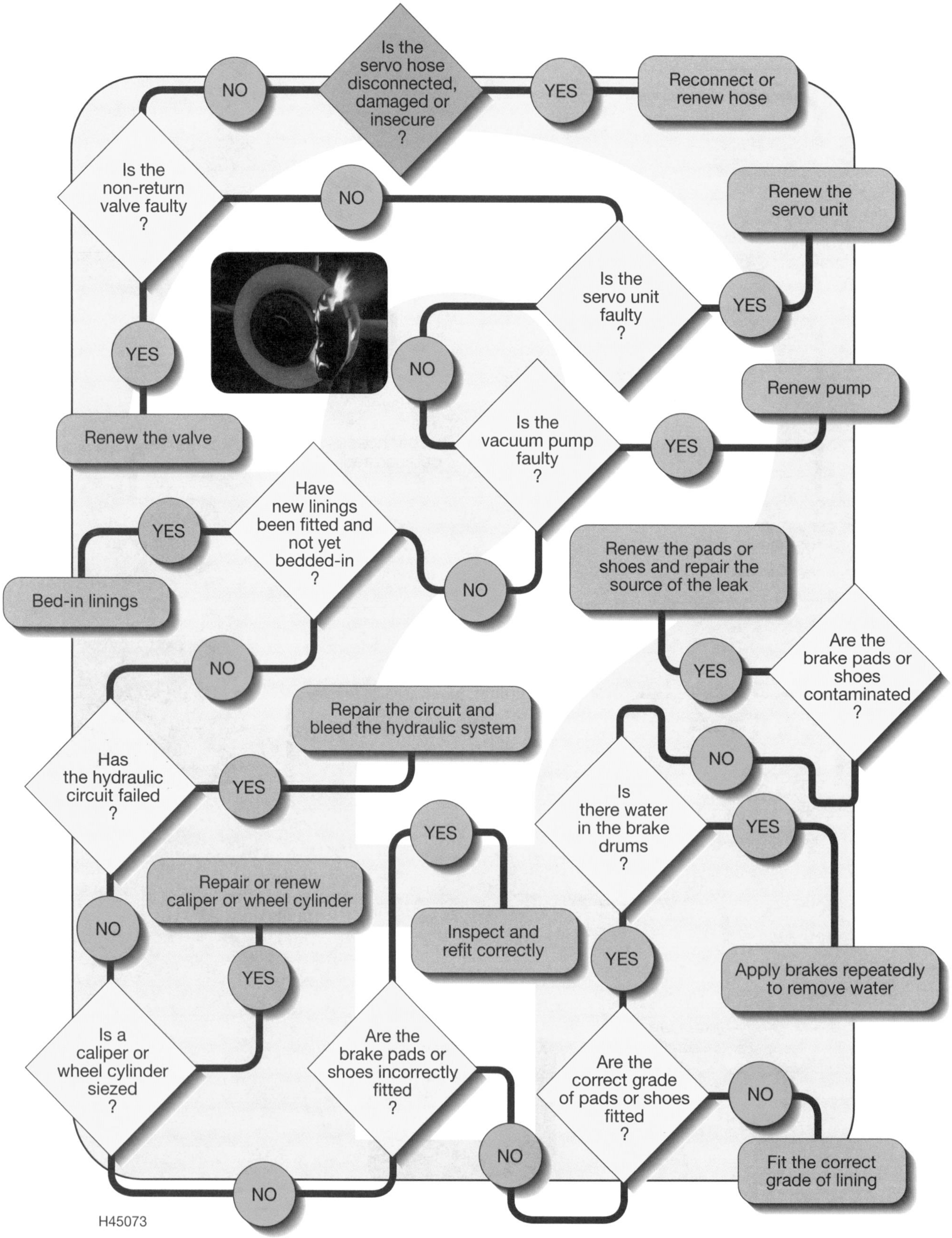

Is the servo hose disconnected, damaged or insecure ?

YES → Reconnect or renew hose

NO → Is the non-return valve faulty ?

NO →

Renew the servo unit

Is the servo unit faulty ?

YES → Renew the servo unit

Is the non-return valve faulty ?

YES → Renew the valve

Renew pump

Is the vacuum pump faulty ?

YES → Renew pump

NO →

Have new linings been fitted and not yet bedded-in ?

YES → Bed-in linings

NO →

Renew the pads or shoes and repair the source of the leak

Are the brake pads or shoes contaminated ?

YES → Renew the pads or shoes and repair the source of the leak

NO →

Repair the circuit and bleed the hydraulic system

Has the hydraulic circuit failed ?

YES → Repair the circuit and bleed the hydraulic system

Is there water in the brake drums ?

YES → Apply brakes repeatedly to remove water

Apply brakes repeatedly to remove water

Repair or renew caliper or wheel cylinder

Is a caliper or wheel cylinder siezed ?

YES → Repair or renew caliper or wheel cylinder

NO →

Inspect and refit correctly

Are the brake pads or shoes incorrectly fitted ?

YES → Inspect and refit correctly

NO →

Are the correct grade of pads or shoes fitted ?

NO → Fit the correct grade of lining

Fit the correct grade of lining

NO

H45073

Vehicle pulls to one side during braking

Does the road have a pronounced camber?

NO → Are the tyre pressures correct?

YES → Check brake performance on a flat road

Are the tyre pressures correct?
- NO → Adjust tyre pressures
- YES → Are the brake pads/shoes contaminated on one side?

Are the brake pads/shoes contaminated on one side?
- YES → Renew as necessary and correct the cause of contamination
- NO → Is a caliper or wheel cylinder seized?

Is a caliper or wheel cylinder seized?
- YES → Overhaul or renew the caliper or wheel cylinder
- NO → Is there a mixture of pad/shoe lining materials fitted to the same axle?

Is there a mixture of pad/shoe lining materials fitted to the same axle?
- YES → Fit new pads or shoes of the correct type
- NO → Are any caliper/backplate mounting bolts loose?

Are any caliper/backplate mounting bolts loose?
- YES → Tighten/replace the bolts as necessary
- NO → Are any suspension or steering components damaged?

Are any suspension or steering components damaged?
- YES → Repair or renew as necessary

H45077

Index

A

ABS systems – 5•1 *et seq*
  ABS facts – 5•2
  advantages – 5•2
  brake pedal position sensor – 5•7
  component systems – 5•4
  electric fluid pump – 5•7
  electronic control unit – 5•7
  electronic systems – 5•5
  fault finding – 5•9
  Ford belt-driven mechanical ABS
    system – 5•5
  four-wheel anti-lock systems – 5•3
  front-wheel anti-lock systems – 5•3
  general information – 5•1
  hydraulic accumulator – 5•7
  hydraulic modulator – 5•6
  integral systems – 5•4
  lateral acceleration switch – 5•7
  limitations – 5•2
  precautions – 5•8
  toothed signal rotors – 5•6
  what is ABS? – 5•1
  wheel speed sensors – 5•5

B

Bleeding brakes – 6•12, 6•38
Bleeding kits – 1•11
Brake caliper – 6•16
Brake disc
  inspection and renewal – 2•24
  replacement procedure – 2•27
**Brake drum removal, inspection and
  refitting** – 3•5
Brake fade – 1•7
Brake fluid – 1•5, 7•3
  renewal – 7•15
Brake hoses and pipes – 1•5, 7•10
Brake lights – 7•6
Brake pad
  inspection and renewal – 2•6
  renewal – 2•23
  replacement procedure – 2•27
Brake pedal – 7•15
  freeplay, "feel", and travel check –
    7•5
  position sensor – 5•7
Brake servos – 6•13, 7•4
Brake shoe
  adjuster tool – 1•11
  renewal – 3•6

Brake spring pliers – 1•10
Brake warning light – 7•6
Braking ratio – 3•4
Broken fasteners – 1•15

C

Calipers – 1•4, 6•16, 7•16
  piston retraction tools – 1•9, 1•10
Conversion factors – 0•4

D

Dial test indicators – 1•12
Disc brakes – 2•1 *et seq*, 7•8, 7•11
  brake disc inspection and renewal –
    2•24
  brake pad inspection and renewal –
    2•6, 2•23
  designs – 2•2
  fixed caliper – 2•6
  floating caliper – 2•16
  general information – 2•1
  operation – 2•5
  sliding caliper – 2•10
  typical brake pad and disc
    replacement procedure – 2•27
Drum brakes – 3•1 *et seq*, 7•6, 7•11
  adjustment – 7•13
  brake drum removal, inspection and
    refitting – 3•5
  brake shoe renewal – 3•6
  braking ratio – 3•4
  duo-servo brake – 3•7
  general information – 3•1
  leading/trailing brake – 3•15
  operation – 3•3
Duo-servo brake – 3•7

E

Electric fluid pump (ABS) – 5•7
Electronic ABS systems – 5•5
Electronic control unit (ABS) – 5•7

F

Fasteners – 1•13
Fault Finding – 8•6 *et seq*
  ABS – 5•9
Filtering mask – 1•13
Fire extinguishers – 1•12
Fixed caliper – 2•6, 6•16
Flexible hose renewal – 6•38

Floating caliper – 2•16, 6•18, 6•28
**Ford belt-driven mechanical ABS
  system** – 5•5
Front brakes – 7•6

G

Glossary – 8•1 *et seq*
Gloves – 1•13

H

Hand tools – 1•8
Handbrakes – 4•1 *et seq*, 7•14
  cable(s) – 4•6
  component renewal – 4•4
  introduction – 4•1
  lever – 4•4
  mechanisms – 2•23
  parking brake pedal or pullrod – 4•5
  shoe adjustment – 7•15
  shoes (drum-in-disc type
    handbrake) – 4•8
Hold-down clip tool – 1•11
Hold-down spring tool – 1•10
Hose clamps – 1•11
Hoses and pipes – 6•38
How to use this repair manual – 1•2
Hydraulic accumulator (ABS) – 5•7
Hydraulic modulator (ABS) – 5•6
*Hydraulic systems, brake servos and
  vacuum pumps* – 1•2, 6•1 *et seq*
  bleeding – 6•12, 6•38
  calipers – 6•16
  fixed caliper – 6•16
  flexible hose renewal – 6•38
  floating calipers – 6•18, 6•28
  hoses and pipes – 6•38
  hydraulically operated servos – 6•14
  introduction – 6•1
  master cylinder – 6•2
  metal brake pipes – 6•38
  opposed-piston calipers – 6•25, 6•33
  pressure differential warning
    switch – 6•10
  proportioning valve – 6•10
  servos – 6•13
  sliding calipers – 6•18, 6•28
  vacuum pumps – 6•41
  vacuum-operated servos – 6•13
  wheel cylinders – 6•36
Hydraulically operated servos –
  6•14

I

Introduction – 1•1 *et seq*
  brake fade – 1•7
  brake fluid – 1•5
  brake hoses and pipes – 1•5
  brake shoe adjuster tool – 1•11
  brake spring pliers – 1•10
  broken fasteners – 1•15
  buying tools – 1•7
  caliper piston retraction
    tools – 1•9, 1•10
  calipers – 1•4
  component disassembly – 1•16
  dial test indicators – 1•12
  fastener sizes – 1•14
  fasteners – 1•13
  filtering mask – 1•13
  fire extinguishers – 1•12
  gloves – 1•13
  hand tools – 1•8
  hold-down clip tool – 1•11
  hold-down spring tool – 1•10
  hose clamps – 1•11
  how to use this repair manual – 1•2
  hydraulic systems – 1•2
  master cylinder – 1•3
  micrometers – 1•12
  one-man brake bleeding kit – 1•11
  proportioning valve – 1•4
  safety glasses or goggles – 1•13
  safety items – 1•12
  special brake-related tools – 1•8
  split ring spanners – 1•8
  tightening sequences and
  procedures – 1•15
  tools and equipment – 1•7
  Torx bits – 1•9
  vacuum gauge – 1•9
  vacuum pump brake bleeding
    kit – 1•11
  vacuum/pressure pump – 1•9
  wheel brakes – 1•6
  wheel cylinders – 1•3

L

**Lateral acceleration switch
  (ABS)** – 5•7
Leading/trailing brake – 3•15

M

Maintenance – 7•1 *et seq*
  brake fluid – 7•3, 7•15
  brake hoses and pipes – 7•10
  brake lights – 7•6
  brake pedal – 7•5, 7•15
  brake servo – 7•4
  brake warning light – 7•6
  calipers – 7•16
  disc brakes – 7•8, 7•11
  drum brakes – 7•6, 7•11, 7•13
  front brakes – 7•6
  handbrake – 7•14, 7•15
  inspection – 7•2
  introduction – 7•1
  maintenance procedures – 7•2
  maintenance schedule – 7•2
  master cylinder – 7•16
  rear brakes – 7•11
  servo – 7•4
  tyres and tyre pressures – 7•2
  wheel bearing check, repack and
  adjustment – 7•6
  wheel cylinders – 7•16
  wheel nut (or bolt) tightness – 7•3
Master cylinder – 1•3, 6•2
  seal check – 7•16
Metal brake pipes – 6•38
Micrometers – 1•12

O

One-man brake bleeding kit – 1•11
**Opposed-piston
  calipers** – 6•25, 6•33

P

**Parking brake pedal or
  pullrod** – 4•5
**Pressure differential warning
  switch** – 6•10
Pressure pump – 1•9
Proportioning valve – 1•4, 6•10

R

Rear brakes – 7•11

S

Safety glasses or goggles – 1•13
Safety items – 1•12
Servos – 6•13, 7•4
Sliding caliper – 2•10, 6•18, 6•28
Split ring spanners – 1•8

T

**Tightening sequences and
  procedures** – 1•15
Tools and equipment – 1•7
Toothed signal rotors (ABS) – 5•6
Torx bits – 1•9
Tyres and tyre pressures – 7•2

V

Vacuum gauge – 1•9
**Vacuum pump brake bleeding
  kit** – 1•11
Vacuum pumps – 1•9, 6•41
Vacuum-operated servos – 6•13

W

**Wheel bearing check, repack and
  adjustment** – 7•6
Wheel brakes – 1•6
Wheel cylinders – 1•3, 6•36, 7•16
Wheel nut (or bolt) tightness – 7•3
Wheel speed sensors (ABS) – 5•5

Preserving Our Motoring Heritage

< The Model J Duesenberg Derham Tourster. Only eight of these magnificent cars were ever built – this is the only example to be found outside the United States of America

Almost every car you've ever loved, loathed or desired is gathered under one roof at the Haynes Motor Museum. Over 300 immaculately presented cars and motorbikes represent every aspect of our motoring heritage, from elegant reminders of bygone days, such as the superb Model J Duesenberg to curiosities like the bug-eyed BMW Isetta. There are also many old friends and flames. Perhaps you remember the 1959 Ford Popular that you did your courting in? The magnificent 'Red Collection' is a spectacle of classic sports cars including AC, Alfa Romeo, Austin Healey, Ferrari, Lamborghini, Maserati, MG, Riley, Porsche and Triumph.

A Perfect Day Out

Each and every vehicle at the Haynes Motor Museum has played its part in the history and culture of Motoring. Today, they make a wonderful spectacle and a great day out for all the family. Bring the kids, bring Mum and Dad, but above all bring your camera to capture those golden memories for ever. You will also find an impressive array of motoring memorabilia, a comfortable 70 seat video cinema and one of the most extensive transport book shops in Britain. The Pit Stop Cafe serves everything from a cup of tea to wholesome, home-made meals or, if you prefer, you can enjoy the large picnic area nestled in the beautiful rural surroundings of Somerset.

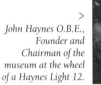

> John Haynes O.B.E., Founder and Chairman of the museum at the wheel of a Haynes Light 12.

< Graham Hill's Lola Cosworth Formula 1 car next to a 1934 Riley Sports.

The Museum is situated on the A359 Yeovil to Frome road at Sparkford, just off the A303 in Somerset. It is about 40 miles south of Bristol, and 25 minutes drive from the M5 intersection at Taunton.
Open 9.30am - 5.30pm (10.00am - 4.00pm Winter) 7 days a week, *except Christmas Day, Boxing Day and New Years Day*
Special rates available for schools, coach parties and outings Charitable Trust No. 292048